MW00804345

BERLIN UNDERGROUND

Berlin Underground

1938–1945

RUTH ANDREAS-FRIEDRICH

⌐⌐⌐⌐⌐⌐⌐

Translated by Barrows Mussey

WITH AN INTRODUCTORY NOTE BY JOEL SAYRE

PARAGON HOUSE • NEW YORK

First paperback edition, 1989

Published in the United States by

Paragon House
90 Fifth Avenue
New York, NY 10011

Originally published in German under the title *Der Schattenmann* by Suhrkamp Verlag (Frankfurt). This edition is reprinted by arrangement with Suhrkamp Verlag and Henry Holt and Company.

Library of Congress Cataloging-in-Publication Data

Andreas-Friedrich, Ruth.
  [Schattenmann. English]
  Berlin underground, 1938-1945 / Ruth Andreas-Friedrich ;
translated by Barrows Mussey.—Paragon House ed.
    p.   cm.
  Translation of: Der Schattenmann.
  Reprint. Originally published: New York, Holt, 1947.
  ISBN 1-55778-159-1
  1. Andreas-Friedrich, Ruth—Diaries. 2. World War, 1939-1945—Personal narratives, German. 3. World War, 1939-1945—Underground movements—Berlin (Germany) I. Title.
D811.5.A579313 1989
943.086′092′4—dc19
[B]   88-33054
                                                  CIP

Printed and bound in Canada.

For Andrik

(Leo Borchard)

A *beloved friend*

A NOTE

on some characters in this book

Although I had known a sister of Ruth Andreas-Friedrich's some twenty years ago when I was in Germany, I didn't meet Ruth herself until July, 1945, a few days after the arrival of the first American and British occupation forces in Berlin, which had been captured two months previously by the Russians. However, during the nine months I spent in Berlin as a correspondent I got to know Ruth even better than I had known her sister and can positively guarantee that she exists.

Du lieber Gott, does she exist! During the Third Reich she not only brought up a daughter (who is now a beautiful young actress and one of the rising stars of the new Berlin theater), but simultaneously held down a full-time job, wrote a couple of best sellers, and sparked the resistance movement described in these pages. For years Ruth was a wheel horse at the colossal Ullstein publishing house, and in terms of American journalism occupied a position somewhere between those of Dorothy Dix and Alice-Leone Moats, her two best sellers having been after the school of the latter's *No Nice Girl Swears*. But it is not Ruth's status as a prose artist that should concern us, nor did it concern her at the time. What did concern her was the problem of getting enough money to feed the Jews and the fellow conspirators hiding in her cellar.

The code name of the resistance group which Ruth sparked was *Onkel Emil*. When one member wrote or telephoned to another on group business, the state of Uncle Emil's health was gone into and prescribed for in detail. It was a small group with scarcely more than a couple of dozen members, most of whom were professional people—doctors, musicians, professors, actors, writers—but there were, in addition, several skilled artisans. One was a printer who could forge to perfection almost anything in the way of a needed official document such as a pass, a military exemption certificate, or a strip of food tickets to feed a famished Jew; another was an electrician who could cut a cable so well that it was virtually impossible to repair. The group took no part in the wholly praiseworthy but tragically cumbersome conspiracy that so narrowly missed getting Hitler, Keitel, and Jodl with the bomb in the black briefcase on July 20, 1944 at the Fuehrer's GHQ in East Prussia. It specialized in aiding Jews, in dodging and helping others to dodge the draft, and in spreading defeatism, culminating in the *Neinaktion* told about by Ruth in the closing part of her story. It goes without saying that anybody detected in such activities could be sure of a swift death.

Though it worked with a small Communist group known as the *Gruppe Ernst* (which in turn was solicitous about the health of Uncle Ernest), the Uncle Emil group held no political beliefs save anti-Nazism. It may occur to some readers that, however despicable the Nazis, the Uncle Emils were traitors to their country. The best answer to such a quibble, I think, is this. Nearly all of them were skilled practitioners at their various callings and could have left Germany before or after the Nazis took over. Exile is surely a terrible thing, but a competent practitioner can get by almost anywhere. Ruth, for instance, could have gone to Hollywood and unquestionably done well. However, after much thought and undeniable temptation, she and her friends decided to stay and slug it out. They loathed the slavery, but they loved the slaves. They really did love their country and they still do, although,

God knows, to look at it now in the shape it's in, it doesn't seem much of a thing to love.

The Uncle Emils worked out of the section of Berlin called Steglitz, which lies in the American-occupied sector of the city, and in passing it may be interesting to note that the group, both collectively and individually, was screened almost to pieces by the various security agencies of the American Army. Our intelligence authorities gave the group and its members not only a clean bill of health but somewhat of an accolade. The Uncle Emils were also the only non-Communist resistance group in Berlin to be recognized by the Russians.

The first time I went to Ruth's apartment, two other characters who appear in this book were also there. One was the physician and professor of medicine whom she calls "Frank." I got to know Frank quite well and to like and admire him. During the war he was underground for several years. The way he came to go underground was as follows. One day he was walking along a street in Berlin when he saw a small crowd gathered. Thinking that somebody had been hurt, he worked his way into its center to see if he could be of help. He found a Russian soldier lying on the ground with his hands tied behind him. A Hitler Youth of about sixteen was kicking the Russian soldier while the crowd looked on. Frank, who is a small, slight man, fetched the Hitler Youth a wallop over the ear and a boot in the pants, causing him to flee. He then untied the Russian soldier and found that he was suffering from three broken ribs and a brain concussion. Frank appealed to the crowd to call an ambulance, but as there were several citizens present wearing Party buttons, nobody dared to, so Frank went off and telephoned for one himself, and when it came he took the Russian soldier to a hospital. On his way home that evening, just as he was entering his street, he was waylaid by a neighbor who told him that a couple of Gestapo agents were waiting for him at his house. Frank thanked his neighbor, and did not see his wife and four small children again until the late fall of 1945, for they left Berlin when the great air raids came and went to live in a Bavarian village with his father, a famous professor of internal medicine, retired. Ruth hid Frank out. During his hiding, he didn't merely hide, he worked against the Nazi Government in every way he could. He had no patience with the argument put forward by so many Germans who did not really like the Nazis but played along with them because "after all, it's Germany." This "after all it's Germany" argument was part of the old Prussian *Pflichtgefühl*, that dreadfully overworked, totally humorless, and rather degenerate Sense of Duty, which could be used as an excuse for anything and everything and has so often got the German people into trouble. To Frank, loving Germany meant doing all that he could to help destroy the monster that had Germany in its grip.

The other character in this book who was at Ruth's apartment the first time I went there was the symphony conductor whom she calls "Andrik." I notice that on the dedication page Ruth reveals that "Andrik" was Leo Borchard. In a codicil to the book she adds that he was killed by the "stray bullet of an American patrol." Maybe a few more details might be added to this undeniable fact.

When the Russians captured the city on May 2, one of the first things they did after turning on the water and the electric current, getting the kids back into whatever schools were still standing (no Berlin schools had been open for the past year), and setting gangs of male and female Nazis to shoveling rubble, was to make Borchard conductor of the Berlin Philharmonic. He and the orchestra gave many concerts to Allied audiences which were much appreciated. One night that early fall, he had conducted for the British and was being driven home by a British cultural colonel in a small German car that the British had requisitioned. There were several other passengers in the car, including Ruth, who was sitting directly behind Borchard. The colonel and Borchard in the front seats were discussing music intently, when suddenly they saw a light being waved in front of them. The colonel thought it was somebody trying to thumb a lift. "Sorry, no room," he said in a general sort of way, and went on talking music with Borchard. They were still talking music when they passed the spot where the light was being waved. Ruth heard a whistle trill and some shouting. Her old campaigner's instinct told her to duck, and she obeyed it. It was fortunate that she did, for a few seconds later a stream of bullets came through the rear window, and one of them cut some hair off her scalp. The rest went into the back of Borchard's head and completely blew his face off. The colonel, it seemed, had driven through an American check point. The outfit that had furnished the detail for the check point was a famous and tough one, and there had been numerous recent complaints from on high about German cars which had not responded when challenged. Wanted Nazis had been known to escape. An order had been issued that all cars were to be stopped at every check point at all costs. It was nobody's fault in particular, just an unfortunate linking of phenomena. But it was rough on poor Borchard after he had managed to go through the whole war unscathed.

Ruth is still living in Berlin and edits a women's weekly newspaper called *She*, but is by no means satisfied with it. Ruth is never smug about anything she is engaged in, which is one of her great virtues. Her other virtues are her energy, her pugnacity, her courage, and her wonderfully good heart. We, the people of the United States, have undertaken to educate the Germans under our control in the best ways of our democracy. If we are ever to get anywhere with such a staggering project, it is with Germans like Ruth and her friends that we must work.

JOEL SAYRE

This book does not pretend to be a work of art; it is simply *Reed* the truth.

It is not my intention to vaunt deeds of political heroism, to uncover conspiracies, or to tell of armed resistance to Gestapo and Hitler tyranny. The whole world is aware that we did not eliminate Hitler; did not overthrow Goebbels; did not kill Goering. But few people know why none of those things happened.

For twelve and a half years the German people lived within prison walls. What actually took place inside those walls almost never reached the public ear. The Nazis had many adversaries in Germany. These adversaries, having stood out as "Aryans" against Party and Hitlerism from the start of the regime, did not feel that they could conscientiously appropriate the all-too-few opportunities of emigration the world offered for the persecuted. They stayed in the country of their own accord. They had premonitions of what was to come. They knew of all the atrocities that took place, though only through rumor. And precisely because they knew and foresaw all this, they felt it their duty to use their energies on the spot. Then at least not all the intended outrages might be carried out.

Many whose lives were in danger would never have managed to emigrate if all Hitler's opponents had left first. Countless "wanted" persons who went underground could never have stuck it out to the end but for the help of strangers.

The purpose of my book is to show how hard it was to engineer even the simplest aid among bombs and ruins, spies, suspicions, restrictive regulations; you were cut off from the truth, forced to rely on rumor alone, often without transportation, current, gas, water, or telephone. That, I say, is my purpose; for if the nations would love one another, they must first learn to understand one another.

Germany today is the bad child of the world. The tendency is to identify the whole people with the outrages of its leaders. Yet thousands upon thousands had nothing whatever to do with those outrages. On the contrary, year in and year out they risked life and liberty—with no help from foreign nations, no support from any organization or powerful Party quarter —to serve humanity wherever they could.

Those Germans, high and low, their life and their work, are the subject of these pages. I have deliberately refrained from any subsequent emendations. Of course many rumors current in those days have since been explained, many inaccurately transmitted facts corrected through press and radio. But this very uncertainty about what actually happened was so characteristic of the time that it would be a distortion to make changes now.

This book can fulfill a purpose only if each and every word is deeply honest. May it go out into the world to testify that there were human beings living even under Hitler in Germany—human beings who do not deserve to be despised, along with their whole nation, because of an irresponsible government. If that be accomplished, these notes will have fulfilled their purpose by helping in some small measure to raise the German people a hairsbreadth from its present low degree in the eyes of the world.

Ruth Andreas-Friedrich

Berlin, October, 1945

BERLIN UNDERGROUND

Berlin, Tuesday, September 27, 1938.

People look different today from what they usually do. Somehow there is a disturbing hint of sensation in the air. Karla Simeon and I turn down the Leipzigerstrasse. Everyone who hurries past us seems to be desperately considering something —obviously something most disagreeable.

"Mr. Goebbels' 'land of the smile' is showing its best side again," my friend observes sarcastically. "Just look at those dismal faces, will you? What would you think of a drink?"

I think well of it. I always think well of a drink. Specially when I've been blue-penciling articles at the copy desk for eight hours.

Karla takes my arm. "Let's go, then—on to the Kaiserhof!"

We cross the Mauerstrasse. Twilight is falling. A couple of army automobiles like gray shadows whisk around the corner in quick succession, and vanish swiftly toward the Wilhelmstrasse.

About two hundred people are standing in the square outside the Reich Chancellery—not the beaming provincials who everlastingly pound the pavement there, just to take back a "glimpse of the Fuehrer" as their sweetest memory of Berlin. These people seem but little inclined to vent their enthusiasm in Sieg Heils. The crowd stands mute, hands in pockets, shoulders a bit huddled as if against the cold, waiting.

For what? For whom?

The Kaiserhof bar is fairly empty about this time. We sit down in a corner and order two Martinis. Then two more, then two more.

"Look here," says Karla at length, pensively fishing the last olive from her glass, "I think we're in the wrong place. History is being made outside."

The same little crowd of people is still standing in the Zietenplatz. Clustered tight together, they are staring tensely at an uninterrupted procession from Unter den Linden past the historic balcony: cannon, baggage trucks, horses, tanks, soldiers. Soldiers without end. Steel helmets low on their foreheads, eyes rigidly to the front, they sit their saddles, crouch on wagon seats and limbers, march heavy-footed along the asphalt.

The balcony door upstairs opens. Hitler comes out, bareheaded, his hands in the pockets of his tunic. He moves quickly to the railing. A couple of officers follow at a respectful distance. I recognize Raeder, and see the gold embroidery of several generals' uniforms in the twilight.

I steal a glance at the faces of those around me: tight lips, wrinkled brows. They stand there with their tails between their legs, with the embarrassed, guilty look of people who know perfectly well that they don't want to do as they must.

Not a hand is raised anywhere.

The tanks roll, the people keep silent, and the Fuehrer, uncheered, vanishes from the balcony. White-gloved SS men shut the door, and draw the curtains inside the window.

A young workman beside me blows his nose loudly. "If that don't mean war, I'll eat my hat," he growls through his teeth.

His neighbor, a fifty-year-old postman with uniform cap and pouch, looks around cautiously before venturing a nod of agreement. "And we're the suckers," he whispers, then jumps with fright at his own boldness. When he notices that I am watching him, he falls into an abstracted silence.

I smile at him as nicely as I can, and even tread slightly on his toe, simply so that I can give him a cheerful "Pardon me," and thus express my agreement. Then I wriggle out of the crowd.

Karla is waiting for me at the next lamppost. "It's war, it's war, and how I don't want it to be my fault," she declaims.

"Neither do I," I sigh. "But we shan't be able to help it."

Not a doubt of it; Hitler wants war. What we have just seen was a test, a trial of popular feeling. Will the ice bear, or won't it yet?

We said "No"—goodness, what am I boasting about? We *thought* No. We mean No. And we don't want it.

But what does our want signify? What does it signify in Nazi Germany if two hundred people act as though they were expressing an opinion? After all, their sole achievement is summoning the pitiful little courage not to notice Mr. Hitler on his balcony. Tomorrow there'll be war, to-*mor*-row *there'll* be *war:* our footsteps keep time with the words.

We part on the Potsdamer Platz. "Good-by," I say absently. I don't feel like going home; so I just pound the streets, almost until morning.

Have the people any idea what they are being forced into? They're sitting in the cafés the same as any other night, drinking their beer or brandy; and over the front door it says, "The German's greeting is Heil Hitler!" Next to it a motto is fading: "God bless us all, both great and small."

No, I don't want any part of it! Why must we go to war when we want peace? Why does almost everyone do what he loathes deep down in his heart?

Looking in at Hiller's shortly after one A.M., I find Heinrich Muehsam. He's sitting in a corner, writing at a table piled with papers. Letters to himself—to me too, perhaps: the same as he does every evening. Now that the paper has chucked him out for non-Aryan descent, he is discovering Berlin by tram, brooding over why women don't like him, and scattering his cleverness, charm, and energy to the desert air. He used to be an editor at our shop. Now he lives on the compensation from a motor accident, and just waits for the Fourth Reich. He waits and waits.

Wednesday, September 28, 1938.

Naturally I oversleep. It's striking nine o'clock from St. Mark's steeple when I open my eyes. I'm in a good mood, serene and cheerful—as you mostly are before you have really awakened and faced the day. Then suddenly you remember there's something there, something menacing and disagreeable. A burden on your soul, which you can't quite remember, but which you know will occur to you in a moment. It will be disagreeably vivid, like pain when the morphine wears off. What was it, now? Of course. It's war. How stupid of me!

Danger has been hanging over our heads for almost a month. It began with the great campaign of enlightenment about the martyrdom of the German minority in the Sudetenland—first small type on the back page, then huge headlines on the front. Outraged mothers, their children at the breast, pregnant women molested by "Czech beasts." A very crucifixion of anguish. We had never dreamed that there were such abominations in civilized Europe. And when the newsreels took pains to catch the atrocities on celluloid, most people surrendered to ocular proof. There were very few who asked themselves dubiously, "How did the cameraman ever manage to grind his film unharmed in all that row?" Even the face of our sensible scrubwoman, a sworn foe of the Nazis since 1933, streams with tears as she listens to the radio stories of Sudeten-German fugitives.

4

"Why, Mrs. Kramm, *you* aren't being taken in by that propaganda, are you?" I ask in astonishment.

"Oh, I know it's all a lie," Mrs. Kramm sobs, "but it's so sad!"

The doorbell rings, four times. That's for me. I leap into my bathrobe, rush into the hall, and there's Karla.

"Well! They called it off!" she pants breathlessly.

"What—where—who?" My brain seems to fail me.

"Why, the war, of course," Karla explains impatiently. I still don't understand.

"You seem to have had a hard night," says my friend with a patronizing air.

"If you'd at least allow me to get some clothes on, and start the tea," I apologize. Karla allows me.

Teeth brushed, clothes on, tea boiling, bread fetched. Karla sits mutely in the armchair. She knows my mind is hard to get at before the first cup of tea. But then it comes out like a waterfall. "No war, you see! Peace! Real, honest peace! It's going to be negotiated tomorrow, at Munich. Between Hitler, Mussolini, Daladier, and Chamberlain. I've got the authentic story." *Authentic* is the catchword of our day, or rather one of the innumerable catchwords. A profession of honesty as against atrocity stories and whispering campaigns.

In this case "honesty" is represented by Erich Tuch, a cousin of Karla Simeon's and the alleged right-hand man of one of the best known Nazi bigwigs. If anyone has the authentic dope, it must surely be he, stirring up history every day and every hour with both hands. He stirs and stirs, and thinks his own thoughts. But the Nazis don't know that, and must never find out.

"Well, go on!" I implore Karla.

"Erich was in there when we were standing outside! He

saw everything—everything! Even us! Among all those two hundred people in the square outside the Reich Chancellery. Right then the war was balanced on the razor's edge. Hitler went out on the balcony to give his soldiers a warrior's greeting. He had never been so determined to take by storm what they refused to let him have peaceably. We helped spoil that for him, with our grumpy faces and our hands in our pockets. He stood for half an hour inside the curtain after he went in, watching our resentment. And so they had a change of heart, and postponed the thing. Just you watch, starting tomorrow the tortured German minority will be gone from all the papers."

Taken aback, I go over to the radio, and tune in the Prague station. *Vyshehrad, Vyshehrad,* says the station identification plaintively. Then men sing a melancholy chorale. It sounds like the dirge for a murdered victim. *Vyshehrad, Vyshehrad.* My heart quails.

I go around the rest of the day as if I were dreaming. The fierce tension of the past weeks has even robbed us of the energy to be joyful. *Vyshehrad, Vyshehrad.* War or peace? They both seem equally awful and equally guilty to me.

Thursday, September 29, 1938.

Erich Tuch has flown to Munich with his chief. The decision is expected this very day. Our editorial writers are sitting with poised pens. All the city desks are working at forced draft. They save room for the headlines up until the last moment.

Morning edition—noon edition—evening edition. Still nothing. Still nothing. We huddle over the radio. The telephones ring incessantly. You smoke one cigarette after another from sheer nervousness.

Hitler is conferring with Mussolini. Secretly; even more secretly; in dead secrecy. The Axis partners are one heart and one soul again.

Fat Hollner, our magazine-section editor, flutters from room to room like a bird of ill omen, shaking his head, and croaking, "Oh dear, oh dear, I just hope everything comes out. Two wolves against two lambs. And who do you suppose is going to eat whom?"

It's a queer thing. Every day millions of pounds of printed paper go rolling out of this building, vomiting a torrent of National Socialist propaganda over mankind. And yet there's hardly one person under our roof who agrees with what he writes, sets, prints, edits, or carries from office to office. As long as the walls have no ears, people mutter by two's or in small groups behind every door.

The few hundred-percenters are known; they are toadied to—and shunned. People warn you of them, stop talking or change the subject whenever they come into the room. And no one dares tell them to their faces what he thinks, what is bothering him, and what he trembles at. Those among us with acrobatic consciences hold the view that anyone with eyes cannot help reading between the lines how fiercely our pens rebel at writing down the prescribed lies.

I can't help myself: I don't see anything between the lines. If there's any pulse in them at all, it's certainly no more than the beat of a chicken heart.

But after all, where is courage to come from when it will cost you your neck to show any? People who live in glass houses shouldn't throw stones. The courage of one's convictions under a dictatorship is ruled by different laws from the opposition in a democracy. Neither Mr. Chamberlain nor M. Daladier has grasped this truth so far. And anyway, who knows if it's a moral gain for us to have realized it?

Friday, September 30, 1938.

They've brought it off after all. The wolves against the lambs. It was announced with fanfares late last night. By October 10, Czech troops will evacuate the Sudetenland. France, England, Italy, and Germany have agreed to cede the Sudetenland to the Reich. *Vyshehrad, Vyshehrad:* your appeal was in vain.

People in Munich are wild with enthusiasm. And Daladier takes childish delight in his prima donna's privilege of taking a dozen bows before the curtain (or rather, to be precise, on the balcony). Democracies are not in the habit of spoiling their statesmen. No wonder the rhythmic Sieg Heil of our well-drilled masses is music to his ears.

Saturday, October 15, 1938.

The days go on; work goes on. Everything seems to have calmed down wonderfully. You take your coffee regularly at Schmitt's again, get annoyed at trifles, and tend to be absorbed in the monotony of every day. But when I met Dr. Muehsam in Hiller's yesterday evening, he had a worried look; he stared pensively at his various letters, scattered among wine glasses and half-empty dishes, and sighed, "I don't like this quiet. Look here: what can a dictator do without successes—I mean without visible successes? He puts himself out of business.

Only kings or the presidents of liberal states can afford to rest on their laurels. But tyrants are hunted men, forever tossed between *Hosanna* and *Crucify him!* If they aren't to topple over themselves, they have to keep everyone else on edge. The crowd wants games and bread. When the big foreign-affairs spectacle is over, the clown jumps out of the box. Do you know who the clown is? The German Jew, naturally! Ahasuerus goes on in the intermission. It's Ahasuerus' turn again, as it has been a thousand times throughout history. Believe you me, they'll paint him up and rig him out so that no one could ever recognize his weeping face under the make-up. Everything is the Jew's fault. Trample him! Thrash him! Laugh at him! Laugh at the poor man that gets his ears boxed."

"Why, how do you mean?"

"How do you mean?" grumbles Dr. Muehsam, wiping the sweat off his nose. "Why, are you blind? Can't you see what's smoldering under the blanket—one anti-Semitic decree hard on the heels of the next? Exclusion of the Jews from the German body politic. Mixed marriages between Germans and Jews prohibited. The Jew cannot be a citizen of the Reich. Complete exclusion from cultural life. No Jewish writers, painters, actors, newspaper or movie people. First we stepped out. Now we're being isolated. And after isolation comes extinction. It follows like A B C." He downs a glass of Spanish white wine, and smiles. "If only this beloved country hadn't been home for a hundred years past!"

Dear God, how I know that misery, that desperate rebellion against racial and blood laws. Can't everyone be at home where he wants to be at home? When I was little, I can't ever remember having heard the word "Jew." You distinguished between good people and bad people, decent and rotten, lovable and unattractive. Our saying "Jew" and "Aryan" only proves how far even those who think otherwise have got away from a simple human valuation. In America every immigrant is an American within one generation. In Russia he's a Russian. Why? Because he's formed by the landscape he grows up in. Because he's formed by the language he speaks. Not just the sauerkraut he eats, not just the snow that lies on his roof in winter, but the clouds hanging high or low above his horizon, the atmosphere he breathes, the way people around him bury their dead, sell fish at market, or express their love.

"Home," says Dr. Muehsam, "is where you see chalked on the wall, 'Paulie is a dope.' Where you used to play marbles and cops and robbers. Not all the Hitlers on earth can take that away from you."

"They can't take it away, but they can throw an awful shadow over it." I remember the countless emigrations I have shared in since 1933. Anyone who can possibly break away has long since gone—to the United States, to Bolivia, to Sumatra. My friends are scattered all over the globe. Lucky for those who got off with a scratch, who suffered no more than the loss of three-quarters of their property. You can make more money, you can get over the loss of possessions. Human hurts you never get over.

And how they were hurt. Stupidly, senselessly. Take the affair of my deputy parents. When the Nuremberg Laws came out, they got ready to leave—with a heavy heart, God knows. I had lived with them for five years; for five years I had known nothing but kindness from them. I and everyone else who knew them. They had a cook, a delightful factotum. At the time of his departure, Dad had the misfortune not to be sixty years old, and the cook was so unlucky as to be six months below the canonical age. So the law decided that Jewish men were voluptuaries who must certainly have designs on the virtue of their Aryan staff. And despite his spotless reputation, despite his twelve years' employment of the cook, despite the presentation of a ticket to America, Dad had to move out of his own house, and spend his last two weeks in Europe at the house of friends—simply because the cook's bedroom was found by the official yardstick to be less than ten meters from his own. Jewish sensuality, then, was estimated at nine meters' distance.

Thursday, October 27, 1938.

Andrik Krassnow is back from his guest appearances in Sweden. His friends turned up yesterday to celebrate his return. As always, there were endless conversations, conjectures about the future, and passionate discussions of "the situation."

Andrik and I belong together; we have for seven years. He has the room next to mine in our apartment house. He's a conductor, and lived in Finland for a long time.

We were sitting together by the radio on the evening of January 30, 1933, when Adolf Hitler's appointment as Reich Chancellor was announced. We hadn't voted for him. We never did vote for him, either from conviction or from fear. When the heelers used to appear, late on election afternoons, to fetch tardy fellow Germans to the polls, we used to put an indelible pencil in our pockets, because indelible-pencil crosses won't erase. And finally, when the crosses didn't matter any more, and a whispering campaign scared the timid with the rumor that every ballot urn had a secret counter to unmask those who voted No, we said nothing more at all. We tore up the ballot into tiny bits, and put it in the envelope, blank—the big circle for Yes, and the tiny circle for No. If in the end, as many people claimed, they simply counted the envelopes that were turned in in their favor, we had a clear conscience, if not always an easy one.

Andrik hates the Nazis, just as I do—just as almost everyone in our group does, whether personally affected or not.

Andrik was the first to suffer. The radio denounced him as politically unreliable because he ventured to remind a new-made Party member of his former attachment to the German Socialist Party. This worshipful Party Comrade, unluckily, was a member of the orchestra with which Andrik was supposed musically to adorn Hitler's birthday on April 20, 1933. The orchestra refused to play under him. Sworn statements were entered that he was considered a foreigner, that he favored the Jews in the orchestra, and that three years previously, when the German anthem was being played somewhere, he had wrinkled his nose. He had not wrinkled his nose, he had only sneezed; but who can explain a thing like that beyond doubt three years after?

At the time we had moved heaven and earth to defeat this silly accusation. After all, you can't give up your career just for a single sneeze. But no matter where we turned, we found closed doors. No one would take a chance. Accordingly Andrik was simply not allowed to appear any more.

Now he was back from Sweden, bringing real whisky, twelve cartons of Camels that he had smuggled adroitly through customs, and all sorts of news from outside the cage.

"Thomas Mann has written a new book; Georg Bernhard is disgracing the tradition of the *Vossische Zeitung* by his incredibly commonplace *Pariser Tageblatt*. Toller is reported dead; they say he hanged himself. Bruno Walter is creating wild enthusiasm in America. Good old Secretary of State

Schäffer is 'in' safety matches now; he's at Norrköpping, upholding the Kreuger trust. Brüning is dangling between England and America, thinking over his mistakes, and saying nothing."

Twenty pairs of eyes are fixed on Andrik's lips. The smoke in the room is so thick you could cut it with a knife. But it smells of foreign countries—of freedom. That makes it good; one hardly notices. They're sitting on chairs and stools, on tables and sofa cushions. Wherever there's a tiny spot, somebody has squatted down with his glass of whisky and ash tray, puffing, drinking, and gazing into space. Karla and Erich Tuch, Dr. Hollner and the Hirschbergs, the Angels, the Levys, Dr. Muehsam, Flamm, the Hinrichs, and all the rest.

"Suppose the Gestapo were to nab us now," Hollner glooms. But no one listens to him.

"Have they any idea outside how things look here?" Karla inquires.

And Andrik frowns. "That's the dismal part of it. Anyone who gets out is cut off. Four weeks of emigration, and they forget it all—what you can write, and what you can't write; how you might help, and how you mustn't help. Human beings simply have no imagination about injustice. What they don't see with their own eyes they can hardly conceive of. Even the Jewish *émigrés* are no exception. And yet more than one of them began by casting his vote for Hitler."

It was a fact; they really had. Dozens of our Jewish friends had made that mistake shortly before Hitler came into power. Firmly convinced that he would have shot his bolt within a month, they voted for Adolf Hitler to "put an end to this nonsense once and for all." It was not the nonsense that was put an end to, but they. The "nonsense" was beaten out on their backs.

13

"The best thing would be for Brüning to come back," growls Levy the lawyer. "Better a silent man than a loud-speaker, anyway." He's right. Brüning is one of the few emigrees who still keep their reputation among almost all groups in Germany, and who might even be imagined to return, possibly to return better than they went.

"He's saying nothing, and learning from his mistakes," Andrik says. "He judged people by himself—and they weren't that way. That was his one mistake. Hitler judges people by himself, too. He succeeds because they are that way. One man wants to make the masses free through responsibility; the other makes them free of responsibility. Only an independent person likes responsibility; dependent people dread it like the plague. Hitler's best trick has been to stand up in front of the people and yell, "The final responsibility before people and history rests upon the Leader! I will lift that odious burden off your shoulders. Put it on me; I alone will take the consequences."

Will he really take them—the consequences he has been steering us toward for five years? Suppose a war comes? Can he die for all of us? Would he die for all of us—or would he send one after another to death? And then what about responsibility for lost lives, for human misery and endless grief? The masses don't see through the trick—not so far. And we must persevere until even the dullest has understood.

This evening we talk a great deal about that question—so much and at such length that we quite forget the customary subject of conversation in all opposition groups, as fruitless as it is permanent: Blood vengeance on all the Nazi bigwigs.

Not that any treasonable plans are hatched in the process —far from it! The Germans are no revolutionists; not even the German Jews are that. Otherwise someone would long since

14

have drawn the logical conclusions from his martyrdom. They simply imagine how they will punish the bigwigs for their misdeeds when it's all over—Hitler, Himmler, Ley, Goebbels, and Goering. Everyone has his own particular passions, and describes them in full detail, amusing himself by the hour with these sadistic mental gymnastics. "The sour-grape game" is what Karla and I call this pastime.

Tuesday, November 8, 1938.

The evening papers report that a Jewish refugee has shot at a member of the German Embassy in Paris. Some people say the affair has a political background, and is an act of vengeance by tormented Jewry against the Nazi regime. Others are mumbling about a homosexual love affair, about blackmail and jealousy—a second Horst Wessel mess. Odd, this train of thought that leads back to the quarrel about Hitler's martyr. Politics or sex? Sex or politics?

The new history books say of Horst Wessel: "Leader of Storm Troop V in the Red workmen's quarter of Berlin. Created the battle song of the Movement, *Banner High (Die Fahne Hoch)*. In January, 1930, he suffered a cowardly, murderous assault in his residence by the Red Front. Murderer: Ali Köhler. Died on February 23, 1930, after six weeks' illness."

They have twined laurel wreaths for him, killed thousands of Communists in his name, set fire to the Reichstag, named squares after him, streets, regiments, even heavenly hosts. The day of his death has become a popular holiday, his battle song the national anthem. No effort has been spared to turn the ex-dueling fraternity student into the chief saint of the Move-

15

ment. And yet even the most passionate Nazi propaganda has not quite sufficed to free its hero of the suspicion that in private life he was a very unsavory character indeed, whose death involved not the honor of Germany, but the dishonor of a certain sort of sexual behavior.

Hero or pimp? Is history really so lacking in resource as to employ the same means twice for one and the same political purpose? That time it was the Communists; this time it's the Jews. Yesterday a pimp, today a homosexual. Suppose the rumor *is* an invention; the fact that it was invented on both occasions shows how much it's in the air.

Andrik grins when I tell him about it. "Count, methinks this Mortimer has died to suit your plan," he quotes. "Let's see the paper." He skims through it from top to bottom. "Well, they don't seem to take it too seriously," he says, with a sigh of relief. "A little note on page three, and no remarks. I would at least have thought . . ."

Wednesday, November 9, 1938.

Andrik thought rightly. The Paris assassination has become a world sensation overnight. "Cowardly attempted murder of Embassy Councilor Ernst vom Rath by the Jew Grünspan," all the morning papers shriek in huge type. "World Jewry takes off the mask." Then follow columns of description of the victim's career and merits. A new medical bulletin every hour. So far the injuries don't seem to be fatal. Woe, if they should prove to be so! In busses, on the street, in shops and cafés the Grünspan case is discussed both loudly and in a whisper.

I see no signs of anti-Semitic indignation, but there is an oppressive uneasiness like that before a thunderstorm. Along the Kurfürstendamm, the Tauentzienstrasse, and the Leipzigerstrasse the shops that have been required by proclamation to mark themselves as Jewish by putting their names in white are conspicuously empty. As usual, people don't dare. . . . They're afraid of making themselves unpopular. *Der Stuermer* has screamed too often, "Don't buy from Jews."

On the way to the office I look in at Dr. Muehsam's. He's at the typewriter, copying letters—childhood letters that he wrote himself, to his mother, to his Nanny, to a boyhood friend long since gone to America. They are tied up in bundles a year at a time. "Dear, sweet Mummy," is one I catch a glimpse of.

"Is he going to die?" I ask him. "And if he dies, then what?"

"Of course he's going to die. Otherwise the whole thing would be useless. If they're going to avenge him, they've got to weep for him first. The greater the grief, the more fanatical the hatred. Didn't you know that political incidents seldom happen until everything is ready for it down to the last hobnail—until all the decrees are issued, all the preparations made, all the steps agreed on? There's no doubt of it, the Jewish war is upon us. For myself, I propose to remain a pacifist. Even a Jew can't do more than die."

He turns back to his machine. "Dear, sweet Mummy," he types earnestly.

Outside, they're hawking the new editions. "Ernst vom Rath's condition worse." As I go through the revolving door at Grünfeld's store, I almost feel as if I were entering a house of death.

Thursday, November 10, 1938.

The doorbell rings at seven in the morning—eight, nine, ten times in succession, as if someone were beating a tattoo on the button.

Outside the door is Dr. Weissmann, the lawyer. "Hide me, they're after me!" he pants.

I stare at him. "Who? What? I don't understand."

"Do at least shut the door. Are you alone? Where shall I . . . Where can I go, for God's sake?" He pushes past me into the room, falls into a chair, and covers his face with his hands. His topcoat is torn, his hair hangs down over his face. He looks as if he had been wallowing in a mud puddle.

"Why, what's happened?" I ask, horrified.

"Are you living on the moon?" he asks bitterly. "The devil is walking in Berlin! The synagogues are on fire. Jewish blood is flowing from the knife. The Storm Troops are on the march, smashing windows. And you ask me what's happened!" His voice cracks in his agitation. "They're hunting us like rabbits," he grits. "They made me run halfway down the Kurfürstendamm, and yelled after me, 'Jewish swine, mass murderer, drop dead, you stinker!' They threw stones and dirt at me—the louts, the ruffians, the damned Storm Troop hooligans!"

"And the police?"

"The police just looked on. They let anything that's on fire burn, and anyone get killed who's supposed to be killed."

"So he died after all?"

"Who?"

"Why, vom Rath."

"Yes, he's dead," Dr. Weissmann nods. "And now they're holding requiem for him with torches and oil barrels, by violating churches and mass murder. They almost caught me, but I slipped down a side street. So they beat up somebody else instead."

I go all hot and cold with horror. Andrik, Andrik, how right you were! No Mortimer's death ever so suspiciously suited a plan. I look at the clock. It's half past seven.

"Wait," I say. "I'll get rolls and milk. First we'll make tea; then we'll see what to do next." By nine o'clock, after breakfast and a bath, Dr. Weissmann is in Andrik's bed, in Andrik's new Swedish pajamas. He's taken care of for the moment, thank God.

At half past nine I ride to the office. The bus conductor looks at me as if he had something important to say; but then he just shakes his head, and looks away guiltily. My fellow passengers don't look up at all. Everyone's expression seems somehow to be asking forgiveness. The Kurfürstendamm is a sea of broken glass. At the corner of the Fasanenstrasse people are gathering—a mute mass looking in dismay at the synagogue, whose dome is hidden in clouds of smoke.

"A damn shame!" a man beside me whispers.

I look at him lovingly. This, it occurs to me, is really the time to call your neighbor "brother." But I don't do it. One never does; one just thinks it. And if you really do pluck up courage for a running start, in the end you just ask, "Pardon me, but could you tell me the time?" And then you're instantly ashamed of being such a coward.

Yet we all feel that we are brothers as we sit here in the bus, ready to die of shame. Brothers in shame; comrades in humiliation. But if everyone is ashamed, who smashed those windows? It wasn't you, it wasn't I. Then who is X, the great unknown?

The office is fluttering like a dovecote. I take refuge for a moment in Hollner's room. "Well, now, what really happened?"

He sits at his desk, a lump of misery, pushing his pipe from one side of his mouth to the other; he groans, "My dear girl, I shan't live through this. We ought to be so ashamed we could sink into the floor. Synagogues—houses of God—temples of the Lord, sim soaked down with gasoline. And on top of all that, thy act as if they'd done something brave."

Hollne hs me a couple of typed pages, and points a finger at t heavy headline, "Anti-Jewish action in Berlin and the Reich."

"Aha—DNB correspondence! Which means in plain German, 'All evening editions will reprint. The editor is at liberty to replace ornamental adjectives with substitutes of his own choice.'"

Hollner gives a melancholy nod. "And that's the kind of stuff one has to stand for; that's what one has to stick one's neck out for—sign as responsible editor—act as if one *believed* this miserable rubbish."

I hastily skim the closely typed pages: "On the announcement of the decease of the German diplomat, Party Comrade vom Rath, laid low by a cowardly Jewish murderer's hand, spontaneous anti-Jewish demonstrations developed throughout the Reich. The profound indignation of the German people found vent in many quarters in violent anti-Jewish action. In many parts of Berlin the show windows of Jewish shops were smashed and the showcases of the Jewish owners demolished. The Jewish shop-owners had the impudence to make their Aryan employees remove the broken glass with their bare hands, calling forth passionate remonstrances from passers-by. . . . The synagogues, places where the antisocial and antinational doctrines of the Talmud and the Shul Khan-Arukh are propagated, were set afire, and the interiors consumed. The synagogue on the Wilhelm Platz also suffered. Arms are alleged to have been discovered there. The synagogue at Eberswalde went up in flames. The same fate befell the Jewish temples at Cottbus and Brandenberg." I turn the page in disgust. "Fire in the Wilmersdorf Synagogue this

20

morning between six and seven o'clock . . . Dome collapses
. . . Demonstrations in Nuremberg . . . All surviving Jewish shops demolished . . . Spontaneous demonstrations
against Jewry in Leipzig." The same words over and over
again in endless sequence.

So now I know. The Jewish war has begun. It started last
night at two o'clock, with an attack all along the line. And
on Schiller's birthday, too. If one could only find out who is
for and who against it!

"Why, one doesn't dare look people in the eye any more,"
says our duty editor, who is rumored to have a tinge of Nazism.
"Anti-Semitism, well and good. But not like that."

Only tall Meyer, our political editor, rubs his hands cheerfully. "At last we're showing 'em, the damn scoundrels," he
triumphs.

"It's odd that the spontaneous popular rage happened to
burst out alike exactly at the same time all over the Reich,"
I say, as if this were something that had just casually occurred
to me. But the barb goes home.

Meyer looks at me blankly. "Hm," he mumbles, staring
thoughtfully into space. Then he shakes his head in annoyance. "What are you always crabbing about? The Fuehrer
must know. . . ."

"Obviously. The Fuehrer knows! That's just what I mean,"
I cut him off dryly, slamming the door behind me and leaving
his peon brain to absorb this drop of poison at leisure.

A standing assembly is convened in Karla's office. Even in
the hall I can hear the buzz of excited voices. When I turn
the knob, everyone falls silent as if at a signal.

"Oh, it's only you," is my friend's welcome. "Why didn't
you say so to begin with?" She turns back to those around her.
"They dragged our landlady's son out of bed at two in the

morning. Orders from the Storm Troop unit. Fall in at once. Of course it was the Storm Troops. Who else would it have been?"

"And in full war paint, too," our local editor breaks in. "I saw them with my own eyes marching up the Kleiststrasse. Masses of them. It was organized, let me tell you! It was all managed! One cog fitted into the next. And meanwhile the common people were under the covers, sleeping the sleep of the just."

"Decent people are usually asleep between two and five," our secretary observes. "You can't set fire to churches before you get up."

As Karla and I cross the Hausvogteiplatz on our way to lunch, we hear a strange noise in the distance. Someone seems to be dropping china on the sidewalk from the sixth floor. We stop. The noise comes from a side street. "We've got to go see this." Karla is already off at a trot.

Scarcely a hundred paces away, on the left side of the Mohrenstrasse, a dark mass of people is gathered outside a ready-to-wear shop. Three heavy iron bars swing like sledgehammers at the huge windows. A creak, a splintering, a tinkle that lasts for seconds. Then all is silence. Crash, jingle, crash, jingle, the next window is in fragments. Before it stand five fellows in crumpled civilian clothes, wearing peaked caps, their faces distorted with exertion. Crash, jingle . . . They thrust, they pound; they work like precision machines. None of them deigns to glance at the bystanders. There is neither hatred in them nor indignation, neither frenzy nor anger.

One of the fellows—obviously the foreman—casts a searching glance around. Two quick steps and a blow, and the chandelier inside crashes down. The pictures shake from the walls like cones off a pine tree. Iron heels noisily shatter the waxen visage of a show-window mannikin. Broken glass everywhere.

The crowd stands silent, hypnotically attracted, hypnotically repelled, encircling the scene of action at a timorous distance.

"Ready," cries the foreman, signaling with his eyes and shouldering his rod; the little troop marches on in close formation. Left, right, left, right—a thousand times they have practised marching so. Then, "Halt!" outside the next "Jew" windows.

Is this a pogrom? Is this the spontaneous rage of the people finding vent? Is the spark leaping into the powder keg, releasing the stored-up fury of a nation with a thunderous explosion? No. Nothing of the kind. But if those five were ordered tomorrow to kill all the chimney sweeps in Germany with flails, they would go to it, and not leave one alive. They would be without passion and without mercy, not because they hated chimney sweeps, but because they loved obedience —loved it so much that even the soul stood at attention before it.

And how about the rest of us? How about this hundred of us against five, the millions of us against a few thousand? We are wiping the sweat of terror from our brows, tugging abstractedly at our collars. . . .

"We really ought to spit at each other for standing by without opening our mouths," says Karla, trembling with rage.

"Of course we ought to spit at each other. But who's any the better for your opening your mouth if they grab you by the collar the next moment, and very quietly string you up? Martyrs need an audience. Anonymous death never did anyone any good." Wise as I seem to myself, I somehow can't seem to enjoy my wisdom. There's some catch to it somewhere.

We've lost our appetite for lunch. "We'd better go home," says Karla. "Who knows what we'll find there?"

Sure enough, we find various things. Not just Dr. Weissmann in Andrik's bed—the whole apartment is crammed. Levy has arrived, and Jochen Cohn; they're sitting on my couch, playing écarté—"To divert our minds," says Levy apologetically. He looks exhausted and unshaven.

Jochen Cohn rubs his forehead in embarrassment: "The idea of our descending on you like this. . . ."

"Where's Andrik?" I inquire.

"He's looking for Dr. Hirschberg. Nobody answers his phone. Probably they've shipped him off."

"Shipped him off?"

"Yes, certainly, shipped him off. To the felons' paradise, the Jews' heaven—by special delivery in Prussian trucks. Anyone that didn't disappear in time might just as well make his will."

Two more guests have made themselves at home in Andrik's room. "Just for one night," they plead shyly. "Just until the worst is over."

The telephone rings. "Are you at home?" I recognize Franz Wolfheim's voice; it sounds hoarse and excited. "Open the front door for me. I'll be there in five minutes." He'll make our sixth guest. I'm beginning to feel claustrophobic.

When Franz Wolfheim arrives, we hold a council of war. Two on my couch. Two on Andrik's. The shortest and thinnest one can sleep in the armchair; if we pull up a chair, he can even stretch out. Dr. Levy is billeted on the floor with two Persian carpets and all the available cushions. By the time Andrik arrives, everything is arranged.

"Did you bring him along?"

He shakes his head. "Too late! They got there ahead of me. Sperling is gone, too, and Peter Tarnowsky, Ernst Angel and little Schwartz. I saw them getting him from his apartment, three SS men, and shoving him into a truck. There were seventeen people standing inside, packed like sheep. He was the eighteenth. Give me a drink. Otherwise . . ."

We all need a drink. I pour out what the household affords. By one o'clock the house is quiet.

Friday, November 11, 1938.

They've dragged them all away—all the Jewish men they could get hold of. Not just in Berlin, but all over the Reich, without warrants or any legal formalities at all. They had to go along just however they happened to be; we hear that some of them didn't even have shoes on. Only those who were warned in time have escaped the raid. Thank Heavens, a good many were warned. Hundreds managed to disappear at the houses of friends; hundreds sought shelter with strangers—and found it. One little seamstress took in two Jewish fugitives; she didn't even know their names or where they came from. Workingmen in the Frankfurter Allee brought back to the Jewish shop-owners the merchandise that was scattered over the street. They didn't say a word, just tugged sheepishly at their caps. The chief surgeon of a hospital is hiding a wounded rabbi in the back room from the bloodhounds of the Gestapo.

While the SS was raging, innumerable fellow Germans were ready to die of pity and shame. Almost all our friends have people quartered on them. When we telephone, we talk in hints and ciphers. Then we rack our brains by the hour over what the person at the other end of the line could have meant. "Karl has suddenly been taken sick." Who the hell is Karl, anyway? "Thea had guests come in yesterday—those country cousins, you know them, the ones with all the children. Gerhard? Gerhard is working out of town. We don't know just when he'll be back." What Gerhard? What children? What do you mean, country cousins? But our deductive powers grow by the hour.

This afternoon I go to see Lisel Hirschberg. She is sitting, turned to stone with grief, on an overturned chest amid broken glass and general desolation. "Two officials from the criminal police came for Kurt yesterday afternoon," she says with empty eyes. "They didn't even let him put on his hat. An hour later the doorbell rang. When I opened the door, ten hooligans burst in, asking if the Jew Hirschberg lived here. I couldn't get a word out; I just nodded. That started them off. They were like a bunch of vandals—they knocked all the silver off the buffet with one sweep, tipped over the bookshelves, dragged the linen out of the cupboard. They chopped up our wooden Madonna with an ax, tramped on the Dürer engraving, and threw Kurt's valuable collection of woodcuts into the kitchen stove. They carried on for thirty minutes. At the end they said, 'You have your racial compatriots to thank for this.' And they didn't even know that I'm Aryan." She smiles her soft, melancholy smile. Then suddenly her self-control leaves her. "Kurt," she sobs. "I do love him—I do. And he didn't do anything."

"Nobody has done anything. That was exactly our mistake." I begin to realize something. "We didn't see how different other people are. We judged others by ourselves. That's how we judged the Nazis; and that's how we made them great.

You, and I, and Andrik, and everyone else. The Jews are just the first in line. But you wait; our turn will come. Not because we did anything, but because we tolerated it. The great rise of injustice."

"But what could we have done?" Lisel Hirschberg stares at me blankly.

"We should have spoken up louder for the good cause—for love of one's neighbor, for peace, for our ideals. But all we did was let the Nazis speak up for theirs." I reach for my hat and coat. "Let's at least profit by our mistakes. If we can't get them released, we must at least find out where they are. Come, get your things on; we'll go see Lukaschek. If anyone knows anything, he will."

Lukaschek is a lawyer, and a passionately devout Catholic. Ever since 1933 he has believed that the great about-face would come, and has been working for it.

I was not mistaken in him; Lukaschek is not one of the tolerators. Lukaschek acts. His waiting room is full of people; they sit and stand in every nook and cranny. Women with horror still in their eyes, women who look pale and sleepless, women weeping soundlessly to themselves. They have all found their way here. Lukaschek is acting. With fixed attention he is sitting behind his desk.

"The first batch went to the freight station. That same night. We gather they went to Oranienburg. The Silesians? No, the Silesians aren't there. We hear they went to Buchenwald—to Buchenwald, near Weimar. They were left standing in the spotlights on the square outside the station for two hours. Your husband there? Yes, he was seen. He was all right. He's definitely expecting to come back. . . . We don't know anything at all about the third transport yet, but inquiries are under way. . . . No, Dr. Oppenheim wasn't there. There's no trace of Rotholz. . . . Wait a minute, I'll give you an introduction—for the Gestapo. It may do some good."

He does not send one woman away unconsoled. When I leave his office with Lisel Hirschberg, she has in her pocket a letter to Kriminalrat Müller, and I know where I can turn to do my share more vigorously in the future.

They are still sweeping up broken glass in the streets. The empty caves of show windows goggle like blind eyes in a flayed face. Oh, Ernst Angel, oh, Peter Tarnowsky, oh, all you poor creatures that have been carried off! An icy wind is blowing, and I shiver when I think of you.

Sunday, November 13, 1938.

The Gestapo's rage has worn itself out. The wave of arrests seems to be over. Instead, the government is issuing one decree after another, signed by Goering. Frick, Goebbels, Gürtner, Schwerin-Krosigk, and Funk attended the cabinet meetings.

Elimination of the Jews from German economic life. As of January 1, 1939, no more Jewish business houses, artisans, or business managers. Reparation is to be made by all Jews of German nationality through the payment to the German Reich of one billion Reichsmarks. All damage done to Jewish business concerns and dwellings on November 8, 9, and 10, 1938, through popular indignation at the campaign of calumniation by international Jewry against National Socialist Germany is to be repaired forthwith by the Jewish proprietors or tradespeople involved. The cost of repairs is to be borne by the proprietor of each Jewish concern or dwelling. Insurance claims due to Jews of German nationality are confiscated for the benefit of the Reich.

That day Ernst vom Rath was taken to Düsseldorf for a state funeral, and thousands of innocent Jews were rolling away toward some unknown agony.

Only little Schwartz, the violinist in the X String Orchestra, has come back; he made it in two days.

"They kept us locked up for fourteen hours," he tells us. "A hundred and fifty men in one room. Finally they took us into the courtyard, and made us form in ranks of fifty. Nobody knew whether they were going to shoot us or release us. We stood and waited, heels together, hands at our sides. Finally somebody in uniform appeared—a *Scharfuehrer*, Group Leader, something like that. He went clanking along the ranks, and yelled, 'World War officers front and center!' Thirteen of us came forward. Form ranks again, click heels. What regiment, wounds, decorations? There were nine with the Iron Cross first class. The man in uniform stands there and gives a searching look, folds his arms, and shouts, 'The first seven fall out, get out of here, quick! The others get back in ranks!'

"I was the seventh man. We didn't dare look at one another. We never glanced back; we slunk out like traitors. Seven out of a hundred and fifty." Little Schwartz looks as if he wanted to cry. "I can't get over it," he wails. "A fellow should have stayed there."

Schwartz is a newlywed; he has a daughter nine weeks old. "She's going to be named Catherine," he said. "Catherine can be pronounced in all European languages." His emigration papers are in order; all he has lacked so far was the courage to leave. Some people have to go round by way of the Gestapo to lose their unwanted love of country.

At eight o'clock in the morning a messenger brings me a city telegram: "Come at once." I rush over to the Buggestrasse. Mrs. Schwartz opens the door; she has no make-up on; she looks sleepless and harassed.

"Thank God you're here," she says, and dashes off. The entry smells of dust, sweepings, wrapping paper, and packing cases. I hear the baby yelling in the distance—Catherine, whose name you can pronounce in any language. At present the future cosmopolite is lying in a laundry basket, with chaos around her. It seems as if the entire household had been dumped out with one sweep: piles of books, bundles of linen, open drawers, half-filled trunks, bulging wastebaskets, nails, excelsior, stacks of dishes and pots and pans on the floor, on the beds, on the dining table, and in the bathtub. I wade knee-deep through the debris of moving, stumble over a mountain of clothes hangers, and finally almost put my foot in a pan of fried potatoes.

"My God," I stammer, overwhelmed.

Schwartz comes rushing from the music room. "It's all right, it's all right," he reassures me. His vest is flapping. As he shakes my hand with his right, his left hand is doing up his tie. "We're off this evening—10:50 from the Zoo Station. Tickets, visa, emigration permit, everything in order. We can catch up on our sleep in London." He stares at me as if the hangman were at his heels. "Ten-fifty," he repeats. It sounds like a magical formula.

But then he grows thoughtful again. "You **must** do me a service. Really, it would be a great favor. My wife has a piece of land somewhere, half an acre. To be truthful, there's nothing but trees on it—not even a fence around it. It's in Saarow on the Scharmitzelsee. You take the place. In trust."

I remember that a great many of my Aryan acquaintances have become apparent capitalists in the same way during the past three months. "Before the Gestapo gobbles it up," their Jewish friends say. And so apartment houses and businesses, building lots and woodland change owners overnight. Underneath, everything stays just as it was, only it is no longer the experienced Mr. Abraham who turns up for board meetings of Müller & Co.'s embroidery factory, but Dr. Franz von Hollberg; Miss Schulze collects the rents in the apartment house at No. 12 Köpernickerstrasse, instead of Dr. Cohn. One has only to find some dodge that will make the transfer look credible. Everything else is a gentleman's agreement, in trust, on a simple word of honor.

"All right, let's transfer it," I assent. At eleven-twenty we sign the contract at the office of a notary in the west end. A footman in livery serves two whiskies and sodas on a silver tray. Little ice cubes float elegantly in the tall crystal glasses. Imagine there still being such things!

At eleven-forty Schwartz and I are standing on the Kurfürstendamm; the usual noon idlers are strolling past—chorus boys, smart women, pedigreed dogs, and snobs. It smells of gasoline and autumn. The cars are rolling around the Memorial Church, an endlessly revolving circle. The religious merry-go-round, as a wag once remarked. People throng the sidewalk cafés. They are sitting wrapped in blankets, enjoying the sun, and drinking something bright-colored through long straws.

"Beloved city," murmurs little Schwartz. "Beloved town! Shall I ever see it again?"

"Of course you'll see it again!" I grow brusque with emotion.

Luckily an empty cab is just whisking past. We leap in and race through the city. We buy and buy and buy—silk stockings, leather suitcases, hatboxes, handbags, bedspreads. We scatter money like confetti. We rush in and rush out. We race upstairs and down. Sometimes the whole thing strikes me like some silly comedy. What's this nonsense for? Why this useless snatching at possessions, indiscriminately, aimlessly, just to get rid of the paper money?

Parcels pile up in the cab, threatening to bury us. The taximeter mounts; by the time it shows thirty-four marks fifteen, it is seven o'clock at night. We stop in the Buggestrasse. I feel as if we had bought out Berlin.

Schwartz wrings his hands and groans, "All this to pack? Our train leaves in four hours."

But Karla has turned up during the afternoon, and so has Andrik. We pack as if we were being paid for it. Into the trunks with it—into the trunks with it. At last everyone has to stand on top; the overflow threatens to snap the locks. "The transfer company will take care of the rest."

Schwartz grabs for the trunks, and is half way to England already.

Andrik takes my arm. As we open the apartment door, he asks pensively, "Do you suppose we'll ever be going so suddenly . . . ?"

I can't help laughing. "Not with all that baggage, if we do—even if I am 'Mistress at Saarow.'"

Tuesday, December 6, 1938.

Lucky for all those who have left the country. As of today, certain districts of the capital are put under the so-called "Jew ban." Henceforth Jews of German nationality and stateless Jews may neither walk nor drive through any street, square, park, or building in such districts. Anyone who happens to live there must obtain a police permit to cross the ban limit.

Word from Kurt Hirschberg. He's in the Sachsenhausen concentration camp near Oranienburg—only thirty kilometers from Berlin. "Dear Lisel," he writes, "I am all right. My health is good. You can send me a parcel of food. You can write, too. Twenty lines. Get in touch with lawyer Landmann." And underneath, "Dear, dear Lisel! Your Kurt."

"He's here! He's here! He's back," it comes stumbling, sobbing, and rejoicing over the wire.

"Andrik!" I shout into the next room. "Kurt Hirschberg is back."

We drop everything, and rush over to the Sächsischestrasse. Lisel is at the door. Her eyes are red with weeping.

"Ssh!" she whispers, putting her finger to her lips. "Ssh! He's asleep! The doctor just left."

"The doctor?"

She nods. "He's all done up—hands, feet, ears. Frozen. They made them stand out in the cold at twelve above zero. Punishment level No. 1, he said." She indicates the bedroom door with a nod, and begins wiping the tears from her face again. "He's gone through absolute hell." We nod. Any words of consolation would seem silly.

Two hours later we are sitting by Kurt Hirschberg's bed. The doctor has bandaged his head and arms. His shaven head looks like a wax mask through the white bandages.

"Imagine your being back," we say, trying desperately not to let him see our horror at the change in his appearance. "Was it very bad?"

"Very," we hear from the pillows. "Very, when you had to stand in ranks for fifteen hours, in groups of three hundred, lined up like Prussian recruits. Hat in hand. Valuables in your hat. Fifteen hours. Nothing to eat. Nothing to drink. Not a single chance to step out of ranks. Three men died that night, of heart attacks and urine poisoning. It was bad . . . Bad . . . Very, very bad.

"It's bad to sleep in overcrowded barracks, packed together like sardines in a tin. If one man turns over in his sleep, a hundred and seventy-five others have to turn with him. The straw bedding rustles. The man next to you groans. A hundred and seventy-five men, knee to knee, arm to arm. You aren't asleep, you aren't awake; you lie as if you were stunned. It's bad . . . It's bad, it's awfully bad.

"It's bad when they make you sing sentimental songs with your limbs frozen stiff and despair in your heart—'Deep brown is the hazelnut, deep brown are you.' You have no coat. You have no gloves. Your head is shaved. You stand out in the cold, shivering and singing, 'Deep brown is the hazelnut.'

"It's bad when they let out their power jag on you. A smack in the face. Rifle barrel between your legs. Hey, watch your step! Damn Jew! People that don't obey get hung up by their elbows; locked in the standing cage; beaten and flayed and shaken until their teeth rattle.

"We froze, we obeyed, we stood at attention when they strung up two of our companions on the gallows beside the

34

lighted Christmas tree. We sang 'Deep brown is the hazelnut,' *O Tannenbaum,* and 'But the wagon rolls.' Because we stuffed newspaper under our shirts to keep from freezing stiff, we stood outside the door for two hours as a punishment. Hands at our sides—bare hands at twelve above. We . . ." He stops. "It's bad when you can't cry. Bad, bad, unimaginably bad when . . . When you . . . aren't a human being any more." He says it without emotion, without anger—as if he were recording some biological discovery.

"When are you leaving the country?" Andrik asks tonelessly.

"As soon as I can get a visa for England. I hope in the next month."

Monday, January 16, 1939.

Gradually they're all coming back—the ones from Buchenwald and the ones from Sachsenhausen, with shaven skulls and eyes overfull of suffering. Peter Tarnowsky, Kurt Sperling, Ernst Angel, Heinz Rosenthal, and Paul Weiss.

Some of them have one story to tell, others another. At Sachsenhausen you could work, but you froze to death, and the punishments were harsh. At Buchenwald near Weimar work was prohibited. For hundreds of people there was one privy. The first seven days there were known as Murder Week. Bad food, intestinal grippe, diarrhea. People writhed in spasms. Fall in to fall out; a queue outside the privies. Forward, march into the hereafter. In Berlin people are complaining that the coffee is giving out. "Germans, drink tea!" the coffee merchants advertise. There's no tea at Buchenwald. No coffee. And no privy. At Buchenwald several hundred people died in seven days—clubbed, shot, harried to death.

"Deep brown is the hazelnut," I sing, trying to forget that I read in a refugee paper about a young Communist who was flogged to death to the tune of *Am Brunnen vor dem Tore* on the phonograph.

Friday, February 24, 1939.

The "lift"—the luggage truck—is trump in Berlin—not the passenger elevator of smart hotels, but the container for permissible *émigré* baggage. For six weeks there has been hardly any other subject of conversation. November 10 opened the eyes of even the most devotedly home-loving Jews. Everyone who can possibly manage it is trying to get out of the country. It's not easy to get an emigration visa; it almost seems as if all the countries had conspired to make emigration difficult for the German Jews. In one, they restrict immigration; in another, they forbid it altogether. Urgent applications are delayed, important letters lie unanswered. Affidavits are mislaid; sponsorships have to be begged for.

A person with no connections abroad, no influential sponsors, must resign himself to staying here as an unwelcome alien. *Sauve qui peut!*

We pack "lifts," we break up households, we auction off dishes, and peddle libraries. Seven sets of Heine. Nine copies of *The Magic Mountain*. Eleven of *All Quiet on the Western Front*, and twelve Bibles.

If you aren't packing furniture, you are poring over the atlas. Where's La Paz? Oh, yes, in Bolivia. New Zealand is supposed to have opened up temporarily. They need doctors in Uruguay. Farmers can emigrate to Palestine.

The globe is shrinking; Brazil seems a stone's throw, London like an afternoon's excursion to Wannsee. If we should want to go visiting our friends later, we'd have to get a round-trip ticket around the world.

Intellectual occupations are in poor demand. Everyone who can scare up the time and money tries at the last moment to learn some manual trade. Every day you hear about new short courses. Lawyers' wives are learning dressmaking, learning to put up rollmops from pickled-fish dealers. One man turns to manufacturing popular-priced egg liqueurs, another to the production of dress patterns. There are short courses in gymnastics, quick courses in massage, infant care, cooking, baking, pressing, mending, glove making, slipper making, millinery, necktie making. Instruction in every living language. Essential vocabularies for the Spanish doctor, the English jurist, the Russian engineer, the French mechanic.

Sauve qui peut! Next week the Hirschbergs are leaving for England; the week after that, the Weissmanns for America. The Wolfheims and Levys are gone. The Fischers, Rosenbergs, and Angels are getting ready to go. For the second time since Hitler came to power, our circle of friends is scattering to the winds. We shall be pretty lonely when we've sold off the last set of Heine.

Monday, March 6, 1939.

"Haven't you been noticing," my friend Hinrichs inquires, "that they're taking an alarmingly keen interest again in the Czech German minority?"

Hinrichs is a professor at the University. Now that the Nazis are meddling in his business, he is trying hard to do something not so much for his science as for humanity. Next to Erich Tuch he's our most reliable source of information.

I shake my head. I think of the seven million Czechs that Hitler so grandiosely forwent before he occupied the Sudetenland. "What do we want with seven million Czechs?" he yelled. And the absolutely endless, scornful laughter of an obediently applauding Chamber of Deputies rewarded his happy phrase.

Thursday, March 9, 1939.

The Czech-atrocities-against-German-minority propaganda steam roller is getting ready to go. Hinrichs' forecast was not erroneous. One after another they're coming out of the advertising files: the outraged mother with child at the breast, the assault on unoffending fellow Germans, waylayings and murders, riots, disturbances, provocations. The idea that the Germans themselves might have given any cause for such doings is indignantly denied. It is downright slander for anyone to say that they are forming Nazi cells in a foreign country, recruiting followers for Hitler, and grossly blackguarding their government wherever there is a chance. The fifth column is on the march in the remnant of Czechoslovakia. Today it's disguised: tomorrow ... *Vyshehrad, Vyshehrad,* I think sadly. Will the world put up with this looting expedition as it has with all the others?

Saturday, March 18, 1939.

It did put up with it. We are tearing our hair; we cannot conceive that Mr. Hitler has been allowed to win this game again. Until four days ago the billows of Czech atrocities against the German minority were breaking like stinking sewage over the press and infecting the radio, eating their poisonous way into the minds of the credulous.

Then the bomb burst. On March 13 Tiso, the Slovak prime

minister, arrived to see Hitler. One day later Slovakia declared itself independent. On March 15 our papers announced: "The Fuehrer today received the Czechoslovak president, Dr. Hacha, and the Czechoslovak foreign minister, Dr. Chwalkowsky, in Berlin at their request, in the presence of Reich Foreign Minister von Ribbentrop. The Czechoslovak president stated that in order to achieve final satisfaction, he was confidently placing the fate of the Czech people and country in the hands of the leader of the German Reich."

And so what does he do, our Leader, overwhelmed with the trust of the Czech people? He "expresses his determination to take the Czech people under the protection of the German Reich, and to guarantee it an autonomous development of its national life in accordance with its special nature." One lie upon the heels of another.

The fifth column, flinging aside the mask, marches into the Czech capital as a German army. Hitler sets off for Prague with a great retinue. On March 16 the Protectorate of Bohemia and Moravia is incorporated in the "Greater German Reich." Today they appointed Mr. von Neurath as Reich Protector in Bohemia and Moravia. Not a shot is fired. Not a word of protest anywhere.

Have you died, Vyshehrad? Have they put a gag in your mouth?

Monday, April 17, 1939.

Today the Fischers are flying to London. Tomorrow Mrs. Rosenberg is leaving us. We are getting to be familiar callers at the Tempelhof airport. Almost every one of the departing travelers leaves us some legacy behind. "Don't forget my mother. . . . Look after Aunt Johanna. . . . And see here, you will drop in on Uncle Heinrich now and then, won't you?"

That's why the emigrations have been never-ending for us since 1933. There's always somebody left behind—a daughter, an uncle, a son; some near or remote relative who is now doubly in need of consolation, through the departure of his loved ones and the growing Jewish terror.

We drop in on Uncle Heinrich. We look out for Aunt Johanna, and we don't forget Heinz Rosenthal's delicate little mother. There are lots of other Uncle Heinrichs in Germany, and countless Aunt Johannas. Sometimes it's enough to make you tear your hair. "You will come soon again, won't you?" begs Aunt Johanna, with the eyes of a terrified child. "At last one gets a sight of you!" grumbles Uncle Heinrich. "I thought you must have gone over to the Nazis."

The great plague has infected us all—victims and lucky ones alike—so deeply that even the merest want of time raises suspicions of a change of sentiments.

Thursday, April 20, 1939.

Hitler is celebrating his fiftieth birthday, with trumpet and drum, with reviews, fluttering banners, Bengal lights.

Yesterday evening the so-called East-West Axis was opened —the splendid street leading by way of the Brandenburg Gate to the Reichskanzlerplatz. Hundreds of iron flagpoles line it on both sides. "For future hangings of bigwigs," people call them privately. The flags flutter, picturesquely illuminated by searchlights. Sensation-loving crowds are milling below. Laughing, chattering, on the lookout for adventures, they push their way in a packed, black mass toward the Victory Column. Getting through is quite out of the question.

"Is it sensation they want, or is it Adolf Hitler?" asks Andrik, shaking his head, as we try to fight our way through to the Friedrichstrasse.

The big parade comes off at noon—an advance showing of the National Socialist war potential. For two and a half hours the tanks, guns, and ammunition trucks go rolling on. Again masses of people line the streets. In front, a row of Storm Troopers bars the way; behind them are German Girls' League and Hitler Youth. The Storm Troopers make a game of blocking the little girls' view with their broad backs. "Just put your heads between our legs," they suggest with a smirk. The smirk that goes with the suggestion is not a nice one. Nor is the smile with which forty out of a hundred Girls' League girls accept it.

"Sieg Heil!" the crowd howls. On a kitchen stepladder in the middle of the push sits a workingman, lean, unshaven, in a blue mechanic's overall. He looks pensively at the rolling trucks. "You take all that, and no gas," we hear him growl, "and it's just junk." People around look up at him, horrified. When they see that no one is protesting, they venture an approving smile. And again one wonders helplessly, what do they really think? Are they against it or for it?

"For it! All Berliners are for it!" declare the foes of the Nazis in the provinces. "Otherwise they wouldn't keep yelling 'Yes!' at the Sportpalast."

That wretched Sportpalast! It's known by reputation all over the world. The place will hold a couple of thousand; and Berlin has about four million inhabitants. Why is it that so few people understand the real inwardness of our "yeses" at the Sportpalast, the tumultuous joy of the men lining the way, the ovations at all the bigwigs' speeches, the Sieg Heiling of the Reichstag deputies, the boisterous popular approval at every Nazi function? Misleading though it is, the puzzle is very easily solved.

"All Party Comrades and all those known to be politically reliable will attend a community reception of the Fuehrer's speech," is the name of the solution.

The county supervisors, block leaders, factory stewards, plant foremen, Girls' League and Hitler Youth leaders, all the officially appointed supervisors of German public opinion are held responsible that there shail be nothing but yes-shouters present to cheer on official occasions. Any politically unreliable person, anyone suspected in the slightest degree of possibly saying No must be kept away.

It's not fair to reproach us with the Sportpalast. We have no more and no less to do with it than the listener at the radio, the native of Honolulu, or the farmer on Lake Michigan.

Friday, June 23, 1939.

The opponents of Nazism are trying hard to save at least a fraction of their Jewish friends' property, and get it abroad to them. The emigrant's baggage grows lighter from month to month. The German traveling public going abroad, however, has been crossing the frontier in grander and grander style during the last few months.

"One Persian lamb coat, three rings, two necklaces, one bracelet. Who's going to Italy in the predictable future?"

"Two watches, one diamond choker, one Leica, to Finland."

"Five gold pieces, two silver fox, for Brazil. Send off by parcel post, registered and insured, from the first station beyond the frontier."

"One typewriter and five bags to Switzerland."

You load yourself with jewelry, you swathe yourself in sable and chinchilla. Never in our lives have we looked so "capitalistic." Four new suits in the wardrobe trunk. Six winter dresses, five summer dresses, eight silk nightgowns, twelve pairs of stockings, and three pairs of shoes. A twenty-dollar bill slumbers at the bottom of your powder box. By way of butter on each slice of pumpernickel in the "Sökeland package" there is a thousand-mark note. We heave a sigh when the frontier inspection is behind us.

Through his foreign tours Andrik has the most opportunity to cross the border. In two weeks we shall be going together to France and Sweden. Letters of request are already arriving from both countries: rollmops, Westphalian ham, frankfurters, Bismarck herring, Hamburg black bread, Neiss pastry. Behind each wish lies a twinge of homesickness. Each errand reveals the unspoken confession: we can't get free of the land we have left. We're longing to be back—back at home.

Every day our traveling baggage grows bulkier, and Andrik's shopping list longer.

Saturday, July 8, 1939.

Tomorrow evening we shall be in Paris. At last we will be able to talk again without whispering, without circumlocutions or looking anxiously in all directions. I've just been to see Heinrich Muehsam. One never knows what may happen in the meantime.

He still hasn't found the jumping-off place; he's typing his childhood letters, and philosophizing over the way of the world, as wise as any Buddha.

"Are you really going to risk staying here?" I ask.

He looks at me. "Where else should I go? To be unhappy in Canada? Uprooted in the United States? Frantic with homesickness in the Philippines? Quite aside from the fact that neither the Philippines nor the United States, let alone Canada, the emigrant's paradise, would take me to their bosom." He smiles. "There is a certain degree of belonging-here that cuts off any idea of flight. If they don't actually force me . . ."

"God forbid! God forbid!" I say, horrified. "Knock wood! Don't tempt fate! The Thousand Years' Reich isn't over yet."

Paris, Sunday, July 16, 1939.

From morning until evening people are coming and going in our hotel room. Friends, acquaintances, friends of friends, acquaintances of acquaintances. Everyone wants to hear how things look in Germany. They want to exchange impressions, receive greetings, unburden their souls. They aren't all the same as they were, either, before our long or short separation. With a good many of them it's a bit hard to make oneself understood. Why do they suddenly think we're in favor of the Nazis just because we're going back to Germany? Why do they say "we Jews" instead of "we friends" the way they used to? Weren't we their friends when we helped them to get out?

Hitler invented race segregation. They themselves are doing Hitler's work when they follow his distinctions. Now and then I find our conversations a bit saddening.

But Andrik straightens me out. "Now don't you go making

the mistake of thinking that all Jews are bound to be angels. Not everyone whom the Nazis have forced to oppose them really shares our views. Many a Mr. Abraham, Isaac, or Jacob would be a Nazi with pleasure if they had only let him be one."

"But the *émigrés*—" I try to object.

"There is no such thing as *the émigrés*," Andrik interrupts. "There is only your *émigré* friend Mr. A or your *émigré* friend Mrs. B. Our whole trouble comes from generalization. All Poles are this way; all French are that way; all Jews are bound to be thus and so. Character assessment by schedule F. A hundred thousand on one pattern. If we don't break ourselves of that habit, we'll never go right—neither with international understanding nor with tolerance."

I can only agree with him, and I don't require "all" refugees to share all our opinions.

Stockholm, Tuesday, August 22, 1939.

Germany has made a nonaggression pact with the Soviet Union. The news struck the world yesterday like a bombshell. Andrik comes back from town with a bundle of newspapers under his arm. "I guess it's here," he says gravely. "I'm afraid we shall have to leave."

Neither of us knows whether to heave a sigh of relief or to gasp with horror. Ever since 1933 Hitler's opponents have been certain that the "Thousand Years' Reich" would wind up in a war sooner or later—a war that Germany was bound to lose. We've had six years to get used to the idea. Now the end with its horrors seems almost more bearable to us than horror without end.

45

Our trip home has left us in no doubt about the seriousness of the situation. Reservists with knapsacks and cartons are thronging streets, station platforms, waiting rooms. "We don't want any war," their scared faces say. At Stettin Station all is unimaginable confusion. "The first day of mobilization," the porter whispers in our ear. "They sent the children home from school, and convened the Reichstag. The crazy business is going to start tomorrow." The man must take us for foreigners, to talk so openly. Or has the looming threat of war put even the threat of the Gestapo in the shade?

At home there's a note on the table: "Call me at once! Urgent!" It's Karla's handwriting.

I rush to the telephone. "Too late, my love!" she greets me. "I hope you've put your house in order for the next few years."

Unluckily my brain, grown unused to cipher conversations, doesn't take hold. "What can she mean?" I wonder. What's too late? What does she hope I've "put in order"?

Sunday, August 27, 1939.

Now I see what she meant. Effective immediately, food ration cards are introduced throughout the Reich. Up to last night we could have bought things. By the time I telephoned to Karla it was too late. The shops were closed for the day. Starting tomorrow, the German people will be living on a strictly regulated rationing system. Twenty-four hundred grams of bread a week, 500 grams of meat, 270 grams of fat, 62.5 grams of cheese, 100 grams of marmalade, and 250 grams of sugar. Besides this, a certain quantity of prepared foods per month, and 400 grams of coffee substitute. Whole milk for children and invalids only. All other vital foodstuffs will be distributed after a "preceding proclamation in each case."

A pretty prospect when you are just back from a six-week trip.

Right under the decree are two columns in boldface about the "inhuman maltreatment of the German minority in Poland."

Monday, August 28, 1939.

The troops are rolling eastward. Hinrichs has been called up. Not a soul in Berlin believes that peace can still be saved.

Wednesday, August 30, 1939.

Yes, the die is cast. Every step Hitler has taken since yesterday reveals his intention to march into Poland, cost what it may. Hour by hour Erich Tuch whispers the cues to us for this new scene in history.

Henderson calling on Hitler. The Fuehrer demands not only the return of Danzig, but the incorporation of the Polish Corridor. "Poland needs access to the sea," he said not long ago. Today she doesn't seem to need it any more. A Polish envoy with full authority to negotiate must appear in Berlin within twenty-four hours. This is an impossibility; Hitler and Ribbentrop know it just as well as Sir Nevile Henderson does.

Thursday, August 31, 1939.

Last night a farce unparalleled in history was played out between Henderson and Ribbentrop. The British ambassador meets with an icy reception at twelve o'clock at night from the Reich foreign minister. Ribbentrop opens his portfolio, takes out a paper, and reads it off hurriedly in an undertone.

Sir Nevile Henderson is not at home in German; he understands but half of it, even that half not altogether. "May I ask for a copy for my government?" he asks courteously after the reading is finished.

"Too late," says Ribbentrop irritably, and tosses the paper on the table.

Negotiations with England have been broken off since two o'clock this afternoon. The German army is on the march.

A mood of disaster reigns at the office. "Starting tomorrow, the guns will do the talking," says Hollner somberly.

Most of the able-bodied men have already been called up. Tall Meyer, our political man, celebrates the day with the splendor of his SS uniform. But he doesn't seem quite at ease in it. And when Hollner circulates a bottle of cognac as a farewell to peace, he, too, takes a good pull. So heartily, in fact, that afterward he has to be piled into a taxi.

Friday, September 1, 1939.

At 4:45 German troops crossed the Polish frontier on a broad front. The government has popped up with an abundance of new decrees. Streets, shops, and dwellings to be blacked out. Compulsory air-raid duty. As of today listening to foreign radio stations is forbidden under severe penalties.

We have already "sinned" three times, with a blanket over the radio, behind locked doors. France and England are mobilizing. Italy has declared her neutrality. The die is cast. But when will Hitler's die be thrown?

In the afternoon we are invited to tea at Dr. Flamm's. Since the Nazis pensioned him off as a senior judge of the county court because of political unreliability, he has been making a living by a course of law lectures, trying carefully and shrewdly to enlighten his pupils about the pernicious doctrines of Nazism. Andrik considers him the most solidly sensible of his friends.

Now we find him balancing on a ladder, in the act of tacking wrapping paper over the windows. "Germans, black out!" he greets us, driving the last nail into his monstrosity.

We sit around the table, stirring our tea. "This is going to be a long war," says Flamm in melancholy tones. "Heaven knows who'll be left alive at the end."

"Certainly not Mr. Hitler!"

Flamm makes a wry face. "What good will Hitler's death do us if we bite the dust before he does?"

Outside a strange sound is heard—up and down, down and up, a long-drawn howl.

Andrik springs up. "Air-raid alarm!" he cries, startled. We look around, not knowing quite what to do.

"Down into the cellar!" Flamm advises.

A lonely plane buzzes overhead; we watch it tensely through the open basement window. Twenty minutes later the scare is over.

Another unaccustomed sound is heard—a long, piercing hum. "The all-clear," the local experts call it. They undo their gas masks, and smugly beat a retreat.

We say nothing about this new experience; it's disagreeable, and almost makes us feel as if we'd disgraced ourselves.

On our way we see stars over Berlin for the first time—not paling sadly behind gaudy electric signs, but sparkling with clear solemnity. The moon casts a milky gleam over the roofs of the town. Not a spark of electric light falls upon the streets.

"The metropolis is going back to nature," Andrik smiles. "It's almost enough to turn one into a romantic." He takes my arm and squeezes it.

"How fond I really am of him!" I think tenderly.

Monday, September 4, 1939.

State of war between England and Germany. Three days ago Mrs. Rosenthal got a letter saying that her English visa was on the way. Now the trap is sprung. She weeps. How many others are weeping today over a similar fate?

Dr. Muehsam smiles philosophically. "Now we're all tarred with the same brush," he says, and seems almost pleased that the decision to emigrate, at least anywhere on the European continent, has been definitely taken out of his hands.

Tschechenstochau has fallen. The Warthe is crossed. German air forces have been bombing the Polish towns in "wave assaults" since yesterday. France also is at war with us. Yet neither Frenchmen nor Englishmen are marching across our frontiers. Why don't they, too, cross some river or other, and put an end to the madness of war before the best blood of all nations has been drained?

Thursday, September 21, 1939.

They haven't acted. Today Adolf Hitler is speaking from the German city of Danzig. The war against Poland is finished—after eighteen days. Three hundred thousand prisoners. Neither the British nor the French prime minister seems to know that Hitler abhors nothing so much as a two-front war,

that he would rather risk an alliance with the very Bolshe\
he has been blackguarding for six years than expose himself
to any attack from the rear.

Tuesday, October 10, 1939.

A rumor is running through town this morning like wildfire:
the English government has fallen; a ten days' truce is pro-
posed. Our office claims to have heard on reliable authority,
direct from the Air Ministry. All Berlin is on the telephone.
"Had you heard. . . . Is it really true?"

About noon comes the denial, issued by Goebbels in person.
The peace-loving rumor mongers, including the Reich Ministry for Air, have been victimized by fishwives' gossip. No one
has any peace proposals. The war is going on.

And in the ARP course, tenants and landlords are constantly reminded that they need not permit persons of alien
race in their basements.

We are ashamed to face our Jewish friends; and being
ashamed, we go to see them more and more often. "Remember
when . . ." our conversations begin. "Do you still recall . . ."
is usually the end.

Monday, October 30, 1939.

Karla is dropping mysterious hints of some "great affair" in
prospect. She's practising revolver-shooting with Erich Tuch
in the privacy of her apartment. "Just in case," she says oracu-
larly. "After all, one never knows."

We wish we did "know," but our friend remains shrouded
in obstinate silence.

51

Yesterday evening an infernal machine went off in the Munich Bürgerbräu. It was just after Hitler had finished his address to the old fellow warriors and the wearers of the Blood Order, and had left the meeting. A reward of five hundred thousand marks is offered for information of the perpetrator.

"Boy, if it had worked, we'd all be dead drunk under the table by now," is Hollner's greeting to me at the office.

Karla is remarkably quiet. Does she know more about things than she cares to tell?

The evening papers are foaming at the mouth with rage. "There is no question that the English Secret Service had a hand in this outrage," they screech. "But this time the British gentry have mistaken their man. The gloves are now off with the enemies of the State in Germany who fatuously expect to carry on their criminal activities in the pay of the Secret Service. The gloves are off, with German thoroughness."

For the moment German thoroughness consists in suspecting everyone else—anyone but the right person. Flamm and Andrik believe another "Reichstag fire" has been staged—that is, that the government arranged its own bomb outrage. In many quarters a rumor is current that Himmler did it to prove his power, and Hitler wanted to display the "favor of Providence." There is no trace whatever of the real culprit. Six old Party warriors were killed; more than half a hundred injured. Oddly enough, there is not a single prominent figure among them.

Karla smiles like a sphinx. Erich Tuch won't come to the telephone.

We consult with Hinrichs, who has just arrived on leave, strange and a trifle alarming in his Air Force captain's uniform. "If the damn thing had only gone off sooner," he grumbles. "What good are infernal machines to us if they don't explode when they should?" He, too, knows nothing about the supposed perpetrator. Just one thing he is sure of: the Secret Service was not in on it.

Monday, December 4, 1939.

People are still whispering about the mysterious Bürgerbräu affair. The rumor that it had been staged from among their own ranks gained such alarming currency among the people that the government resolved to turn up a culprit, cost what it might. The man whose picture and description are now appearing, with considerable delay, in all the papers is named Elser. Ostensibly he was apprehended just as he was passing the Swiss frontier with the plan of the beer-hall basement in his pocket. What an odd duplication of criminals' mistakes! When Van der Lubbe had set fire to the Reichstag, and the flames were singeing his jacket, he hastily put his Communist Party membership book in his trouser pocket—forehandedly, so that if he were caught it should surely be found. Elser does the same with the plan of his outrage. What good is the plan to him in Switzerland? Is he going to frame it and hang it over his bed as a souvenir? No practised conspirator lets himself be caught with compromising documents.

Berlin, Wednesday, January 24, 1940.

"Incredible, what heights the National Socialist Pegasus sometimes attains," says Andrik, shaking his head as he leafs through a slender pamphlet. I look over his shoulder. "Christ-

mas in the Third Reich," by Fritz von Rabenau. Above is the
swastika; below, a Christmas tree with angels flying around.
Twelve poems about Adolf Hitler.

"Listen to this," says Andrik, clearing his throat meaningly:

> "Silent night, Holy night,
> All is calm, all is bright.
> Only the Chancellor stays on guard
> Germany's future to watch and to ward,
> Guiding our nation aright.

> "Silent night, Holy night,
> All is calm, all is bright.
> Adolf Hitler is Germany's star
> Showing us greatness and glory afar
> Bringing us Germans the might."

He flings the pamphlet on the table. "Well, how do you like
that for a work of art?"

My flesh crawls. And for this Stefan Zweig and Franz
Werfel had to leave the country; for this Heinrich Heine's
poems have been prohibited for seven years past. To the
young people of today Hermann Hesse is already but a name;
they know nothing of Becher's lyricism, of Barlach's drama,
of Else Lasker-Schüler's sweet, fairy-tale poetry.

The intellectual disaster has been worse than the material
one can ever be. The mischief, falsification of history, distortion of truth, and slanders upon art that have been pounded
into people's heads through years cannot be effaced from
those heads so easily. Each one of us bears the stamp of the
Third Reich somewhere. Even the downfall of the government
will not conjure democrats out of Nazis, personalities out of
Mass Man.

Hitler has accustomed the people to ecstasies. There's got to be a "bang" somewhere all the time. People are constantly going to excesses.

The upsetting of all values has spread to everyday speech. We don't call anything simply "beautiful" because it is beautiful any more, simply "great" because it is great. Anything that doesn't strike us as "tremendously great," "divinely beautiful," or "uniquely wonderful" has as little savor in our mouths as unseasoned food. Germany has lost its ear for gentle notes.

Nietzsche knew. He foresaw it, even in his day. "The German, his garments all tattered, Once had in his head thoughts that mattered. Now he tends to his clothes, And the little he knows, Between tailor and Bismarck [*read* Hitler] is scattered," he jeers in a jingle.

And this very Nietzsche is the man Goebbels wants to proclaim as a forerunner of National Socialism.

Sunday, March 10, 1940.

We sit crowded around the radio in my room. Flamm, Hinrichs, Dr. Muehsam, Karla, Andrik, and I listen to Hitler's speech for Heroes' Memorial Day.

"Must we actually listen to this pernicious nonsense?" pouts Muehsam, pulling like a suction pump at his not altogether genuine Havana.

"We must," replies Hinrichs severely. "An ostrich policy is irresponsible. If we don't realize clearly what 'they' are up to, we'll lose our grasp of the situation. And without a grasp of it . . ." He stops.

Andrik is standing by the radio, his head bowed a little, his gaze turned thoughtfully inward, just as he stands there almost every hour, to catch the air waves in his supple hands.

Hoarse male voices thunder, "Sieg Heil!"

"That's brought in and amplified ten times," says Andrik contemptuously, turning down the volume.

"Fellow German men and women," we hear the hated, barbershop voice, "as Leader of the Nation, Chancellor of the Reich, and Commander in Chief of the German armed forces, my life today is devoted to one single task: thinking day and night of victory, struggling, working, and fighting for it, if necessary not sparing even my own life, recognizing that this time Germany's future will be decided for centuries to come."

Hinrichs grins. "Good of him to be willing—if necessary—not to spare even his own life!"

"Ssh!" says Andrik, turning up the voice of his "Supreme Commander in Chief" for a moment to thundering volume.

It goes on: "The war forced upon the greater German Reich by the capitalistic potentates of France and England must end in the most glorious victory of German history."

"There we have it," says Flamm, agitated. "Megalomania in every sentence. And the worst of it is, people believe his faking. Ninety per cent of the people are taken in by that guff."

"It's the same ninety per cent that are always taken in in every country by propaganda guff," returns Andrik calmly. "Why do you expect the German people to be the exception?"

"Because I love them," says Flamm softly. "Because I can't endure to see them heading for the abyss."

Wednesday, June 19, 1940.

Three and a half months have passed—fourteen weeks, during which the German nation has been reeling drunken with one victory after another. Put out the flags; take in the flags. Every window, every gable, every tower, all a sea of swastika'd flags. Order for display of flags: "As of today, for a period of one week." Ringing of church bells: three days. Once again Christian tongues have to join in praising the bloody victory of arms.

Norway and Denmark are occupied within a few hours. Five days beforehand people were already whispering about a "great action." The surprise assault followed. "The Reich Government will assume the protection of the kingdom of Norway during the present war. It does not intend by this step to infringe upon the territorial integrity or political sovereignty of the kingdom, now or in future."

Quisling is the name of the betrayer of that independent kingdom—Vidkun Quisling. On the same day that the German press announces the victory over Norway, a brief notice appears on page 2 of the paper: "The SS Reich Fuehrer and Chief of German Police announces that Ludwig Koch was shot on the nth for resistance." "Resistance" has been for some time an abbreviation for: "Sentenced to more than eight years' imprisonment for political offenses." Prison takes board —bread, tinned food, potatoes for useless mouths. Anyone under sentence of more than eight years' imprisonment is to be eliminated from the national community as an antisocial element. "Because of resistance." We know of people who have been charged with "resistance" when they were in a hospital, in a cast.

A month after the occupation of Norway, a lightning campaign against Holland, Belgium, and Luxembourg. After four days' resistance Holland capitulates; Belgium lays down arms after eighteen.

"The struggle that begins today will decide the fate of the German nation for the next thousand years," Hitler cries to the German troops crossing the western frontier on May 10.

"If France will only hold," we pray in secret. Calais is taken, Ypres stormed; Dunkirk falls on the fourth of June. The last remnants of the fleeing English divisions escape in skiffs and on rafts, half rowing, half swimming, across the Channel. For the first time in the war we have the sudden, awful thought: "Suppose he follows up—throws his whole force on the British Isles. . . ."

"Then they'll keep on fighting in Canada," Andrik reassures us. But even *his* serenity lacks the deep undertone of conviction.

Flags float from windows. If there is a gap in the red wall of pennants, the block supervisor appears and calls the culprit to account. Two hours' grace to buy flags. Anyone who hasn't put out flags by that time is taken away. What lies we have to invent to make our nonflying of flags credible from the standpoint of State!

The triumphal march goes on—goes on so gloriously that even Italy plucks up courage to snatch a scrap of loot at the last moment. France melts away like a sand castle washed by the tide.

Paris fell last Friday. When the report came in over the radio, the employees of the paper were all at lunch in the canteen. "Paris is taken—put out the flags!" Everyone looks unhappily at his plate. Two fat tears fall into Karla's raw eel with parsley sauce.

"Hurrah!" comes a sudden shout from a corner. Everyone winces. "Hurrah!" again, but this time with noticeably less authority. One of our scrubwomen has jumped up, grabbed her glass, and is cheering, "Long live the Fuehrer!" Icy silence at every table. She sits down again, disconcerted.

Erich Tuch is back from Compiègne—"Not from the opening night, but from the dress rehearsal, anyway," he observes mockingly. The armistice between France and Germany was signed in the forest of Compiègne on June 22, at 18:50 o'clock, in the same parlor car where Marshal Foch dictated the armistice terms to the German envoys of the First World War.

"What you did to me, I'll do to you," Adolf thinks; he has the old-fashioned parlor car brought out of the museum and put up with the most minute exactness on the very same spot as in 1918.

"So there it stands," Erich Tuch reports. "Soldiers are scrubbing away at it. An engineer officer oils the rusty hinges. Twelve hours before the historic scene I'm strolling through the mild summer evening. Suddenly a sound. I stop. Ahead of me, scarcely twenty paces away, the Fuehrer turns up at a bend in the path. He doesn't notice me; he's walking along with head high, eyes fixedly to the front. Now he raises his hand in salute; stops, and smiles graciously in all directions.

" 'Has he gone crazy?' I think. 'Whom is he saluting there? Whom is that gracious smile for?' I creep cautiously after him. More nodding and waving to right and left. The 1918 parlor car gleams through the trees. No sentry anywhere near. With head high, Hitler approaches the monstrosity, mounts the steps with dignity, and turns the newly polished knob. In a flash I see it—he's rehearsing his act. I peer out slyly from behind a tree. Damn, the door seems to be sticking. He shakes at it savagely. 'Get back there, on the double!' I think. What fun! Sure enough, he turns around, climbs down, and starts the scene over. Salutes, nods, the gracious smile of the victor. Then the dictator of Germany disappears inside the car."

"Do you know what voluntary contributions are?" Andrik asks me this morning. I know what he's getting at. Yesterday Hitler opened the second war Winter Relief Fund with great to-do. Only one dish for Sunday; money collections on the street; industrial contributions; badges to be sold.

"A voluntary contribution is when they deduct a certain per cent from your pay the first of every month," I reply obediently.

Andrik grins. "Right! And what is sabotage of the Fuehrer's work of building up the nation?"

"Saying that you can't afford the forced deductions, for financial reasons."

"Excellent!" my friend approves. "Did you know that yesterday Emil Nitschke, a compositor, fifty-eight, was fired without notice from your paper because he said he was unable to fit the voluntary contributions for Winter Relief into his monthly budget?"

I did know. The man has worked in the shop for twenty-six years. "You can thank God that we aren't reporting you," the personnel manager remarked in firing him.

Everyone knows that the millions for Winter Relief go not to the unemployed but to the armament program. How else could you strike a balance between the constantly declining number of unemployed and the constantly growing proceeds of Winter Relief? Otherwise all the unemployed in the whole Reich must long since have become rich.

And still we go on contributing—on the street, in factories, in metro and bus, at the ticket office, at the box office, at the door of the apartment. Not because you want to, but because you can't escape the pressure.

Each time the take is bigger. "The last collection has increased another twenty per cent," they announce to the people.

Do you suppose Emil Nitschke the compositor will be one of those to profit by our voluntary forced contributions? I hardly think so.

Friday, October 25, 1940.

Last night we had our thirty-eighth air-raid alarm since the end of August. If the damage doesn't get any worse in the future, we needn't worry too seriously about this particular specter of war. After each raid the populace turns out, curious and sensation hungry, to view the so-called damage. They gape at a burned attic here, a few paving stones dug up there, a half-collapsed house over yonder. In general they don't take things too hard; they make it a point of pride to show themselves stoics, and are gradually getting used to sleeping the night in the basement.

Monday, December 16, 1940.

Our fifty-second alarm is behind us. We spent it in pleasant company. Frank Matthis has turned up again; we'd lost sight of him for years. Frank Matthis is a doctor, mountain climber, activist, scholar, mischief lover, and dreamer—a most amusing compound of contradictory qualities. He regards himself as a hard-shelled rationalist. When you see him bending over his desk, absorbed in his scientific experiments, you almost believe him. But if you catch him roaming the woods like a Boy Scout, no romantic could be more romantic than he.

Now we are all emerging together from the basement after the fifty-second alarm. The firing was heavier than usual to-night. "They're getting in practice," says Frank, pointing to the red glow that stains the western sky. We join him at the window. The siren of the fire brigade is screeching in the distance. "I shall rub out their cities," Hitler has threatened. He started with Coventry a month ago. Since then people have called the utter destruction of a city "Coventrizing"; they are proud of the new word, and quite forget how cruelly it may be turned against us someday.

"They're getting in practice," says Frank again. His words bring a cold shiver to our hearts.

Tuesday, January 28, 1941.

A cocktail party at Erich Tuch's. Half the Foreign Office turns up—or, to be exact, the "other half" of the Foreign Office. The opposition half. For among the hundred and twenty guests, there is scarcely one Nazi. They talk in cleverly veiled language, as befits diplomats. But underneath the fancy phrases anyone can see they all mean the same thing: We don't think that way! We reject the policies of this gangster government.

"But you do take part in it," says Andrik to Tuch.

"Do we really, though?" the latter asks. "I ask you, what are we to do? Get out? Really we all ought to get out. We can't make any headway against the vigor of those scoundrels. . . .

"Anyone who tries to be honest has got to decide," he goes on hesitantly. "Either he stays in the racket to get in the way, at least to hold back what he can't overthrow; or else he gets out, and leaves the damn government to its own devices, uninfluenced and unchecked." He raises his head. "For my part I've picked the first way," he winds up earnestly. "And if my boss doesn't put a spoke in my wheel . . ."

Mr. von Ribbentrop has decided otherwise. He doesn't like people around him with opinions of their own, no matter how cautiously the opinions are expressed. He has long suspected Erich Tuch—suspected him of being rather cleverer than himself. It isn't a comfortable arrangement for the boss in the cabinet always to be wrong, and his young man in the anteroom always right. So the young man must go—the sooner, the quicker, the further the better.

Erich Tuch is transferred to the Far East. Karla goes with him; they are leaving in the next few days.

"So we can get through Russia before they invade it," Karla explains.

"Russia?" I ask, aghast. "Our allies?"

"You innocent lamb!" Karla laughs. "Do you think he'll give a damn—with nothing else in his head since the fall of France but 'peril in the East'? It's Russia's turn, I tell you. In a month, or two at most, we'll be at them."

"Do you know that for sure?" I ask incredulously.

"As sure as I'm sitting here. As sure as the fact that the German army staff is in the midst of preparations right this minute."

I shudder. Another marauding expedition in this war that has been "forced on us." Now at last I see the true meaning of an alliance that made mock of every Nazi principle: keep one adversary out of the way while you're busy with another.

Once you've disposed of him, you can afford to drop the mask of friendship.

I'd like to discuss things with Andrik at once. But there isn't time; I have a date with Mother Lehmann, Ernst Angel's mother-in-law, on the Kurfürstendamm in half an hour, to buy stockings and sewing things. In three days the first national clothing card will become invalid. Jews have no clothing cards. We must manage to look out for them with our own points. Tomorrow is the last shopping day.

Since the first of the week Frank, Flamm, Andrik, Karla, and I have been collecting all the leftover points from everyone we know—for fourteen Uncle Heinrichs and twenty-two Aunt Johannas.

"If only America doesn't get into the war," Mother Lehmann sighs. "If they do come in, we'll *all* be killed."

I'm too near agreeing with her to comfort her very well. Our good-bys are depressed. Things look ugly in the world.

Three days ago Hitler forced the Yugoslav government to ally itself with the triangular pact of Germany, Japan, and Italy. Today the papers report an uprising in Belgrade and Agram.

Monday, April 7, 1941.

Karla and Erich Tuch have gone. German Army units have been fighting on Yugoslav soil since yesterday. This time the invasion was probably not on Hitler's program. The defection of Yugoslavia was a surprise even to him. "He's raving and chewing the carpets," Karla whispers in my ear on the platform.

"And Russia?" I whisper back. "Will they give up Russia now?"

"Postponed, but not called off," she whispers. They tear us apart. A great many people have come to say good-by.

"We'll be seeing you," says Erich Tuch, holding up four fingers. "We'll be seeing you in . . ."

"The Fourth Reich," we finish silently for him. And nod to show him we understand.

Sunday, May 4, 1941.

The fifth "lightning campaign" of the war is over. Today Hitler made his great report in the Reichstag to all the leaders of Party and army. There's nothing more to prevent the invasion of Russia. "Postponed, but not called off," Karla said. We do what we can to spread the word.

Monday, May 12, 1941.

"Turn on the radio," Frank Matthis tells us over the phone. We turn it on.

". . . letter left behind unfortunately showed in its incoherence such traces of mental derangement that it is feared Party Comrade Hess is suffering from delusions. . . . The National Socialist movement must be prepared to learn that Party Comrade Hess may have crashed somewhere during his flight."

"Well, well!" says Andrik. "*Et tu, Brute?*"

"Do you think he . . . ?"

"Of course he's done a bunk. Done a bunk, like Putzi Hanfstaengl." He claps his hands with delight. "Oh boy, oh boy, what a scandal! It's almost too good to be true. Let's hear what the others have to say."

Pillows over the set. Tune in. "This is London. This is London. Rudolf Hess, Hitler's personal representative, landed near Glasgow in Scotland on the night of May 10-11."

The whole country is talking and guessing about the Hess affair. The stammering utterances of the government, changing every hour, are such clumsily obvious lies that no one takes them seriously. "If," people are saying to themselves, "a man is the Fuehrer's personal representative, he can't be crazy. But if he is crazy, and has been for years, they wouldn't have made him the Fuehrer's personal representative. What's the truth? Where's the lie?"

The wits have already appropriated the case:

> *Es geht ein Lied im ganzen Land* *
> *Wir fahren gegen Engelland*
> *Doch wenn dann wirklich einer fährt*
> *So wird er für verrückt erklärt*

("You hear them singing, high and low,
It's off to England we shall go.
But let someone just try it on:
It's crazy the poor man has gone.")

Even the Nazis are making long faces. They can't decide which version they'll take. Does Hitler know about it? Did he himself send out his representative to make a separate peace? Or did Rudolf Hess fly of his own accord, because things were getting uncomfortable in the Greater German Reich?

The English radio gives no information. Opinions are divided at the shop, too—some say crazy, some say not crazy.

* The chorus of a popular German wartime song.

"The question leaves me cold," Frank Matthis declares. "The main thing is that he's gone."

"And that the bigwigs are wild," Andrik adds gleefully.

Sunday, June 15, 1941.

"Had you heard?" my milkman says confidentially. "Stalin is coming to Berlin. Two hundred women have been put to work sewing flags."

"You don't say!" I am astonished. "Two hundred women? Really to sew flags?"

"Absolutely for sure. I heard it from an absolutely reliable source." He pours my half pint of skim milk into the jug. "Aryan skim milk," they call it, for now that even fresh milk with the cream taken off is rationed, non-Aryans aren't allowed to buy it.

A little while ago a woman said angrily, "You can drink that slop yourself." Now she has to go to the police station every day for three months, and repeat out loud, "There is no skim milk. There is only decreamed fresh milk."

As I go home with my purchase, I meet a neighbor on the stairs. "Heil Hitler!" he says smartly. "Have you heard the latest? Stalin is arriving in the next few days, by special armored train." He measures me with a glance of triumph. "Heil Hitler!" he repeats smartly, and marches on iron heels down the stairs.

"Stalin is coming. . . . Stalin is on the way," the rumor runs like wildfire through town. That afternoon Andrik and I are invited to a diplomatic tea.

"Next Saturday it starts," says a man from Ribbentrop's office. "On October 15 our victorious armies will be on a line from Astrakhan to Archangel."

"And suppose the Russians resist?" I venture to object cautiously.

"They won't have time."

"Suppose in retreating they destroy everything, so that our troops can't get supplies?"

"They won't be allowed time for that either." The man from Ribbentrop's office seems to have victory in his hip pocket.

"You know, I presume, that rumors to the contrary effect were current among the people?" Andrik asks politely.

The Ribbentrop diplomat makes a contemptuous gesture. "Intentionally spread by our office. Of no consequence at all. We'll straighten that out when the time comes." He looks challengingly around. "Or do you gentlemen hold different views, by any chance?"

No one holds different views, or at least no one says so. Only Ambassador Nadolny shakes his head sorrowfully. "Don't be deceived, gentlemen," he warns gravely. "Russia has never been suited to lightning wars. What's the good of our being in the Urals? They'll just go on fighting beyond the Urals. No, that mouthful is one we can't chew. Let me tell you, it's . . ." He stops. Those around act as if they had not heard him. No one wants to lose favor with the Ribbentrop man.

Monday, June 23, 1941.

It began punctually to the minute, the lightning war of self-defense against Russia. Our soldiers crossed the Niemen on almost the same day as Napoleon 129 years before. Our propaganda can pick up where it had to leave off so suddenly in September of 1939: United front against Bolshevism! Guard Europe from the Soviet menace!

"German people! National Socialists!" says Hitler. "Weighed down by grievous cares, condemned to months of silence, the moment has now come when I can at last speak openly." He talks and talks. He says Moscow broke the German-Russian pact; that he meant so well, and was so wickedly deceived.

Sunday, June 29, 1941.

Goebbels has thought up a marvelous surprise: victory bulletins as a country-fair sideshow. On the principle of seven days' scrimping for one day of plenty, he's been gathering victories for a week, to pour them out upon the people now as if from a watering can. Every fifteen minutes a blast of trumpets; a few beats of a Lizst prelude; special bulletin: Brest-Litovsk. Special bulletin: Bialystok, Grodno, Minsk. Special bulletin . . . Special bulletin . . . Special bulletin. We put our hands over our ears. We don't want to hear any more. It's abominable taste to dress up the bleeding and dying of uncounted men for a Sunday treat. History speeded up by the camera! But no matter where we go, the radio screeches, Special bulletin—special bulletin.

"We'd better go to bed," Andrik snarls.

Saturday, August 23, 1941.

We are winning, winning, winning. And each victory makes Hitler's arrogance worse. Goebbels has begun adoring him as "the most brilliant general of all time." His personal deification is already assuming frightening forms.

"Our hour has struck," says Heinrich Muehsam anxiously. "After such successes as these he can afford to do anything."

It's here. As of today the Jews are outlawed, marked as out-
casts by a yellow Star of David that each one must wear on
the left chest. We feel like crying aloud for help. But what
good is our outcry? Those who would help us don't hear us—
or perhaps don't want to.

"Jew," is written in Hebrew characters in the middle of the
yellow Star of David. "Jew!" the children jeer when they see
someone with a star walking along the street.

Thank God, the greater part of the people are not pleased
with the new decree. Almost everyone we meet is as much
ashamed as we. And even the children's jeering has little to
do with serious anti-Semitism. There's no great difference
between pulling the legs off flies, sticking butterflies on pins,
and shouting at Jews.

The yellow star makes segregation easier. It lights the way
into the darkness—the darkness called the ghetto. For some
days now the third and last Jewish migration has been going
on. People taken away from their apartments; forced evacuation with destination unknown. "To Jewish concentration
camps in Poland," some predict. "To certain death," say others.
Every night the cars go through town, taking them away,
between sundown and sunup. Every night new fugitives are
camping out on the sofas of their Aryan friends. "If you aren't
at home they go away. Everything's all right if you aren't at
home," says Mrs. Rosenthal, and her teeth chatter with
horror.

Sometimes the business of "not being at home" works;
more often it doesn't. More than one person is picked up on
the street, or taken away from work. No one knows the rules
by which people are carried off. This man was caught; that

man is unmolested. Why? By what prerogative? "We'll all have our turn," sigh those that are left. "What's the difference whether it comes a month sooner or a month later?"

Friday, October 17, 1941.

The Germans are outside Moscow and Leningrad. "The victory has been won," boasts Mr. Dietrich, our Reich press chief. "Budenny's armies annihilated, Voroshilov's armies bottled up. Timoshenko's armies on the verge of collapse."

"From such blows as these no army can recover," Hitler adds proudly.

"Stick it out, stick it out," says Andrik grimly. "Moscow isn't Astrakhan, by a good deal. Leningrad isn't Archangel."

The Nazis are booming the slogan that we "must defend the Greater German living space on the Urals."

"Stick it out, stick it out," groan Frank Matthis, Hinrichs, Flamm, Hollner, and all those who think as we do.

Thursday, October 30, 1941.

The Germans are stopped outside Moscow and Leningrad. Hitler is minimizing our losses, ignoring them as if they were nothing to him. His soldiers aren't even allowed to die for him officially.

Wednesday, November 19, 1941.

They say Udet is dead, Goering's friend and most popular Air Force general. Frank brings word direct from the Air

Ministry. "Nobody knows what he died of," he says excitedly. "Something's fishy about this, I tell you. Depend upon it, there's something queer behind it."

"Has there always got to be something queer about it when one of them kicks off?" I ask, ill-humored because the wrong man has caught it again.

"Certainly not," Frank returns mildly. "However, normal people usually die before the coffin is taken into their house, and not a day afterward, like, for instance, Mr. Udet."

"I'll be damned!" says Andrik, astounded. "I must say that does look very much like—"

"The silken cord," Frank interrupts. " 'Put yourself out of the way!' they're supposed to have told him. 'We no longer require you, Colonel General Udet.' "

"And why is he no longer required?" Frank shrugs. "Nobody knows. Some say this, others say that. Bad planning of airplane production, debts, embezzlement, drinking, envy on the part of Field Marshal Milch. Possibly the Nazis themselves don't know. Anyway, Ernst Udet is dead. And day after tomorrow they're giving him a state funeral."

"You can't give a man a state funeral when you've killed him yourself," I exclaim in horror. "Why, his . . . He'd turn over in his grave."

"Lots of people must have done that, then—not just Mr. Udet and Ernst vom Rath with his state funeral," Frank laughs scornfully.

Lost in thought, Andrik looks at him. "If the murderer comes before the bier of his victim, his wounds will bleed," he declaims, half aloud, to himself.

Frank claps his hands over his ears. "For God's sake never mind the Nibelung stuff! The warrior hero's faithfulness unto a stab in the back has always sat heavy on my stomach."

The dead man's wounds did not bleed—not even when the Fuehrer and the Reichsmarshal raised their hands in the German salute at his bier. Yet it is definitely true that they did send him the "silken cord," that he was warned to take his own life.

"To us the idea is quite inconceivable, my dear Udet, that you are no longer among us," Goering laments in his memorial address, wiping a manly tear from his eye. How can people be such liars—such bold and shameless liars?

Saturday, December 6, 1941.

"If you aren't at home, they go away," Mrs. Rosenthal said. "Everything's all right if you aren't at home." But some time or other you have to be at home. You can't be forever sleeping on strange sofas, aimlessly walking the streets, or sitting in stuffy movies. Once in a while you have to look after the flowers at home, the laundry, you have to . . . Now and then everyone needs the feeling that he is not homeless.

Margot Rosenthal takes the star off her jacket when she starts out in the evening. And before she goes back to her apartment in the morning, she slips into the nearest doorway, and sticks it back on her chest. Almost everyone does that, now that an unwritten law forbids Aryans to have any dealings with star bearers.

Last night Margot Rosenthal did not come to our place, though we had made a definite engagement. Surely nothing can have happened to her?

Monday, December 8, 1941.

"The one on the second floor? The Jewess, you mean," says the concierge. "They came and took her away. Day before yesterday. Oh, along about six."

So she's gone! Crushed, we start home. "Japan at war with U.S.A. and England," newsboys shout. We scarcely listen. It doesn't interest us. At the moment only one thing interests us: where did they take Margot Rosenthal?

Wednesday, December 24, 1941.

The ghetto at Landshut is where they took her—her and nine hundred fellow sufferers. Her first letter arrived today, on Christmas Eve. "Send us something to eat, we are starving," it says. "Don't forget me," it says. "I cry all day."

There shouldn't be any Christmas trees as long as people are alive who have to cry all day. In a week the fourth war year begins; the tenth year of our official anti-Semitism.

Monday, February 23, 1942.

"Oh, century, oh, science! It's a joy to be alive," Andrik groans, tearing his hair.

With us sits Dr. Jakob, our dentist in better times. Now he's a star wearer, and has been trying for three months to "baptize his Jewish grandparents." They call it "Aryanization procedure" when a Jew tries to prove that his parents really weren't his parents at all; that at least his father . . .

Never before have there been so many marital infidelities, and so many daughters and sons ready under oath to assert their mothers' vagaries. This is not a matter of vagaries, but a downright substitution of children. Three of our group have sworn to it before a notary. They have taken oath that Hugo Jakob, dentist, does not look in the least like either his parents or his brothers and sisters. (His parents and brothers and sisters went to Palestine years ago. Who cares about resemblances there?)

But here they do care. The Race Research Office is intensely interested in family photographs—photographs of the Jakob family. The more, the merrier.

We dig around in bureau drawers, and scare up something that may do: the Salomons. The brother is dead; the sister went to America at the start of the Nazi regime. They won't mind our inventing a relationship. The Race Research Office is a scientific institute. It works precisely and thoroughly—twenty-three measurements of the ear; relationship of jaw to nose; of nose to eye; of hairline to forehead.

The reply came today: "The case is dismissed, as a certain family resemblance between petitioner and subject photos of brother and sister is definitely traceable."

"You'll simply have to separate," Andrik advises. "Five of you can't make it. Five together will never get away with it." He gives a hasty glance at our furnishings: one couch, two armchairs that might be moved together in a pinch. "No," he repeats. "It can't be done with five. Not the eating or sleeping either."

Dr. Jakob turns hesitantly to go. "If you'd come to see us now and then, even so . . ."

Of course . . . Of course, we stammer. We are unspeakably distressed at being Aryans.

A little actress has moved into the next room. Heike Burghoff, her name is; seventeen years old, and her first time away from home.

"I think Berlin is just marvelous," she says, shaking her straw-blond mane. "If you had any idea how many Nazis there are at home! But here? You hardly even hear anyone say 'Heil Hitler' on the street."

"You still hear it much too much," Andrik growls, contemplating the cheerful snub nose of our new recruit with satisfaction. "But anyhow, if you should happen to find that's so, Miss Burghoff, why"—he turns toward the door—"you can stop in here now and then for consolation."

"That's a real compliment!" I say to Heike Burghoff. "He doesn't offer that to everybody."

Later I help her unpack. "You might just as well call me Heike," she suggests.

"And you'd better call me Ruth," I say, giving her a kiss.

"Nice girl," Andrik remarks when we are alone again. "Nice girl," is what Frank, Hinrichs, and Flamm say too. "An enchanting girl," is what our protégés say after we have made Heike a regular member of our welfare committee.

Thursday, April 9, 1942.

We collect ration stamps. We make calls. Today on Uncle Heinrich, tomorrow on Aunt Johanna. It's a good thing that Heike has joined the party. Every day the clouds gather more ominously over the remaining Jews. Anyone who is lucky enough still to have his own apartment is sharing it with numerous less fortunate people. Three families in three rooms;

a crowd outside the bathroom door; turmoil in the kitchen. Peter Tarnowsky has moved for the fourth time. New people billet themselves on Mrs. Lehmann every day. One can hardly set foot in Dr. Muehsam's quarters for all the bags, furniture, adults, and children. Everywhere the third migration casts its awful shadows before. And now that America is at war with us too, there's no further escape for anyone.

Thursday, April 30, 1942.

"Read this," says Andrik, coming into the room, his face distorted, and puts down on the table a piece of tissue paper with trembling writing. "Beloved friends," I decipher painfully. "Now the full weight of misfortune has fallen upon me. Today I was removed from Grünau. Where to? I am so sick, and don't think I shall survive what is ahead of me. Why could not this cup pass me by? Departure within forty-eight hours was heart-rending. Four hundred and fifty people; knapsack, blanket roll, and as much baggage as one can carry. I can't carry anything, and so shall simply leave everything by the roadside. This is farewell to life. I weep and weep. God be with you forever, and think of me!"

"Margot Rosenthal," I stammer.

Andrik nods. "Another batch gone beyond. Not the first, and not the last; only it does hit you particularly hard when you're personally concerned."

Friday, June 19, 1942.

Stone by stone, fragment by fragment, they're crumbling away, being washed off the solid bank and out into the raging torrent. Of our fourteen Uncle Heinrichs and twenty-two

Aunt Johannas, only a very few remain. Now all the Jews have been put in a special class with respect to food distribution. No more meat stamps. No egg card, no smoked foods. Vegetables and fruit dated so far back that practically everything is gone for the next six months. "What can I do with my Evelyne?" wails Dr. Jakob. "Starting in the fall, two turnips a week. And until then . . ."

"Until then, we've just got to stick it out," says Andrik resolutely.

A great many people with guilty looks are lugging shopping nets full of vegetables through the streets of Berlin. "Those are good people," Frank remarks with satisfaction. "The Vegetable Luggers' Thieves' Gang." Through opposition to injustice a new group of allies is taking shape as if of its own accord.

Wednesday, July 1, 1942.

Heinrich Muehsam, Mother Lehmann, Peter Tarnowsky, Dr. Jakob. His little Evelyne, his wife and the Bernsteins, his father- and mother-in-law. Eight people awaiting their fate. Now it's Heinrich Muehsam's turn. Among packed bags and frantic tenants we see each other for the last time.

"Come back," I manage to choke out.

He smiles, as wise as Buddha and as gentle as Lao-Tse. "I'll . . . I'll be back. We'll all be back. Perhaps not like this. But somehow." He bends down to me, and his eyes are close to mine. "I'll be seeing you," he says slowly, emphasizing each syllable.

"Good-by," he says, and kisses me on the mouth. On Wednesday, July 1, 1942, they took Heinrich Muehsam away to Theresienstadt—to the ghetto for privileged Jews. Because he was baptized a Protestant, and has a wooden leg.

"One thing is certain," Frank declares emphatically, "the day of lone wolves is over. The strong man is not mightiest alone now. We've got to form a shock troop—all over Berlin, in every neighborhood, we've got to have our people. Sworn allies that we can absolutely rely on. Our old crowd is not enough; and not all of them are suitable, either. New people have got to be found in every camp. Each one must bring in his own clique, his connections, his angles. What one man lacks another can take care of. The whole trick is to assign the parts properly."

"And still not to let the Gestapo get you," Andrik agrees.

We are sitting around the radio, once more pursuing our career as "radio criminals." The Germans are still winning in Russia. They are still talking about the last, the very last scrapings that Stalin is flinging into the field against them. But Moscow is many kilometers behind the Russian front now, and even though a couple of dozen letters come into the office every week from enthusiastic apostles of final victory among our readers, inquiring about the possibilities of settling in the Crimea and Caucasus, even the Caucasus matter has not been settled for good. The war can still be lost beyond the Elburz peak.

"We're an odd lot of patriots," says Hinrichs. "To hear us talk, you'd almost think we were the opposite."

Flamm shakes his head violently. "Everyone who's fighting for Hitler is working for the ruin of Germany."

"What about defense of the Fatherland—so-called patriotism?"

"This time they're backing the wrong horse. It's nothing to do with the Fatherland, it's got to do with Hitler's ambition." His brow reddens with agitation. "Imagine the Germans' still not realizing that! Why don't they chuck their rifles in the ditch and go home? 'Run your war alone,' they ought to tell him. He's sending them to death out of pure selfishness."

Andrik is spinning the dial. "If only there weren't so many people killed in the process!"

From the radio comes a martial male voice: "In a tempestuous advance our troops have taken——"

"Turn it off," Frank urges sourly. "Let's talk about something more useful." He takes a notebook from his pocket. "Two pounds of meat stamps have come in this week. A pound and a half of canned goods, one woman's tobacco card, six pounds of bread, three hundred grams of margarine. Who needs what? Who'll divide it up? Who'll take care of the distribution?"

"There's got to be a dress found for Evelyne," Heike reminds us. "The child is growing so terribly, and when fall comes . . ."

Wednesday, September 2, 1942.

All our cellars are crammed to the ceiling with Jewish baggage —three lots, four lots, five lots. We can scarcely find our own way among them. Anyone who has to go now is allowed only the barest necessities; and even the necessities seldom reach their destination.

"Come and help me pack," Mrs. Lehmann writes. "The time has come. They're fetching me tomorrow."

All evening we pack in her room, working with scissors, needle, and thread. A hundred-mark note in the lining of her coat, wedding ring in the bedquilt, fountain pen under the bow on her hat, dollar bill in the hem of her skirt. "Hidden reserves," Mother Lehmann jokes.

In the next room lives a Jewish subtenant, compulsorily billeted there for the past few weeks. Yesterday they handed him the warrant for his evacuation. We are sitting sewing. In the next room footsteps are going to and fro: six steps to the right, six steps to the left. No rest, no pause, to and fro.

"What's the matter with Mr. Erichsohn?" I ask in surprise. "Is he packing?"

Those who are sitting around cast down their eyes in embarrassment. Someone behind Mrs. Lehmann puts a finger to his lips.

"He isn't having any more," somebody whispers to me. "He's decided differently. But she isn't supposed to know. She has enough on her soul now."

"What about him?"

"Him? Have you anything better to offer him?"

Beyond that sliding door a Mr. Erichsohn is fighting his last mortal fight, alone, considerate, discreet. Tomorrow, when the car comes to fetch him, they will find his body.

Rest in peace, unknown Mr. Erichsohn—you who aren't having any more, and have decided differently.

Sunday, October 11, 1942.

We convene at Hinrichs' place. There are a lot of people there —churchmen, public figures, civilians, professional colleagues, people on leave—a collection of the most varied opinions. On just one point they all agree: only a lost war will mean the end of the Nazis.

In one corner, leaning quietly back in an armchair, is a grave man. He watches everyone closely with his big eyes. He says little, and scarcely mingles in the excited discussions.

Only now and then he nods agreement. "Yes, that's so. . . . Certainly, I expect you're right about that!"

"Who is that man?" I ask Hinrichs after the taciturn unknown has taken his leave, ahead of anyone else.

"Moltke. Count Helmuth von Moltke. Our best mind." He takes me confidentially aside. "He'll be heard from one of these days. Large groups are behind him, from right to left. He's working for. . . ." A major in the Air Force approaches us—"Canaris," Hinrichs adds swiftly in an undertone.

"Now they're kicking the half-Jews out of the secondary schools," says the major. "If this goes on, they'll be evacuating them too."

I had already heard about this step; we have been racking our brains over it for days. The children must be taken care of. Frank has four protégés, Heike two. Five have made reservations with Andrik, and those that Flamm expects can hardly be dealt with single-handed. Luckily there are still enough Germans who hold it an honor to snap their fingers at the Jewish laws. The first action against half-Jews brings most encouraging growth in the membership of our "thieves' gang."

On the way home I think of the quiet man with the serious eyes, and I promise myself that his name shall never cross my lips—never so long as there is a Gestapo, so long as it is dangerous in Germany to kick against the pricks of the Third Reich even in thought.

Saturday, November 21, 1942.

"What do you hear from *him*?" I ask Hinrichs. "What does *he* think about the situation?"

Hinrichs serves as a well-trained speaking tube, interpreting to us the work, hope, and faith of this man who, in profound secrecy, is weaving his web for a future Germany.

Through a hundred tiny channels we spread the message. We are soft-spoken and infinitely cautious. Now and again we meet the taciturn man. Then we talk to him as we would do anyone else. "It's you," we think reverently. "You know the road that will lead us back out of darkness someday—someday, at last."

Sunday, November 22, 1942.

The Russians have broken through the front. In Africa the English are making tremendous strides. A good many people are already betting that the war will be over within six months. Every day less spares human lives. Each German defeat is one more step toward peace. How right Flamm is! The slogan of defending the Fatherland is our most dangerous enemy. Every man who lets himself be drafted prolongs the war.

Is it the evacuation of the Jews that we're fighting for on the Russian steppes? The disgrace of the concentration camps? The misery of starving prisoners of war? Are we fighting for Hitler's megalomania? Or Goebbels' lewdness? Are our men getting themselves crippled by the millions so that Mr. Goering can build himself new palaces? No, a man who loves his Fatherland must not fight for Adolf Hitler.

Wednesday, December 2, 1942.

The Jews are disappearing in throngs. Ghastly rumors are current about the fate of the evacuees—mass shootings and death by starvation, tortures, and gassings. No one could deliberately expose himself to such a risk. Any hide-out is a gift from heaven, salvation in mortal peril. The "thieves' gang" moves these guests around from one to another. You take them one night, we'll take them the next. Permanent guests are suspicious looking. The constant coming and going makes the neighbors mistrustful, anyway.

The Jakobs have abandoned their apartment. For weeks now they have been living in a tumble-down tool shed. By turns one or two members of the family camp on our narrow guest sofa.

Peter Tarnowsky doesn't put his nose out of the door any more. He doesn't answer the bell, and retires into the world of Kant, Hegel, and Schopenhauer. He still can't imagine that he might be included in the disfranchisement, the removal, the killing—he, Dr. Tarnowsky the lawyer, a World War officer, Knight of the Iron Cross, a man of honor from head to foot?

"We've got to get stamps, we've got to get stamps!" Frank urges. "I have a place for two to sleep tomorrow; for three the day after. Starting December 15 there's a good safe apartment available in Lankwitz. Send the sick ones to me. Anyone who needs certificates can come to me or to my colleague Dr. Kühn."

Dr. Kühn is a Communist; just recently he suffered some months in a Yugoslav prison. Now he's working again as if nothing had happened—conspiring illegally, a fanatical fighter for his cause. We know little about this cause of his; his circle is different from ours. But when we need one another, there we are.

We have kept needing one another more and more often these past few weeks.

Wednesday, December 30, 1942.

"Cabbage turnips alone won't do it," says Heike. "Sometimes you have to think of man's soul, too."

"What are you hinting at?" I inquire, interested.

"Our Christmas tree still looks pretty fair, and Evelyne certainly won't mind the half-burned candles."

"Then you mean. . . ."

"Certainly I mean. You can't just keep sitting in a tool shed all the time."

We get all our stamps together, and arrange a banquet. Heike "overhauls" the Christmas tree, Andrik digs out the Christmas records, and shortly after nightfall Mr. and Mrs. Jakob, Evelyne, and her Bernstein grandparents appear for a belated Christmas celebration.

We sing a carol.

Four-year-old Evelyne looks wide-eyed at the splendor of the candles. "I ate a pear once, too," she says solemnly. "A real pear!"

Somewhere there's a knock on the wall. Possibly one of the tenants is driving a nail.

"Ssh!" whispers little Evelyne. "Now we've got to be very, very still." She sits down in her chair with hands folded, and looks intently at her parents.

"It's nothing," her mother reassures her, patting her head. "It's nothing, Evelyne. You can go right on talking."

Andrik turns his head away. Heike fusses around the Christmas tree. I cast down my eyes, and don't dare look at our guests.

Friday, January 29, 1943.

All men and women are required to register for home defense. In the eastern Caucasus they are "disengaging from the enemy according to plan." And what has been happening for weeks in the city of Stalingrad can hardly be called an advance by even the most charitable interpretation. On September 18 of

85

last year the papers received an article from the press service, ending with the words, "Stalingrad has fallen. Stalin's command to hold the city at any price did not avert fate. When Adolf Hitler the Captain and German soldierhood set themselves a goal, that goal is achieved. Even if death and the devil are in league against it." There was a footnote below: "Hold for official special bulletin on the fall of Stalingrad."

The fall of Stalingrad is at hand. But it looks different from what they were dreaming of in German headquarters four months ago.

Saturday, February 6, 1943.

Stalingrad has fallen. Three hundred thousand German soldiers will not be coming back. Their commander, General Paulus, is alive. Why is it always the ones who arrange a war that survive it, never those that have to fight it?

From Theresienstadt comes word that Mrs. Lehmann has died. The arranger of that "campaign," too, is in the best of health.

"We've got to get stamps, we've got to get stamps!" Frank urges. By Hitler's birthday Germany is to be "Jew-free."

Jakob's emergency quarters have been confiscated for an automobile repair shop. Our available sofas are all occupied. We telephone around town.

"Not inside a week," they put us off. "Now if it were just one . . . But five people! No, five is out of the question."

"For heaven's sake, split up," Andrik implores. "It needn't be for long."

"We'll stay together," Dr. Jakob persists. "We'll stay together!" say Mr. and Mrs. Bernstein. Like thieves they steal into their own apartment at night, in stocking feet, not even daring to turn on the lights.

During the night the telephone rings. "A pay station is calling you," says the sleepy operator.

"Hello," I say.

"My son-in-law has been arrested," a trembling voice stammers. "We're so afraid. We don't know what to do." It's Mrs. Bernstein! She has already hung up.

I wake up Andrik and Heike. "What *are* we to do—what *are* we to do?"

They look at me hopelessly. "There's nothing much we can accomplish before morning."

Flamm has connections with the jail. Kühn knows the chief warder there. Once we have found out where he is, it will be easier.

Saturday, February 13, 1943.

Nobody answers at Jakob's apartment. We don't dare ask the other tenants. If she can, Mrs. Bernstein will certainly call up again. Kühn is informed, and Flamm likewise. Both have promised to try every possible avenue.

Sunday, February 14, 1943.

Mrs. Bernstein didn't call up today, either. Our uneasiness grows by the hour. We've been over outside the apartment three times. The bell is cut off. We just barely managed to sneak away unobserved.

There's nothing for it: we've got to risk it. Mrs. Bernstein hasn't been heard from. This afternoon I shall call on the people next door to her. I understand they're sensible.

A friendly lady opens the door.

"I beg your pardon, could you tell me if Mrs. Jakob is at home?"

She shakes her head, and bursts into tears.

"Will she . . . will she be back today?"

Another shake of the head. Silently the woman draws me into the room. "She won't be back. She won't be back ever," she says, sobbing.

"And the Bernsteins? And little Evelyne?"

"All gone. All taken away on Saturday."

Stunned, I fall on the nearest chair. "All taken away," I repeat mechanically.

The strange lady sits down opposite me. "You're a friend of Mrs. Jakob's?" she asks sympathetically.

I nod.

"It was agonizing! So awful, you can't help crying when you think of it."

"Tell me," I ask softly. "Possibly we can do something, help somehow."

"Help? When the Gestapo has stormed the house like a fortification—burst open locks and sawed through steel bolts? I ask you, who's to help—who *can* help in a case like that?

"At nine o'clock in the morning a truck stops outside. Six men jump out; they run upstairs and ring the bell madly. The door doesn't open. They ring some more. For ten minutes they pound on the bell push. Then they come in here. 'Are those people over yonder at home?' they ask sharply. 'I don't know,' I stammer. I knew, dear God, I knew all too well that they were at home. All four of them. One of these fellows gets on my telephone and telephones next door. I can hear the bell ringing through the wall. 'Have you got a ladder?' he yells at me. I nod. They get the ladder and push it carefully out of the kitchen window. A window of the next apartment is open. The ladder won't reach; it's two rungs short. 'Damn scoundrels,' the brownshirt grits out. Then they start to take the place by storm. Front door, back door; they kick; axes and hacksaws. God keep you all, I pray to myself. The door is solid; finally it gives way and gapes open. It falls banging into the corridor. Three minutes later the four go down the stairs, one after another. They don't talk, they hardly move. They walk as if they were dead."

"Dead," I seem to hear it echo in the room. The woman wrings her hands.

"They sat there for two hours! Do you know what it means to be besieged in your apartment for two hours? You don't dare whisper, you don't dare breathe. They'll be here in a moment. . . . They're bound to be here. And the child—the child all that time. . . ."

"She ate a pear once, too. A real pear," I murmur mechanically.

"I beg your pardon?" the lady asks in surprise.

"Oh, nothing," I tell her in my confusion. "Nothing at all. I just happened to think. . . ." I get up. "If I hear anything, I'll let you know." We shake hands.

"My name is Mrs. Meyerowitz. Maria Meyerowitz!" says the lady. She hesitates. "My husband was a Jew too."

Goebbels is running a "demonstration of fanatical will" in the Sportpalast. "For the salvation of Germany and civilization!"

"Only the supreme effort, the most total war," he adjures his listeners, "can and will meet this peril."

Total, totaler, totalest. I didn't know that even ultimates could have superlatives. Probably people who are unsure of themselves have to fall back on such things. They have to struggle from one exaggeration to the next. After all, what would still pull in the "Greater German Reich" if not the superlative of all superlatives?

The best people in the world . . . the wisest people in the world . . . the most chivalrous people in the world. Breker's sculptures, Speer's buildings, Goebbels' propaganda speeches, the thundering pathos of George.

"People that boast have need of it," says the proverb. Things don't look good on the Russian front.

Sunday, February 28, 1943.

Since six o'clock this morning trucks have been driving through Berlin, escorted by armed SS men. They stop at factory gates, in front of private houses; they load in human cargo—men, women, children. Distracted faces are crowded together under the gray canvas covers. Figures of misery, penned in and jostled about like cattle going to the stockyards. More and more new ones arrive, and are thrust into the overcrowded trucks with blows of gun butts. In six weeks Germany is to be "Jew-free."

We race around. We telephone. Peter Tarnowsky, gone. Lichtenstein the publisher, gone. Our Jewish dressmaker, gone. Our non-Aryan family doctor, gone. Gone, gone, gone! All of them! Without exception. Only yesterday I was talking to Tarnowsky on the telephone.

"I shall cling to the categorical imperative," he said. "They won't overstep the fundamental laws of morality."

They have overstepped them. They have simply trampled them underfoot. Apparently the SS has no ear for Immanuel Kant, and does not stop to ask whether Peter Tarnowsky is a man of honor, a man of honor from head to foot.

Are we to go and confront the SS—attack their trucks and drag our friends out? The SS is armed; we aren't. No one is going to give us weapons, either; and if anyone did, we wouldn't know how to use them. We just aren't "killers." We revere life. That is our strength—and our weakness.

Tuesday, March 2, 1943.

The English have avenged the monstrous deed with a shattering raid on Berlin, the like of which has never been seen. A hundred and sixty thousand are said to have been made homeless. The city and all the western and southern suburbs are on fire. The air is smoky, sulphur-yellow. Terrified people are stumbling through the streets with bundles, bags, household goods, tripping over fragments and ruins. They can't grasp it that they—they in particular—should have been the ones to suffer so. From cause to effect is a long road. Very few people know enough to follow it. Hardly one realizes that today's consequence may have been yesterday's cause. The cause of Coventry, the cause of Dunkirk, the cause of Jewish

91

atrocities, of rubbing out cities, of concentration camps. The broom that is sweeping Germany Jew-free declines to go back to its corner. And the spirits that we have summoned up will not let us go.

Sunday, March 7, 1943.

At least a few have come back—the so-called privileged ones: the Jewish partners in racially mixed marriages. They were all segregated from the others, and taken to a collecting point last Sunday for examination and final determination. That same day the men's wives set out to find their arrested spouses. Six thousand non-Jewish women crowded around the portals of the building in the Rosenstrasse where the "Aryan-connected" ones were being held. Six thousand women called for their husbands, screamed for their husbands, howled for their husbands, and stood like a wall, hour after hour, night and day.

SS headquarters in the Burgstrasse are only a few minutes away from the Rosenstrasse. The incident was extremely disagreeable to those in the Burgstrasse. It was not considered an opportune moment to open up with machine guns upon six thousand women. Conference of SS leaders. Debates, back and forth. The women are rebelling in the Rosenstrasse, threateningly demanding the release of their husbands.

"Privileged persons are to be incorporated in the national community," SS headquarters decides at noon Monday. Anyone who chances to have been lucky enough to marry a non-Jewish wife can pack up his things and go home. The rest are shipped off in freight trains, direction unknown, destination unknown.

Farewell, Peter Tarnowsky, lover of Kant, Hegel, and Schopenhauer. Farewell, German, man of honor from head to foot. Farewell—farewell forever!

Tuesday, March 9, 1943.

Apparently the soldiers are refusing to go on. Hinrichs tells us about it. A rising is planned, a regular *coup d'état*.

"Is the news from—him?" I ask cautiously.

He nods. "The news is, but not the intention. The army will have to furnish the impulse. They have the arms. They are the only ones who might—perhaps—succeed in such an attempt. The rest of us can only follow. For us to be ready then —ready to set up a sensible government—is what we're working on. That's what he's working on; he has been for five years now."

Wednesday, March 10, 1943.

What's going on in Munich? Something is supposed to have happened in Munich—something subversive and rebellious. People say the students have risen. Thousands of leaflets are supposed to have been distributed; there are inscriptions on walls, "Down with Hitler! Long live Freedom!"

We listen around. We are all on fire to hear the details. Is the storm still raging, or has it been smothered? News has got around that Freisler, the presiding judge of the People's Court, was in Munich a little while ago on a "special mission."

The truth! We want the truth!

Now we know the truth. A secret courier has come from Munich, a liaison man from the M group. He brought a report of the situation, and two leaflets: the last remains of the Munich student rising. It's all in the past now—rising, rebellion, arrests, sentence.

The following, however, is what happened there on February 19. A new Gauleiter is appointed, a keen Nazi, Paul Giesler by name. He addresses the assembled students in the university auditorium. He blasts the unwillingness of the university young people to offer themselves to the Fatherland, and denounces coeducation. He says jeeringly that its sole purpose is to catch husbands, and he bawls all the louder the more he feels resentment growing among his listeners.

The women students leave the hall. Suddenly an interruption: "We won't have our fellow students insulted!"

Scraping of feet, trampling, yells. Giesler has to yield. Hundreds of leaflets flutter down from the gallery. A protest march forms outside. At that moment the police appear, lock the doors of the auditorium, and break up the march. "Long live Freedom!" is written up as if by a ghostly hand on all the walls.

At the Munich university there is a proctor's man, or rather an assistant proctor's man by the name of Schmidt. He notices a couple of students, on the approach of the police, dropping a brief case down the light shaft. That sort of thing must be reported. Schmidt informs the Gestapo. A few hours later three students are arrested: Hans Scholl, Sophie Scholl, and Christoph Probst. The men are combat soldiers, furloughed to study medicine. The girl, Scholl's sister, is studying the natural sciences.

Freisler is ordered down from Berlin by telephone. The very next day the People's Court meets under his presidency in Munich.

"Would you kill Hitler if you had the opportunity?" the accused are asked.

"Yes, immediately!" they reply with one voice. Hans Scholl takes all the blame, chivalrously shields his sister.

"We have been enslaved, and must regain our intellectual freedom," he declares in his defense. And when Freisler announces the sentence, he retorts proudly, "In a short time you'll be standing in my place!"

Two days after their arrest, on February 22, at 16:30 o'clock, Hans Scholl, Sophie Scholl, and Christoph Probst mounted the scaffold. "Long live Freedom!" were their last words. Sophie Scholl's leg had been broken during questioning. She had to be carried to the guillotine. "God, Thou art my refuge in eternity, Amen," she prayed. . . .

Thus far the report. We read it behind barred doors— Hinrichs, Frank, Andrik, Flamm, Heike, Wolfgang Kühn, and I. Then Hinrichs unfolds the leaflet. Clustering close around him, we listen reverently to the proclamation of our fellow believers at Munich:

"FELLOW STUDENTS, MALE AND FEMALE!
"Our nation stands aghast at the destruction of the men of Stalingrad. Three hundred and thirty thousand German men have been senselessly and irresponsibly hurried to death and destruction by the brilliant strategy of the World War lance corporal. Fuehrer, we thank you! The German people is in a ferment. Shall we continue to entrust the fate of our armies to a dilettante? Shall we sacrifice the remnant of Ger-

man youth to the basest power instincts of a Party clique? Never again!

"The day of reckoning has come, of reckoning between our German youth and the most abominable tyranny our nation has ever tolerated. In the name of the entire German people we demand back from the State of Adolf Hitler our personal freedom, the most precious possession of the Germans, of which the State has most shabbily cheated us. We have grown up in a State where all free expression of opinion is ruthlessly gagged. Hitler Youth, Storm Troops, and SS have tried to uniform, remake, and anesthetize us during the most fruitful and formative years of our lives. . . .

"For us there is but one watchword: war on the Party! Get out of the Party organization, where they mean as always to keep us politically impotent. Come out of the lecture halls of the SS subordinate and superior leaders and the Party lickspittles! True science and intellectual freedom are at stake. . . .

"Freedom and honor! For ten years Hitler and his companions have wrung those two glorious German words dry to the point of loathing, worn them out, twisted them as only dilettantes can who cast a nation's most precious possession before swine. . . . Even the dullest German's eyes have been opened by the dreadful blood bath that they have poured forth over Europe, and are pouring forth every day anew, in the name of German national freedom and honor. The German name will be disgraced forever unless German youth arises, avenges, and atones at last, at once crushing its tormentors, and building a new intellectual Europe. . . ."

Hinrichs lays the paper carefully on the table. "The assistant proctor's man Schmidt has received a reward of a thousand marks and a civil-service rating for his nationally and politically valuable work of denunciation," he says laconically.

Frank jumps up. "Where's the typewriter? Who'll type? Who'll dictate? If we don't distribute this leaflet, we don't deserve to have read it."

Heike sits down to the machine. Frank dictates. When we break up, fifty copies are ready to distribute. More will be made tomorrow.

Wednesday, March 24, 1943.

"What's that funny smell?" I say to Andrik. It's twelve o'clock at night, and we have just got home.

"Something's singed," he agrees as he sniffs the air.

Heike's room is dark. "Are you asleep?" I ask, opening the door. A cloud of smoke, pungent but not disagreeable, blows in my face. Heike is lying open-eyed in bed.

"Did you start a fire?" I sniff around her room. "Why, it isn't . . . it isn't incense?"

She clears her throat sheepishly. "I . . . I made a vow," she mumbles shamefacedly.

"What kind of vow, Heike, baby?" I ask affectionately, sitting down on the edge of her bed.

"For freedom," she whispers. "So we won't forget the people in Munich."

Andrik throws the switch. The overhead light goes on. Blue wisps float through the room.

Now I can see Heike's face. Her eyes are red; her little round nostrils are sooty black. "That's wonderful of you," I say, patting her cheek. Beside the bed stands a white enameled chair. Above it on the wall hangs a plaster cast of a mask of Schiller. The Schiller mask, too, has its nose blackened. Four thin lines of soot go like ribbons from the seat up the back of the chair. I mean to smile, but I can't do it. "Really, it's wonderful of you," I say again. "Lovely! We should all make a vow for freedom—all of us, not just you."

I straighten out her blanket and kiss her. "Good night, Heike, baby, and—stay the way you are."

Andrik turns out the light. "If only there were more," he says, touched.

Saturday, March 27, 1943.

We have found a way to smuggle the leaflets and reports to Switzerland, and another way, through Sweden, to England. It can't do the Scholls and Christoph Probst any harm now if their subversive activities are broadcast to the world. To us, on the other hand, it's enormously important for people abroad to learn that even in Germany there are human beings, not merely Jew baiters, disciples of Hitler, and Gestapo Cossacks.

The rest of the world knows far too little of that. If you talk about it prematurely, the Gestapo invariably hears ten minutes before those for whom the news was intended. And before the report reaches its destination, those who sent it are dead.

Since the start of the war we have had very slight connections with foreign countries. Each contact must be painfully achieved. We have no organization behind us, and no powerful party to cover our rear. What we do is individual work. But this individual work, done by thousands upon thousands of Germans, is done on behalf of humanity despite oppression, persecution, and tyranny. Here is something that should not be forgotten, when the day of reckoning comes, by those who have an easier time than we in being kind and helpful human beings.

Monday, July 26, 1943.

"Look! How do you like this!" cries Frank, rushing into the room, brandishing a newspaper. "I'll give you three guesses! What's happened?"

"Peace," Heike guesses.

"A bigwig has done a bunk," Andrik suggests.

"Something new against the Jews?" Flamm stammers, his voice failing.

"Wrong all round!" Frank triumphs. He strikes an attitude: "Mussolini has abdicated," he says solemnly.

"Impossible!" Our heads bump sharply above the paper. There it is in black and white: "Change of government in Italy. Mussolini retires as Chief and Prime Minister. Marshal Badoglio appointed his successor."

"And where is our sweet friend now?" cries Heike, beaming. Andrik turns on the radio: London. He almost pushes his ear into the cabinet. "Vote of no confidence for the Duce in the Fascist State Council," he follows along. "His son-in-law Ciano votes against him. Uproar, shouts, catcalls. . . . The Chief of the Italian State escapes by an emergency exit. . . . He hurries to the Villa Savoia, to see Victor Emmanuel. He demands backing, emergency measures, full authority.

"The king shrugs. 'Your successor has already been appointed.' The Duce is arrested. He kicks and struggles. He's carried out of the king's palace lashed to a stretcher."

Andrik stretches with a sigh of relief. "Well, he's taken care of," he laughs with malicious delight.

Sunday, August 8, 1943.

A roll of drums in the courtyard. I jump out of a deep morning sleep. What's on fire? What goes on?

"Men and women of Berlin!" a hoarse voice rattles out. "The enemy is ruthlessly continuing his aerial terror against the German civilian population. It is urgently desired, and is in the interest of every individual who is not obligated for professional or other reasons to stay in Berlin—women, children, pensioners, and those who have retired from active life —that such persons move to regions less subject to air attack." Roll of drums!

"Did you hear?" Andrik asks sleepily.

"Did you hear?" Heike calls from the next room.

Mr. Goebbels is losing his taste for Berlin.

"I'll stay here," I declare firmly.

"So will I," Andrik yawns, rolling over.

Tuesday, August 10, 1943.

Great migration to east and west, north and south. Mr. Goebbels' night watchman's announcement has thrown the whole city into an uproar. The stations are mobbed; people are fleeing to the country by the thousands, knapsacks on their backs, cardboard valises in their hands.

"The Jews didn't have any more than that," says Andrik.

"Except for the gassing," I remind him.

"Wait and see," he replies, frowning. "This isn't over yet."

Neudorf, Tuesday, August 24, 1943.

"Now at least it's just ourselves," Heike observes with satisfaction as we stumble into the basement, carrying gas masks and ARP gear. It struck midnight a moment ago. The siren is a sound so familiar that we scarcely take it seriously any more. You lie down and sleep in the cellar. You sleep as long as you can, and when the all-clear goes, you totter numbly upstairs, taking great care not to break off your sleep too sharply for this unwelcome interruption. We pull the blankets over our heads.

Andrik is breathing deeply and evenly. I am dreaming at leisure. Only Heike tosses restlessly on her couch.

"I don't know what's the matter with me," she says. "Somehow I just can't get to sleep. Somehow . . ."

Andrik wakes up. "I'm going up," he says, yawning. "If they haven't started shooting by this time—"

"Wait another—" five minutes, I am about to say. I don't get time. Thundering hell breaks loose.

First the antiaircraft booms sullenly from a hundred barrels. Then it is silent. For minutes on end we listen so hard that we can hear nothing but our own breathing.

Then comes a loud howl, as if a siren were going just beyond the wall. *Wheeeeeeeee.*

"Bombs!" Andrik cries out. "Bombs on top of us!"

We fall to our knees, slide along the floor like repentant sinners toward the pillar that is the single support of the house walls.

Wheeeeeeeee! Broken glass scatters around us. Masses of dark-gray dust whirl through the air. Smoke, flames, sulphur-colored fog.

Andrik clutches me in both arms. Heike crouches between my knees like a scared chick. "Holy Mary, pray for us!" says a voice in a corner. We choke and cough.

Fire to the right. Fire to the left. A deluge of flames from all sides.

101

Time stands still; eternity has begun. A frightful bang. "Have mercy," screeches a woman's voice. Stones topple; the storm thrusts a whirlpool of sparks through the shattered windows.

Heike struggles frantically for air. "Put a cloth over your mouth!" I shout at her.

We are on our knees—an hour, two hours, three hours.

At sixteen minutes after three the horror is over. The house is a heap of ruins. The curtains belly in the fiery blast like burning sails. Heike lies blue-lipped, quaking all over, on a mattress in the cellar. "I feel so awful," she groans. "So dreadfully awful."

I feel her pulse; it rushes, lags, hurries, stops.

"Smoke poisoning," says Andrik. His voice is brusque with anxiety. "Haven't you any heart stimulant?"

"Nothing. Just a couple of lumps of sugar."

"Let's have them!" He pops them in Heike's mouth.

"I feel better already," she smiles gratefully.

Until morning we are on fire guard, putting out sparks, salvaging household goods—upstairs, downstairs, upstairs, downstairs.

Morning comes slowly; we seem to wait endlessly for it. Do you suppose the other parts of town look like this too? We see nothing but fire. The moment it's light, we'll pack up—the bare essentials—and be on our way. Out of here, anywhere—anywhere away from this ghastly, sulphur-yellow sea of fire.

"They came back to Hamburg four hours later," somebody beside us says.

Morning is here. That is, not really morning; only the clock shows it must be day. We don't see the sky, we don't see the sun. All we see is smoke, whirling black masses of vapor, and the huge torches of burning buildings. A torrent of fugitives is rolling through the Albrechtstrasse. Over a thousand people are standing like a wall before the locked gate of the station. They are let through singly as each new train arrives.

The hours trickle away. The crowd pushes forward an inch at a time. Isn't that the siren again? Will there be a new alarm?

At last we are on the platform. The train pulls in; people are hanging out of the doors like bunches of grapes. Everybody in that can possibly get in. People push, squeeze, those behind crowd after. Thank God, we're inside the car, if only by the skin of our teeth. Everyone aboard has come from the same inferno as we, sooty, greasy, shocked to death.

We take seven hours for a trip that usually requires forty minutes. At nine o'clock at night, almost crying with exhaustion, we sink into the clammy feather beds of a remote village inn.

Neudorf, Monday, August 30, 1943.

A three-and-a-half-hour rail journey to Berlin every day. Every day four and a half hours on the return trip from Steglitz. Bicycle through the woods, main-line train, change; suburban line, change; subway, change. Then a fourth change, and twenty minutes on foot to our ruined apartment house. For seven days we've been doing this, leaving the village at crack of dawn, going to town, clearing away for a few hours, and returning to the village in the afternoon from the ruins of our various suburbs.

Evenings we sit on the green convertible sofa in the hideous coffee room of the inn, pouring down our parched throats malt coffee by the quart. The inn people stand hostilely about us. We're regarded as interlopers. City dwellers are of no interest unless they have barter goods. Safety from bombing they regard as a personal favor to us. People are very haughty indeed in the country outside Berlin—haughty, Party-minded, and self-seeking. "Just as long as we're all right," the peasants think. They trade bacon for dress goods, eggs for jewelry, butter for silk stockings. "Heil Hitler!" they say. "No matter what happens, we're inflation-proof."

Berlin, Wednesday, September 1, 1943.

We couldn't stand it any longer. Our homesickness for the ruins of Berlin, the shared fate at home, grew so overpowering that yesterday afternoon we strapped up our knapsacks and came back. Better for twelve people to eat out of one soup pot than to live uncomprehended among incomprehensible people. Their abundance doesn't suit our distress; their smug materialism is as alien to us as our brotherhood with death is to them.

"How nice that you're back!" says our neighbor. "I've just made coffee—real coffee-bean coffee. If you come up, you shall have a cup."

Twenty minutes later we are jointly boarding up the windows on the stairway. Thank goodness, we're home at last!

Tuesday, September 7, 1943.

"A young musician has been recommended to me," Andrik says. "Zweidorf the composer sent him. I hear he's a gifted youngster."

"What does he want of you?"

"Lessons—technique of conducting, and musical theory."

"Well, let him come," I advise.

The doorbell rings at four in the afternoon; a slim little fellow, shabbily dressed, stands outside. He has black hair, shrewd blue eyes, and the long-lashed lids of a child.

"Are you Konrad Bauer?" I ask.

He nods. The three of us sit down in the battered living room opposite.

His story is a common one today—parents dead, alone in the world at twenty-one, deferred from service on account of kidney trouble.

"I'm very poor," he ends his account bashfully, casting down his eyes as if he felt guilty.

Andrik looks at him sharply. "If you want to study with me, the first thing is for you to have confidence in me," he says slowly. "Without confidence we can't work together."

"What's wrong with him?" I wonder. "What's he being so severe about?"

Konrad Bauer reddens. He swallows at something that he can't get out. Suddenly he stiffens. "I lied to you," he says. "None of that stuff I told you was true."

Andrik smiles. "I knew it wasn't. Now, out with it, young man."

"I was . . . I've . . . I ran away."

"Just what I thought," Andrik murmurs.

"From Breslau—back on the twenty-eighth of February. When they came in the front way, we got out the back way —my parents and I. We got to Berlin by a roundabout route; now we're here. A friend has got me a job taking his place, in the Gerichtstrasse crematory—playing the organ for funerals. Twenty-two bodies a day. They pay me one mark five per body. But . . . I can't go on living like this. What I want is . . . is to learn," he finishes softly.

Andrik goes over to his music shelves and hunts among the scores. "Here's the Oberon overture. I'll lend it to you, Mr. Bauer. Until—" he looks him kindly in the eye "—our first lesson, tomorrow afternoon at six."

Friday, September 10, 1943.

Italy has split off. At last the first Axis partner has resolved to make an end of bloodshed. "Badoglio's perfidy," we call the Marshal's offer of unconditional surrender to Eisenhower. They would like awfully to minimize this step as the "treason of a tiny clique," but since the armistice is already signed, the German leaders have no choice but to make the best of a bad job, and change over in a hurry from the role of ally to that of archenemy.

All necessary steps have been taken, the army assures us. Since yesterday Germans have been shooting at Italians, and the soil of Italy has once more become a theater of war.

In the east they are resorting to more and more radical "shortening of lines." If you look in the atlas, these unadmitted retreats seem rather to lengthen the front. I expect we shall still be shortening our lines when they're ten kilometers from Berlin, successfully disengaging and victoriously resisting.

Tuesday, September 21, 1943.

The Gestapo took away our commercial artist, Oscar Fischer, yesterday. Right from the office. Two men in plain clothes appeared at eleven in the morning and asked if they could see Mr. Fischer. They were shown in. Two minutes later all three were leaving the building.

"I'll be back soon," Oscar Fischer said. That was all. It was only from the woman doorkeeper afterward that we found out what "firm" the two visitors represented.

Oscar Fischer is a taciturn fellow. We knew he was working against the Nazis, in a group along with Dr. Grosskurth and Dr. Havemann. "They print leaflets," somebody told us. "They're uncommonly courageous people." Now the courageous people have been put out of business. If only the others can manage to escape!

Monday, September 27, 1943.

The others did not manage to escape. Havemann is arrested, Grosskurth, Richter, and Rentsch, all for the same job. We hear that membership lists of the group were found at somebody's apartment. How *can* anyone have membership lists of illegal organizations? How dare anyone keep them in his own apartment, where any search may turn them up? What a ghastly alibi for all those whose names are there!

Friday, October 1, 1943.

"You don't know Dr. Tegel?" Konrad Bauer is astonished. "The miracle worker of Berlin? It's high time you did."

He takes us far out into a remote suburb. Dr. Tegel is a prison chaplain. His "shop," as he calls it, is behind barred windows and bolted doors. He welcomes us like old acquaintances.

"We can spare three milk cards this month, stamps for five

loaves of bread, and possibly a little fat. Do you know of a job for a Jewish orphan girl? She's a trained laboratory assistant, but she can also keep house. We need a place for a refugee mechanic, too."

After ten minutes together we are hard at work, trading ration stamps, planning identification papers, looking over housing possibilities, filling jobs. No preliminaries are needed. A person who feels that he's on the same team as somebody else can make himself understood without explanations. Dr. Tegel is one of us, and it will be an honor to claim that we are followers of his.

Thursday, October 14, 1943.

Konrad didn't turn up for his lesson. Dr. Tegel hasn't heard from him in days, either. If only it wasn't always so frightening. . . .

Saturday, October 16, 1943.

Konrad is gone; there's no doubt about it. The landlady of the pension where his parents and he have been living under cover for months couldn't hold her tongue. The first of the week all three were arrested. Kühn is struggling to find out where they are; so is Flamm. Poor Konrad! Just a week ago we drank to friendship, and started using Christian names.

Monday, November 8, 1943.

Andrik has been a changed man ever since Konrad's disappearance. He runs around distractedly, stares into space, and talks out loud to himself when he thinks no one is looking. Our whole crowd is trying to cheer him up.

"Here, read this," Frank said today, and handed him an army-mail letter. "There are fortunate people, too."

"Dear friend," says the crumpled missive in a vigorous penciled script, "Last week the previously announced court-martial came off. Not to keep you in suspense, I got off easy. Four months' imprisonment. Judging by the prosecution of the judge advocate, who behaved like a wild man, driveling about Jewish-capitalist war criminals, air gangsters, and piratical murderers (he meant the RAF), a considerably severer punishment might have been expected. Luckily the essential facts did not come to light, any more than they had in the preliminary investigations. As a result they could only base their charges on my having sat over wine and cognac with a captured 'terrorist pilot' in company with some people from my outfit.

"You know as well as I what would have happened if the purpose of our 'sitting together' had leaked out—to give our young pilots a true picture of the situation from the mouth of one of the enemy, and show them the hopelessness of the fight without propaganda trimmings. The rest of the circumstances didn't come up either—that the English lieutenant was quartered in hospital quarters, unguarded, that similar cases have frequently happened before, etc., etc. The court was remarkably unsure of itself. The judge advocate general of the Second Air Fleet, before whom the case had come up, wanted to make an example, and demanded merciless punishment—probably for fear of the Gestapo, who had reported the matter in the first place. It happened to be a lance corporal from my own home town that split on me. I wonder if Lieutenant J. D. Blad, who's in the prison camp at Oberursel, has any idea what difficulties he caused me."

"And the fellow writes that straight out in an unsealed

army letter?" I ask, horrified, as Andrik folds the paper.

"Good God, no," says Frank hastily. "It came by messenger; his boy slipped it to me."

"What boy?"

"Why, the orderly. Joe Thäler's orderly."

"Joe Thäler?" I open my eyes wide. "This is from Joe Thäler?"

Frank nods. We've known Joe Thäler for a long time—that is, we've known him and yet haven't known him. So far we haven't been introduced to him, but Frank has told us about him, and raved about the staff doctor who worked with him breaking down Nazism at the Charité, and was almost ready to commit suicide when they called him up for the Air Force. So it's this Joe Thäler. . . .

"You're right," says Andrik. "There are fortunate people, too. If Dr. Thäler comes to Berlin, it would be nice to meet him."

Wednesday, November 24, 1943.

Another major attack, this time on the center of town. We form a bucket brigade on the Lützowufer, from the Landwehr Canal up to the sixth story. Our hands are so stiff from lugging and passing on that the cigarettes fall from nerveless fingers when we take a break. It's a shame, too; cigarettes have got scarce in Berlin. At twilight we hurry home, on foot, for all transportation is at a standstill.

As we open the front door, a figure looms out of the darkness beside us, short, slim, a shadow among shadows.

"Boy, where on earth did you come from?" yells Andrik ecstatically. Two hollow eyes, an unshaven chin: in the darkened rays of the lantern stands Konrad. We drag him into the house. Bath water, shaving things, a clean shirt, a real supper. Gradually he recovers himself.

"Where on earth have you been?" Andrik asks.

"In the Hamburgerstrasse—the railhead for transportation into the hereafter." He pushes a spoonful of soup into his mouth ravenously. "If it hadn't been for my friend Ludwig . . ." he says between mouthfuls. We look at him. "Ludwig Wald—our fire maker in the police cellars. He was months getting ready. He made himself useful wherever he possibly could. Cleaned out the cellars, shoveled coal, sorted potatoes. Finally they put him in charge of the board with the keys on it. The building key is kept there too—or rather, it was!" He corrects himself gleefully. "Until 5:30 on the afternoon of November 23 it was. Then—a preliminary air-raid warning was blowing—Wald cut off the lights. The place was pandemonium. We stole the keys to the gate off the board. 'Come on, it's about time,' Wald said; that was all. The two of us set off. Opened the basement door, the building door, the door to the yard. Behind us they were yelling for lights, screeching and rushing around. Wald was as cool as a cucumber. 'Two weeks from today at the same time outside the State Opera House,' he told me as we parted at the Victory Column. At half past seven there was an alarm. I crawled under a tree in the Tiergarten. Then I set out on foot, and—" he hesitates "—here I am."

"We must let Dr. Tegel know," Andrik says.

Saturday, November 27, 1943.

Dr. Tegel is helpful as always. Konrad gets a job as night watchman in a big downtown bank. Starting tomorrow he will be taking lessons again.

In a fortnight we are to meet Ludwig Wald, the friend from the Grosse Hamburger prison without whom we would never have seen Konrad Bauer again.

Friday, December 17, 1943.

Another disaster! Freisler has condemned to death Pastor Wachsmann of Greifswald, a warrior and courageous Christian. Hinrichs has known him for years and esteems him more highly than almost anyone else. "I'm going to Freisler," he says firmly. "If we don't get him free, at least he ought to be left alive."

Sunday, December 19, 1943.

"The dirty dog! The wretch!" Hinrichs rages. "He tossed me out like a boy not dry behind the ears. He starts off quite reasonably—'Decent sort of fellow, this Wachsmann. A clever man—no doubt about it. But'—his face suddenly freezes into a mask—'an educated man who makes defeatist statements has been declared by the people's court over and over again to be deserving of execution. Clemency is not my province,' he adds coldly. 'The Ministry of Justice makes those decisions.'

"And what was Wachsmann's crime, I ask you? Over a hundred witnesses couldn't think of anything worse to say about him than that he had probably listened to the English radio, and when the Germans were advancing in Africa he had said to somebody, 'We began by advancing in '14, too.'

"I ask you," Hinrichs thunders, "do you cut a man's head off for that? Can a blameless man be put in irons for months for crimes like that? All attempts to get him out of chains have been fruitless. It'll be generous of them if they take them off for the execution."

Monday, January 3, 1944.

The old year ended in horror; in horror the new year begins. Heavy night raid on December 29. Heavy night raid on January 1. The heaviest night raid of the war on January 2.

We move rubble. We nail up corrugated board. Here we are without water, transportation, or current. The telephone is dead too, and we learn only by roundabout ways whether our friends who live at a distance are alive.

A promising start for the year. By the time the most essential repairs are made, at least ten days will have passed. And why make repairs? Why do millions of people keep starting all over to build up what may be in fragments again within the next hour?

I look at the faces of the rubble shovelers and window boarders. I look at my own face in the window—encrusted with dirt, my kerchief rakishly over one eye. And I think I know the answer. We make repairs because we have to, because we couldn't live another day if we weren't allowed to make repairs.

If our living room goes, we move into the kitchen. If the kitchen is smashed, we transfer to the hall. If the hall is in ruins, we set up in the cellar. Anything so long as we can stay at home. The most dismal scrap of home is better than any palace somewhere else. That's why they all come back someday—the people whom the bombs have driven out of the city. They root among the stone fragments of their ruined houses; they go to work with shovel and broom, hammer, tongs, and pickax, until one day a new home rises out of the charred foundation—a Robinson Crusoe stockade, perhaps, but a home nevertheless. You can't live if you don't belong anywhere. That's why the first thing most people save from their burning houses is the pillow from the bed—it's a last bit of home. "The foxes have holes, and the birds of the air have nests; but the Son of man hath not where to lay his head," said Jesus of Nazareth.

The English radio is surprised at our readiness to rebuild; they interpret the feverish activity after each raid as an expression of National Socialist enthusiasm.

Neither rubble shoveling nor pillow rescuing has anything to do with Nazi enthusiasm or resolution to endure. Nobody thinks of Hitler as he boards up the kitchen window. What everyone does think of is that you can't live in the cold, that before evening falls and the sirens wail you must have a corner where you can lay your head and stretch your legs— the way you choose to do it, and not the way someone else wants you to choose.

Wednesday, January 26, 1944.

Goering has just accomplished a masterpiece. If the results hadn't been so tragic, it would have been a huge joke.

Monday noon the sirens went. Three and a half million frightened Berliners marched down cellar. Silence. Not a shot, not a bomb, not a sound of planes. At one o'clock, all clear. Three and a half millions go back to their apartments or back to work.

What became of the attack; what happened? "The raid was a personal invention of the Supreme Commander in Chief of our Air Force," Hinrichs fumes. "The Reichsmarshal was meddling in things that were none of his business, as usual." Indignantly he tells us the details of the bloody farce.

Enemy planes over Holland. An officious adjutant dashes up to Goering, who has just granted himself special leave at Karinhall. Goering doesn't care for air raids, particularly when they show a tendency to take place in his immediate vicinity. So he rushes to the telephone, calls up a fighter airdrome, and roars, "What, aren't you air-borne yet? Enemy planes approaching, and you're still sitting there! Get up there, I tell you! Get up there! And be quick about it!" He hangs up, and then alarms the next field. The fighters buzz up like scared doves. It's a hazy day; poor visibility, uncertain sound detection. The Air Force High Command has its ear to the air. Engine noises? No order to take off has been issued; so it must be enemy planes. So the alarm will have to be given. Air-raid alarm, all over west, southern, and central Germany. And be quick about it!

More than eight hundred fighters go roaring up—the largest number of pursuit planes used against an enemy raid so far. Antiaircraft guns are thundering from the Rhine to the Elbe, sending thousands upon thousands of rounds into the clouds. Ten planes crash; the crews are spattered over the landscape. The consumption of fuel and ammunition is terrific. And when they come to inspect the damage, the planes shot down are German planes, the dead pilots German pilots. Not a single English plane crossed the Rhine that morning.

Friday, February 4, 1944.

Alarm, alarm, and still alarm. You hear nothing else, see nothing else, think nothing else. In the electric trains, on the streets, in shops and busses, everywhere the same scraps of conversation: Completely bombed out . . . roof taken off, wall collapsed . . . windows out . . . doors out . . . bomb-damage certificate . . . lost everything.

Last Sunday Mrs. Meyerowitz was bombed out; she left Berlin yesterday. We have quartered her daughter Dagmar in the maids' room of our bachelor house. It was hard enough to find her a place. The housing shortage grows worse with each raid. With such a shortage, who can venture to receive a half-Jew, of all people? Our landlord does not dream of his good fortune. In registering her for the police, we tactfully evaded the question of our subtenant Dagmar Meyerowitz's racial origin. Why lead with our chins? Already there is muttering about new deportations of Jews. We hear they have made a clean sweep in overcrowded Auschwitz and Theresienstadt. "Two thousand going out of here every week," a man from the Security Service boasted the other day when he was riding a suburban train with us.

Two thousand a week. That makes over a hundred thousand human beings murdered annually by the State in one single camp. During the first deportation they still bothered to cover their mass murder with a slight humanitarian cloak —chiefly when the victim was survived by Aryan or foreign relatives. "Your father, Mr. Paul Israel Braun, succumbed to lung inflammation on October 23," would be laconically inscribed on half a sheet of paper, or perhaps a post card. Whoever got the message suspected what the "lung inflammation" was like, not in a sickbed but in the poison chambers of the ghettos, in gas-filled railway trains, before the bullets of firing squads, or under the murderous treads of the tanks.

"They make them dig their own graves," people are whispering. "They take their clothes away—shoes, shirt. They send them to their death naked. They go naked to eternity."

This horror is so inconceivable that imagination rebels at grasping it as a reality. Some sort of contact is broken here; some conclusion is simply not drawn. It isn't Heinrich Muehsam that they're sending to the gas chamber. It can't be Anna Lehmann, Margot Rosenthal, or Peter Tarnowsky digging a grave in some remote desolation under the whiplash of the SS. And certainly not little Evelyne, who was so proud of having once eaten a pear in her four years of life. No, Evelyne Jakob died differently from those tormented ones; she died more humanly, more comprehensibly, more imaginably.

Is it cowardice that makes us think so, ostrich behavior, a shunning of responsibility?

Perhaps so. But if it is, then that cowardice and that ostrich behavior are among the primitive instincts of mankind, the ineradicable basis of self-preservation.

Who rebelled against the tortures of the Inquisition? Who against the suffering of the Incas, the martyrdom of the Negroes? Tidings of the massacre of the Jews have gone all over the world. Did a single soul lose his appetite for breakfast? Did the farmer in Illinois, the Laplander in the Arctic Circle, the Swede at his smörgåsbord, the Englishman at lunch, the Frenchman at dinner make any personal sacrifice on that account? Were they unable to go on living because the agonies of the victims stopped their breath, lacerated their consciences, and set the furies at their heels?

When we described the distress of one German Jewish woman in burning colors to her Swedish nephew, who lives a comfortable life in Stockholm, far from the horrors of war and Nazi misery, and implored him to strain every nerve to get her out, he answered, "The obligation you ask of me would mean supporting my aunt to the end of the war—

specifically, about three hundred crowns a month. Taxes here have risen 150 per cent, the cost of living 100 per cent. After deducting all fixed expenses, I have a tiny fraction left out of my twelve hundred crowns' salary every month. I am faced with the task of supporting five of us on about a hundred and fifty crowns a month. It would be irresponsible of me to make a commitment that I simply could not keep; when the guarantee of twenty-five hundred crowns that Heinz put at my disposal for his mother was gone, I would simply have to put my aunt out on the street."

He won't have to put her out on the street; the SS has taken the job off his hands.

We who are in our eleventh year under Adolf Hitler's dominion have little cause to boast. But if ever anyone risked his life for his Jewish brothers, it has been the German Aryans—hundreds, thousands, tens of thousands, risking their necks every day and every hour for a few wretched bread stamps, a lodging for a night or two. A little bit here, a little bit there, and still a little bit, scraped together out of their own need, fought for among bombs, forced labor, failing communications, and personal hardship, gained by defying every prohibition, law, and propaganda decree.

No one who has not seen it himself can imagine how difficult even the simplest act of assistance may be under such circumstances. What are you to do if a person you are hiding in your apartment dies of heart failure one fine day? Are you to burn him in the stove, send him up in smoke, blow him out the chimney? What do you do with a corpse that hasn't been registered with the police? "We put it in our laundry basket, covered it with sheets, and carried it out of the house at night," we are told by acquaintances who suffered this particular embarrassment. "In the Tiergarten we fetched it out and put it on a bench." They smile distractedly; they are not pleased with their solution. For forty years they have been respectable citizens.

Konrad's bank, where he was night watchman, suffered a direct hit in the last major raid on the middle of town. Konrad is unemployed and homeless again. He's "sleeping around" among his friends, eating now here and now there; but in the long run it's an impossible situation.

Andrik consults with his colleague Wilfried von Zweidorf. He has connections with the Music Chamber.

The Music Chamber, too, has been bombed out; records of dues, memberships, everything has been dumped in piles, in utter confusion.

Zweidorf marches in as if he were born to command; he is positive, exacting, and astoundingly matter-of-fact. He announces that he and his friend Bauer have been bombed out. That's right, bombed out. A total loss, more or less. Everything gone, even their Chamber cards. Just as a matter of form . . . Wilfried von Zweidorf smiles winningly.

"No doubt you have the information about us. Wilfried von Zweidorf, membership No. 2045. Konrad Bauer—you know, the singing coach—" again he smiles bewitchingly—"membership No. 3627. I've got our pictures with me. If you'd just be so good. . . ."

The lady who issues them is so good. What female creature can resist the smile of a prominent composer—particularly when the composer is young, handsome, and fascinating? She carefully fills out a clean membership card: Konrad

Bauer, pianist and Kapellmeister, membership No. 3627, staples on a blurred profile, signs it, stamps it, and hands it over. "We'll check with our records later," she murmurs.

Wilfried von Zweidorf nods and puts the precious cards in his breast pocket. "Later. Naturally." Exacting, positive, and astoundingly matter-of-fact, he marches out of the place. "Later—in the Fourth Reich," he thinks cheerfully, tips his soft broad-brimmed hat, and vanishes. Konrad has ground under his feet again, and doesn't spend all his time brooding about how his parents are in Theresienstadt, and it's really wrong for him not to be with them.

Wednesday, March 22, 1944.

From day to day Konrad grows more reckless. By the help of his membership card in the Music Chamber he's penetrated into the State Opera. He always tells a most touching story: Bombed home, lost parents, shattered health. It's all true somehow, but different from what he tells. It's only symbolically true, so to speak. But gradually he has dug himself into his fairy tale about having no identification and not being drafted, until he almost believes it himself. Zweidorf covers his tracks in public, exacting, positive, and astoundingly matter-of-fact as always. No one in the place hits upon the wild idea that there could be anything slightly wrong about Korrepetitor Bauer, who directs the stage music behind the scenes at the State Opera.

"There's a peculiar attraction about putting one over on the Nazis just where they feel safest," Konrad smirks. "Goering's Temple of Art, his specially privileged birthday-party theater, desecrated by my presence! Boy, if Fatty knew that!"

"Thank God he doesn't," retorts Andrik reprovingly. "Don't do anything silly, Konrad, the war isn't over yet by a long shot."

No, more's the pity! The end seems to be considerably delayed again. There have been rumblings going round for days that the Hungarians have shown signs of dropping out—that a group were seizing the helm who would no longer submit to the forced alliance with Germany.

But once again Hitler has scented trouble. A signal; a command; troop displacements, reinforcements.

Horthy is summoned to Berchtesgaden. He arrives a statesman; he remains a prisoner. All Hungary is occupied by German troops "with the speed of a blow," as the Nazis like to say. And "jubilantly welcomed by the grateful populace," who cannot thank their German brothers in arms enough for preserving them from the disastrous consequences of an anti-Nazi *coup d'état*. Hungarian soldiers may now continue shedding their blood on the battlefields of Russia.

The applause in Germany is scanty. The popular fury at the so-called betrayers is well within limits. A man who is fed up with war himself is hard to convince that other people may be hungry for it. The propaganda effort was wasted —wasted, like the hopes we had staked on the defection of Hungary.

Thursday, March 30, 1944.

"I've got to see you, urgently," says Hinrichs on the phone. "It's about our friend M."

Can it be Moltke? These days when anyone wants to talk urgently about somebody, it's usually bad news. We make a date for the afternoon.

It is Moltke. At the end of January they arrested him, ostensibly on account of the attempt to warn Consul General Kiep of some danger that threatened him.

"I know about it only from hearsay," Hinrichs reports. "Denunciations aren't usually announced officially." So it's another denunciation! Is there no end to talebearers and slanderers in Germany?

"What scoundrel was trying to win a medal with *that* deed of heroism?"

"If you trace it back, it must have been Dr. Reckzeh, the assisting physician in the psychiatric clinic at the Charité."

"Reckzeh? Never heard of him."

"Nor had I, until yesterday. I wish I never had." Hinrichs sighs. "The thing goes pretty far back. They had some tea somewhere," he begins haltingly. "One of those political groups that are meeting on a tiny scale by the dozen these days—germ centers of resistance. Only it's too bad that one of them hardly knows about another. This particular one was the group gathered around Miss von Thadden, who used to run a boarding school in Munich. A number of tried-and-true followers had met at her place, among them Secretary of State Zarden, Consul General Kiep, Mrs. Solf, and Legation Councilor von Scherpenberg, Hjalmar Schacht's son-in-law. It was Reckzeh's first time there. He had just come back from Switzerland, bringing greetings from a woman friend of Thadden's. The friend was all right, so they mistakenly concluded that he was too. He was supposed to be bringing back word from Switzerland. I suppose they talked fairly openly, about the mad way the war was being run, the probable outcome, the chances of overthrowing the government, of establishing political connections abroad.

"Next day Reckzeh goes and reports the thing to the

Gestapo. They make arrests—first one, then another, than a third. Moltke hears about the intended arrest of Kiep, and tries to warn him. The warning is useless; Kiep's life is forfeit. Zarden, they say, threw himself out of the window on his way to the interrogation. He's dead. The scaffold is waiting for Miss von Thadden. Scherpenberg, equally near death, gets off easy—only two years in prison. Reckzeh is kind enough to testify that in the treasonable tea-table conversation he conceded the Nazis a tiny chance. Mrs. von Scherpenberg is weeping with joy."

Hinrichs falls silent.

"What about Moltke?" I scarcely dare ask.

"He hasn't been back since. What they actually accuse him of is impossible to find out in detail." He looks at me unhappily. "That's the awful part of it. People disappear, and you don't know why. A friend is in prison; but before you find out about it, he may be ten feet underground, with his head between his feet. And those people never lift the veil from their bloody secrets until they—" he hesitates—"present us their bill for their black deed."

"The bill?"

"Yes, the bill! The statement of state expenses, footed up with all the pedantry of a bookkeeper. Or did you think executions were done free—that prison soup was served gratis? Die, but pay up, is their motto.

"Pastor Wachsmann was guillotined at Brandenburg penitentiary on February 21. Soon afterward a functionary asks his sister, 'Are you the heir of the late Wachsmann?' She reluctantly admits she is. 'Are you prepared to assume the costs of the case?' 'What would happen if I weren't prepared to?' 'We would be obliged to distrain the estate.' The sister is horror-struck. Distraining the estate would mean her parting with a thousand dearly loved mementos. 'I'll pay,' she says quickly. 'Might I ask how much . . . ?' 'A few hundred marks. The bill will be sent to you.' A few days later the postman brings her a registered letter. Bill for the costs of the criminal proceedings against Alfons Maria Wachsmann. Total, RM 474.84.

"Itemized, board per day,	1.50
"Transportation to Brandenburg Penitentiary,	12.90
"Execution of sentence,	158.18
"Fee for death penalty,	300.—
"Postage,	1.84
"Postage for statement of costs,	.42"

So a German execution costs a hundred and fifty-eight marks and eighteen pfennigs. Nothing like being business-like. The deceased is not defrauded of a fraction of a penny. Is the cost of electricity included in the execution of sentence —the kilowatt-hours for the guillotine? Are the eighteen pfennigs the executioner's pay by the minute? We will charge our contra-account by way of the Fourth Reich.

Monday, April 24, 1944.

The whole world is waiting for the invasion. Will they try it? Will it succeed? Convinced National Socialists mention it with profound contempt, as if at most it were no more than a practical joke. If only it would begin! One man bets on May, the next on June, the third on July. The pessimists think it won't come at all—the risk is too big, the defense too carefully prepared. The foreign stations are imploring French, Dutch, and Belgian patriots not to rise until orders come from England. And in the same breath they ask why the Germans haven't rebelled yet.

Would that all those who make such a demand of us in resounding accents of moral superiority could know how wrongly they judge us and our opportunities! No one who does not himself live in the country and suffer from the country has any idea what it means to be bound with the chains of dictatorship. Those who did not leave here until after '33 know least of all, and forgot the soonest.

That is why we bear most of our *émigrés* such a grudge, because they demand of us what they themselves could not accomplish. The first time a well-known *émigré* spoke to us over the B.B.C., thousands upon thousands of enthusiastic listeners, behind barred doors, were hanging on his words. They took down his speech by shorthand, whispered it from ear to ear, risked their very existences daily and hourly to spread it abroad. His radio address robbed more than one German of his freedom, and cost more than one German his head.

But when he delivered his sixth, seventh, and eighth addresses, many of them turned off the radio in annoyance. No, they thought, he doesn't belong to us any more. There's a glass wall between us and his glass-clear words. "Get out on the barricades!" he tells us—tells us from his comfortable country house, where no Gestapo man can drag him out of bed at five in the morning, where no one is spying upon his every step, watching what he does, and weighing every word he speaks on the scales of death. "Get out on the barricades!" Amid the hardships of our present life such talk is painful to listen to. A man who has not made his own way to the barricades has no moral right to demand it of others.

Émigré, stay where you are. Rejoice in the sun if you will and can. But spare us your accusations and your contempt.

Whom should I meet on the stair at the shop this morning but our commercial artist, Oscar Fischer. "God love you!" I cry. "You're alive!"

He smiles a melancholy smile. "Not altogether, but a little. As much as you can expect to find alive after a few months of prison, when you live opposite the execution shed." He leans forward confidentially. "Believe me, it gets on your nerves," he whispers morosely. "Not the beheadings. You get used to that. But all the trimmings. The abominable ceremony."

I drag him into a corner. "Tell me, tell me," I urge. "How come they let you out? Where are the others—Grosskurth? Havemann? Richter? Rentsch?"

He looks me in the face, and does not bat an eye. "Condemned. Condemned to death—all four of them. Grosskurth, Richter, and Rentsch were executed nine days ago. Havemann's death has been postponed indefinitely. The Fuehrer had an access of generosity; he reprieved Havemann, the indispensable physicist and pharmacologist, until after final victory. An admirable mercy that goes just as far as the State's advantage will take it." Still his expression never changes a jot. Only the eyes move in his furrowed, parchment face.

"What about you?"

"I denied everything. Day and night, night and day. No, I don't know anybody else. No, I don't know anything more. No, no, and no again. Finally they gave up, and let me out of my orchestra seat in their execution theater."

I pat his hand sympathetically. "It must have been pretty terrible."

126

He nods. His gaze seems to turn inward. His voice is monotonous, abrupt, as if he were reading some report that he had read a hundred times until he knew it by heart. "Straight across the yard was the garage. In the garage was the death machine. On the left was a covered driveway. When they have enough material for the executioner to work on, they cover the front grating with a black cloth. That means Waiting Room for the Hereafter. They come out of the condemned cells, through a hidden passageway, one after another, their clothes off. Naked except for short drawers. If it's cold, they shiver. Not because they're afraid —almost nobody is afraid—but because they're cold. When it's cold . . ." He stops, shaking his head. "They always wait until there are several," he goes on monotonously. "It probably costs too much for one alone. They stand around, and are called by name. While the first one goes into the death shed, the second has to take off his drawers. Neatly folded in a pile. On account of the textiles; and because afterward they won't have to wash them. It goes by turns: name called, take off drawers. Name called, take off drawers. Finally the last man disappears in the garage. Each case takes two minutes. The one humane thing about it is that they never do it before noon, and don't inform the condemned man of his approaching execution until an hour beforehand. So at least they spare them the terrors of the last night. Though whether that's why they do it . . ."

"Except for short drawers," I think, and the blood freezes in my veins. Why does this one circumstance strike us as so utterly abominable, so immeasurably inhuman? Even the rude Middle Ages left the criminal his last shift. Even the thieves on the cross wore a loincloth. The man who at the next moment will be face to face with eternity may not care in what garb he leaves the earth. But to those who survive, textile saving in this connection seems more ghastly than dying, the clothed myrmidons and unclothed culprits more agonizing than the execution.

"They say the bodies have been released," Oscar Fischer interrupts my dismal meditation. "One grave for all of them —I mean for Grosskurth, Richter, and Rentsch. The wives are supposed to have obtained that. It's an unheard-of privilege!"

Someone clatters noisily down the stairs.

"Well, now, Mr. Fischer, about those drawings?" I say loudly.

He catches on. "I know, I know," he nods. "I'll be seeing you shortly."

Friday, May 26, 1944.

Andrik says Konrad is going to wiggle into an army entertainment tour—on his poor wretched Music Chamber membership card. If only it all comes out right!

Saturday, June 3, 1944.

The entire press is assembled in the Air Ministry today to receive an "important decision of the Supreme Army Command." An Air Force general, all gold braid and decorations, makes a short speech. "With the approval of the Fuehrer, the Reichsmarshal has ordered the immediate formation of a female antiaircraft auxiliary corps." He clears his throat. Suppressed muttering. Will they dare . . . ?

The general grows unsure of himself. Perhaps he is thinking of the oft-denounced "gunwomen." "I mean," he says nervously, ". . . I want to emphasize particularly that there will be no shooting involved. The Fuehrer wants no woman behind the cannon. It is not in accordance , . ." he clears his throat again ". . . with his concept of the dignity of the German woman for . . . for . . . well, for there to be all this shooting," he ends, exasperated.

"May I ask you a question, General?" says one of the crowd respectfully. "How are the antiaircraft auxiliaries to behave in case of attack, if none of them knows how to use a weapon?"

The general whispers at length with his adjutant. "The question will be studied," he says hurriedly. "I would request the press to postpone the advertising campaign for the Antiaircraft Auxiliary Corps until this decision has been released."

We are dismissed. There won't be any gunwomen in the future, either in Russia or anywhere else. Certainly not here.

Wednesday, June 7, 1944.

"Hello! Hello! Is this 72 70 35? One moment please, I will connect you with Major Hinrichs," says an excited voice on the telephone.

I rub the sleep from my eyes. Six-thirty in the morning. An unusual time for telephone conversations with the Air Force staff.

The line buzzes: plugging in, wires crossed, cut off, connection restored. The usual performance whenever you try to talk to anyone on the Kurfürst exchange. Then Hinrichs is talking. "Are you up?" he asks merrily. "Did you sleep well? Oh, by the way, I meant to tell you, the shipment got in. That's right! By the early morning train. Looks pretty good to me."

My brain decodes at top speed. Shipment means invasion.

This is the landing on the Continent, the long-hoped-for assault of Allied troops.

"I'm delighted to hear it, delighted," I tell him. He hangs up. Andrik is in Holland. I'm alone with my wisdom and my impatience. Early this morning! Now it's half past six. "Let them come," Hitler has said. "Within nine hours we will throw them back into the sea."

Now they have come. By now half of their allotted time must have gone by. Will they make it?

I rush to the nearest kiosk for the morning paper. The news dealer shakes his head. "The papers haven't come yet." The radio too is silent. Eight o'clock, nine o'clock, ten o'clock. We're on pins and needles. Surreptitiously people venture the first hints. "Two o'clock this morning . . . Desperate fighting . . . Coast defenses gradually broken through." Rumors multiply by the hour, taking on the most preposterous forms. Press and radio are still silent.

At eleven o'clock a delivery truck stops at the corner. Bales of newspapers are thrown off.

Two minutes later three policemen turn up; they whisper to the news dealers, gesticulate, and act frightfully busy. The papers are confiscated even before the bundles are untied. Bale by bale, bundle by bundle, they are swallowed again in the maw of the delivery truck. Waste invasion paper!

At last, by noon, the German government has collected itself. "Invasion by order of Moscow! Battle reports of the impact of German resistance," the papers trumpet forth, displaying the joy of children on Christmas morning. "The long-awaited day of invasion has come. With utmost confidence the German people looks to its troops and its leadership, which are now in the decisive struggle of the war," say the editorials.

130

All afternoon I roam the city, listening here, watching there, deducing, trying to draw conclusions. No, the nation is no longer waiting for victory. Only with difficulty do the anti-Nazis hide their delight at what is happening. The people with swastikas in their buttonholes look uneasy despite the constantly reiterated propaganda enthusiasm. The nine-hour limit has long since passed. Still there is no sign that the enemy is drowning in the Channel, that Fortress Europe has hermetically sealed its gates to him.

Thursday, June 8, 1944.

Seventy hours have passed since the start of the invasion; and English and American troops are still fighting on the mainland of northern France—advancing, falling back, inching their way toward the heart of Europe. Beyond doubt the invasion has succeeded. No matter what bittersweet interpretations German propagandists may devise, they cannot escape the fact that five American divisions got a firm foothold upon the soil of northern France on the evening of June 6, and that by the morning of the seventh it was a certainty: Allied troops had pierced with a single thrust the "ring of iron and dynamite" that Adolf Hitler had built around the European mainland by months of minutely detailed labor.

Everyone is glued to the radio; every soul is a deliberate "radio criminal," for no one can be expected, during these hours of decision, not to keep himself informed through foreign stations. People whisper blasphemous things. And those who cannot keep their communicativeness in check land up in Dachau before they know it. Or in Oranienburg. Or Buchenwald.

But the invasion is a success. With each success the Party

Comrades' faces grow longer, more swastikas vanish from the buttonholes of the Fuehrer's retinue. Remarkable, this rhythmic oscillation in the matter of lapel ornaments. The degree of Party confidence can be read off with mathematical certainty from that one symptom alone. The moment the Nazi bigwigs began to have their first doubts that the Thousand Years' Reich would endure, they issued an order making the wearing of the emblem a matter of honor for every Party Comrade.

Friday, June 9, 1944.

The invasion is progressing. You can count Party emblems on your fingers. Anyone who is still wearing a "woolly crab" on his lapel can at least claim the glory of being an independent personality. People are getting nervous in the newspaper offices; the triumphant outcry of "We knew it all the time" is beginning to lose its pull. High time to put a new catchword to work.

Saturday, June 10, 1944.

It has gone to work. Its name is "enticing in." When Adolf Hitler's prediction that we would throw them back into the sea in nine hours did not come true, Sepp Dietrich, Commander of the Bodyguard, sprang into the breach. "Why, didn't you know," he trumpeted, "that we intended from the very beginning to entice them in? The more, the better. Whole divisions; whole armies; we will draw the main body of the American and English forces on to the fatal soil of continental resistance. We can't put them down unless we can get hold of them. That is the secret of our masterly strategy."

Since that moment we have been "drawing on," "enticing forward," and the strategic fame of our battle conductors is saved again. Overnight the "woolly crabs" return to the lapels. Those who think otherwise say nothing, wait, hope for the swift advance of the Allies; they listen to the English radio, and always know five minutes before the release of the German report what is happening in the world. . . .

Sunday, June 18, 1944.

. . . Such as the use of the long-promised, too-often-threatened first German secret weapon. After the preceding months of whispered propaganda, there was hardly any doubt that it would come. How it would come, though, was a puzzle even to the wisest. Everyone had good authority for a different version of what it would do.

"You press a button. The thing scoots off. The upper half of the British Isles flies sky high, the lower half sinks into the ocean, and the missile comes back with fifty thousand prisoners," the doubters jeer.

"Our secret weapon is frightful," say the believers earnestly. "Twenty-four hours of bombardment, and England will be whining for mercy, for armistice and peace terms. You know . . . splitting the atom. Rearranging electrons . . . A German invention. The effect will be world-shaking."

Well, the secret weapon didn't shake a thing; it hasn't even upset the program of dance music from the Savoy Hotel in London. Ten days after the invasion started, Hitler launched his counterblow. "Against London and southern England," yesterday's papers reported. "Explosives of a new type and of the heaviest caliber."

motely controlled wonder weapon has been chris-
/-1"—for *Vergeltungswaffe*, Retribution Weapon. In
/ords, an eye for an eye, a tooth for a tooth. These
people with a patent on Jew hating ought to be ashamed to
make such a show of Old Testament morality.

In Normandy they are making "successful counterattacks";
and talking already about "east of the Orne," "west of Cau-
mont," "southwest of Carentan," and "north of Ste. Mère
Église." This business of "enticing in" is going ahead at a
great rate. V-1 is king—not, indeed, in London, where one
is said to be hitting every fifteen minutes, but in Berlin, where
Dr. Goebbels is brandishing it in practiced propaganda hands.
Perhaps it was invented solely to keep the German people
in a war mood; for judging by the look of things at the moment, its propaganda effect in Germany is considerably greater
than its explosive effect in England.

Tuesday, June 20, 1944.

The editorial writers of the entire civilian press are wriggling
like fish in a net. The victory propaganda that they are ordered to spread flies too glaringly in the face of truth. They
would like to speak between the lines, but they can't any
more. Eleven years of Party dictatorship, eleven years of daily
taking orders about presentation of articles, regulation of
speech, and prohibited subjects wear a person down, no matter how good his intentions underneath. If you give the devil
an inch, he will take an ell.

And why did they give the devil an inch back in 1933?
Because they feared for their livelihood, for the life and welfare of their wives and children. Because they were afraid of

134

hunger and unemployment, of denunciations, the Gestapo, the scaffold.

We have a Mr. Hitler because we lost a four years' World War, because we went through years of inflation, of economic crisis, of unemployment, exhaustion, and uncertainty; because we have never in history been a united nation, and consequently require perpetual reassurance that we actually are a nation at all. That is the only possible explanation of the "German greeting," the Hitler salute. We had barely twenty-five years of opportunity to learn democracy, to practise the difficult transition from subject to citizen of the world. What is a quarter-century in the education of a people? Almost less than nothing.

It's easy to throw stones if you've been born heir to many hundred years of education as a people; easy to sit in judgment when you're in the midst of abundance, roast chicken, and the good life.

"We'd do differently," these people say. "We wouldn't have crucified Christ, or chosen Hitler, and we would long since have shaken off the dictatorship of Nazi terror."

Would they really have? They with the abundance of their centuries of education?

There are neither bad nations nor good nations, neither inferior nor chosen races. There are only better brought up nations and worse brought up nations—those that history carried early to unity and national development, and those that came late.

Our editorial writers are wriggling in the net; they could not scale the heights from masses to personality. Must they be crucified for that? If so, nine-tenths of mankind might equally well be brought to the gallows. "It would be much nicer if it were nicer," says Erich Kästner. If, that is, the strong understood the weak better, and the weak the strong; if the well-brought-up would take the untaught by the hand like big brothers, and say to them, "Come, we will help you learn what you don't know; we will set you a good example—in responsibility, self-determination, freedom."

But I'm afraid those are dreams that we shan't see realized for a long time.

At the moment the invasion is progressing, and Adolf Hitler is avenging the "crime" of an Allied landing on the continent by constant bombardment with V-1. "Since June 15 at 23:40 o'clock southern England and the London area have been under constant fire, with but slight interruptions, from our heaviest explosives. Extremely heavy damage is to be looked for in this area," the army communiqué proclaims.

In the evening a young girl comes to see me—dark-eyed, with a clear, alert, child's face. Konrad Bauer sent her, with his good-by's, as he is leaving tomorrow with his first army entertainment tour. If Konrad sends a girl to us, she must be something special. It doesn't take long to see that Ursula Reuber is indeed something special, a masterpiece from the workshop of the Creator. She spent six months in the police cellars of the Grosse Hamburger Strasse. The Gestapo held her for the crime of bringing food to her friend Konrad and his parents. "Who's that? She might just as well stay right here," the chief warder barked when she put her little pot of food at the gate of the "Jew camp." And there she stayed— just as she was, with no toothbrush, no word at home; she simply vanished for six months into the basement of the "Grosse Hamburger."

The chance that swept her in there swept her out again. One fine day they released her—because nobody could remember why she was there. They didn't interrogate her;

there was no process of law. The case seemed too trifling for much legal fuss. The official notation on the certificate of dismissal was enough: "First-degree half-breed Ursula Reuber, residing at Berlin-Dahlem, Ihnestrasse 40, has been in police custody for six (6) months." An honorable document. Ursula Reuber displays it with an almost sentimental smile.

"To be truthful, those twenty-six weeks did me good. I had a little volume of Rilke with me, and plenty of time to think about myself." She looks me straight in the eye with her grave, childlike gaze. "A person should be grateful for a chance to think about himself, don't you think? If Dr. Tegel could help me out, I'd like to try to learn to play the organ —Bach and Handel. Bach, mostly. Everyone ought to know Bach. You can't do anything bad if you're listening to Bach."

"Except perhaps if you hear it with the wrong ears," I think to myself. But I don't say it out loud, for it would be a sin to trouble those clear waters. "Do come back very soon," I say. "Come as often as you can. Andrik will be delighted, too, and Heike and Frank. Nice people should stick together."

She nods and beams, and departs with her wisdom about Bach and Rilke—police prisoner Ursula Reuber, nineteen years old, half-breed of the first degree.

Wednesday, June 21, 1944.

We've had another tremendous pounding; my knees still quake when I think of it. At eight in the morning I was sitting over coffee with Heike. A cloudless summer day.

"Bad flying weather," says Heike, squinting expertly at the pale-blue sky. "I think they'll leave us alone today."

She has hardly finished speaking when the phone beside me rings. A man's voice: "Heavy plane elements approaching. State of alarm, 30. Turn on your radio!"

Good God! It's our connection at the Luftwaffe. So there's an alarm after all!

As always when I get word beforehand, my stomach feels rather uneasy.

The police radio has not yet changed over. "Erika, Erika," it sings in fluting tones.

Now the music stops. Tick, tack, tick, tack, goes the signal for the break. The first report is broadcast: Flights from the west, flights from the south. Will they come to Berlin, or will they turn aside?

"Better touch our mascot," says Heike, "it may do some good."

I reach for the old Russian ikon on Andrik's desk, which has been our guardian spirit since the start of the bombing.

Tick, tack, tick, tack . . . The announcer is talking again. "Formations considerably scattered . . . on a western course . . . only a few fighter planes remain," I hear confusedly. Thank goodness, they're turning off. With a sigh of relief we light a cigarette.

Then the siren wails up and down. That's no warning, that's an alarm. We drop the lighter with fright. People are racing outside, with bags and baby carriages, tearing headlong for the nearest basements.

The trams stop with a squeal of brakes. The autos pull over. In less than three minutes every vehicle stands empty and abandoned.

"Put the door mat in the door, so it won't slam if . . ." We are already on our way down. From afar comes a deep, grumbling hum, alarmingly strange, ill-omened, mysterious. Hastily we fling handbags and suitcases into a corner. Gas masks, steel helmets, wet cloths. There's no time to be lost.

There they come. They're over us.

We don't say anything. We don't yell. We press the wet cloths frantically to our lips. While the bombs are whistling outside, it's as still as a church in here.

There is toppling and crashing, quaking, bursting, trembling. To us it seems as if the floor bounded a yard up in the air. There's a hit. Another. And another. We wish we could crawl into the earth. Biting smoke stings our eyes. Did our neighbors get hit? Did we? We have no idea. All we know is that we are poor, naked, and desperately in need of help.

"Fire on the fourth floor," says the air-raid warden. "Bear a hand to put it out!"

We rush numbly up. Bombs are crashing outside, howling down through the smoky air. No one says a word. We reach mechanically for sand pail and pickax. Up to the fourth floor. Blackout paper flutters in the fiery wind like black birds.

But the water! Good heavens, they've turned off the water! The supply always fails whenever there's a major raid. A blessing that at least our bathtubs . . .

While the ack-ack barks outside, and one bombing squadron after another drops its deadly load on us, our damage-control group extinguishes whatever can be put out. Bucket brigades with slop pails, pitchers, bathtubs. The vessels are empty. Now for the bags of sand.

The living room is on fire. Phosphorus flows green under cupboards and upholstered chairs. Sand on it! Sand on it again! The bombs whistle. Far away, closer, very close.

"Look out!" cries the air-raid warden. Again we rush down cellar. But the fire is out, and the last squadron is flying over toward the center of town.

We crouch together, pressing the wet cloths to our mouths. If it weren't for those, the smoke would suffocate us. From far away a siren screeches. Preliminary all-clear. There is still a humming overhead. The drumbeat of light ack-ack is still rattling at short intervals. It barks, stops, barks again, and finally falls silent.

All clear!

Where the next house stood is now a heap of ruins. A woman runs screaming past us. She is wrapped in a horse blanket; terror distorts her face. She is pressing three empty clothes hangers to her breast.

Gradually the street comes to life; more and more people appear out of the smoke, the ruins, the ghastly destruction. They say forty-eight bombs hit our block.

The dead can't be counted yet; they're under rubble and stone, crushed, annihilated, beyond the reach of help.

Two hours later an SS salvage squad appears. They are to help us dig, board up windows, and clear away ruins. They are received with marked coolness. "If it weren't for you, there wouldn't be any ruins," the faces of the bystanders seem to say. "Why do you come now, when it's too late? Why did you get us into all this in the first place?"

The SS men fall to with shovel and pickax, but they look surly. They can feel that they aren't welcome.

Monday, June 26, 1944.

Hinrichs predicts that the Nazis may come to a swift and sudden end. There's something in the air again. But one doesn't dare express it. It's no news to us that there are numerous tiny groups that have formed for positive action against the regime—that the Communists are working, that the Social Democrats have formed a combat group, that the Catholics, too, are not idle, that thoughts of overthrow have long been current in Home Defense and army command. For months the initiate have been whispering, "Goerdeler and Popitz are traveling around the country, distributing posts in the Fourth Reich."

It's alarming enough for such rumors to reach the public. Haven't people learned from eleven years' experience of the Gestapo to hold their tongues? True, silence won't bring any overthrow. That's the tragic part of our plight. If we talk, plan, and recruit allies, we are hanged; among ten people there is always at least one who is treacherous or loose-mouthed. Yet if we are silent, and only vent our indignation within our own four walls, then we still keep the Nazis. The dilemma remains the same. After all, can a tiny group of ten or twenty resolute people cause the Third Reich to topple? And we are only tiny groups—a few in Berlin, a few in Munich, in Breslau, in Dresden, or Hamburg. A handful here, a handful there, like the king's children in the fairy tale, never getting together.

"Don't you think it advisable," Andrik asks Hinrichs, "at least to try to accommodate the plans of Left and Right?"

Hinrichs agrees. The attempt was made today. Dr. Hans Hinrichs and Dr. Wolfgang Kühn meet as spokesmen and negotiators of two resistance groups in Andrik's room. They follow the tried-and-true methods of conspirators: as few names mentioned as possible; they don't burden each other with figures, addresses, and facts that might possibly come to light by questioning under torture.

They talk of "my group" and "your group," and are prepared to pass on the information received only to one trusted man who will relay it to the next dependable quarter.

The discussion goes on for a long time. They feel each other out, making up their minds only slowly through preliminary disclosures. We have taken the telephone out of the room, in case there might after all be some truth in the rumor that the Gestapo is monitoring certain lines. Heike is on guard in the hallway; she sends away all unwanted visitors with some charming excuse or other.

"What do you think of Goerdeler?" Dr. Kühn asks.

"Not much. My people don't think much of him, either. He's too incautious. Anyway, the most he could ever be is a sort of switchman."

Dr. Kühn nods. "Switchman number two. The army is at the first switch. Without the army we can't do anything. We need its machinery, its arms, its impact. I tell you, we've got to disintegrate the army. The chaos of a military revolt is the only situation we can go forward from."

"And how do you see this 'going forward'?"

"Fill all high government positions with men of political training. Mostly from the concentration camps; anyone who has gone through the political schooling of the camps has first claim to a post of responsibility."

Hinrichs rocks his head dubiously. "We see it rather differently. We are concerned primarily with peace. Peace at any price. Not until the great slaughter is stopped can we begin with political reconstruction. Reconstruction in the spirit of democracy, I mean, with full and equal participation of all classes." He toys thoughtfully with his pencil. "Incidentally, what do you think about the church?" he goes on abruptly.

"We're prepared to admit it, indeed even to reach an understanding with it, if . . . well . . . if it should care for such an understanding with us."

142

"May I pass that on to my group?"

Hinrichs nods again. "Without obligation, however. What we have discussed today remains simply a preliminary general contact."

"But at least it is a contact." Hinrichs smiles. And they agree to meet again next month.

"Do you think there was any use in that discussion?" I ask Andrik after the two have left.

"Use or no use, at any rate they're acquainted. And possibly there's a shade less chance that energies will be frittered away at the decisive moment."

Monday, July 3, 1944.

Konrad is here, back from his first army entertainment tour. "Oh, boy, was I walking on eggs," he says, as we sit together over our lunch of fried potatoes. "At every performance I came out in front of the curtain with a 'Heil Hitler.' Address of welcome in the name of the Propaganda Minister. Me! All day it was 'Where's Mr. Bauer? Mr. Bauer's got to talk. Mr. Bauer's got to arrange it. Mr. Bauer's playing the piano, Mr. Bauer's conducting, Mr. Bauer's all over the place.' The pillar of the enterprise. Me and my fake Music Chamber identification, fake name, and a Gestapo warrant out for me. I tell you, I was sweating blood." He pokes around excitedly in his mound of potatoes. "Every damn evening we were invited to some regimental staff. Arguments about art, war, and the sounds of war. One time a fellow thought he was being funny. 'Mr. Bauer,' he yells, slapping his knee with laughter, 'Mr. Bauer, it's too funny! You look just like a Jew!' I grinned back at him—very funny, isn't it? My shoes were running over with sweat. Finally a woman in the office sus-

pected me. I thought to myself, 'Now, Konrad, do or die.'
I acted the aggrieved Teuton, bellowed for a court of honor,
an investigation, and thundered to the assembled troupe,
'Young lady, you take back that insult, or I will turn over the
affair to the Gestapo! As a fellow German and National
Socialist I can trust it to give proof of my Aryan origin.' Boy,
that scored! She came crawling, and I stalked out, every inch
a hero. Every inch an aspen leaf, down inside. Two more
tours like that, and I'll be ready for the booby hatch."

Andrik shakes his head doubtfully. "Why did you have to
be so foolhardy? Can't you be a little more anonymous in the
future?"

"In for a penny, in for a pound," Konrad sighs.

Tuesday, July 11, 1944.

Konrad left this afternoon, this time for Heligoland, where
civilians are allowed only under the strictest supervision. He
still has no identification papers except his fake Music
Chamber card, and a certificate from the Borough of Schöneberg that "Konrad Bauer, technical worker, was bombed out
according to his own statement at 19 Y Street, left rear, second
floor, losing all his personal papers." "Valid as provisional
identification," it says below.

A good many people these days are rectifying their illegal
existence by means of fictitious bomb damage. If you're lucky,
you may even get a one month's set of ration cards; and if
you're very lucky indeed, you may even manage to sneak
back on the official merry-go-round of checking in and out
with the police, and so regain full citizenship.

Konrad B. has not been that lucky. So we must try to
legalize him some other way. Flamm knows a first-class

stamp counterfeiter, but he's temperamental and terribly slow. Dr. Tegel has got his protégés to manufacture business letterheads of nonexistent armament firms. He types out letters saying people are essential war workers, and signs in an illegible, director's scrawl. At least that's something. But it won't stand careful checking.

Lucky that it won't be long now. Yesterday Andrik went to see his friend Adam von Trott, legation councilor at the Foreign Office, a man with a good head, a bold heart, and one of the most active opponents of the Nazis.

When Andrik comes back, he paces the room for a long time, clears his throat, starts to speak, stops, clears his throat again. "Can you hold your tongue?" he asks at last.

I look at him in surprise. "Do you have to ask that after thirteen years?"

"That's not it . . . I know . . . But you see it's about . . ."

"Get on with it," I urge impatiently.

"Well, you see, they really are planning something. Rebellion, *coup d'état,* something of that sort. I have no idea who-all's in it. It's no business of ours, anyway. What matters is that they want to use me."

"You? Where? For what?"

"Liaison man, so to speak. I'm to go to Sweden. Understand? Get in touch with certain groups there. They'll fix up a conducting tour, and arrange the whole business through official channels."

"Suppose they get wise?"

"They won't get wise. It's all going to be done perfectly legally. And I'm not thinking of telling Mr. Hitler about the illegal side of my mission." Andrik's handsome head looks as if Rodin had just carved it out of stone.

"When do you think?" I ask breathlessly.

"Pretty soon. Maybe this month. They'll let me know—telegraph, if necessary. I arranged a code with Trott."

Heavens above, how thrilling! It's coming at last! Really coming! "What are they planning on? Assassination? Army revolt? Are they going to kill Hitler? Do they just want to put him on the shelf? . . ." My questions pour out like a freshet.

But Andrik shrouds himself in silence. "I haven't the faintest," he says. "Anyway, I don't want to know. And I'd advise you not to know anything either, until . . . Well, until it's time."

Friday, July 21, 1944.

It's time! And it has come much sooner than we thought. No one knows any details yet. Hitler wounded . . . Hitler dead! Attempted murder of the Fuehrer . . . Rebellion, violence, revolution . . . Revolution! We're right in the midst of it. Some people are drunk with rejoicing; others, pale with terror. Even yesterday there was a strange uneasiness trembling in the air of the city. When I came back with Andrik late in the evening from a trip out of town, Heike rushed into the room, brandishing a scrap of paper, carrying on like mad.

"Hitler's dead! Hitler's dead!" she yells, falls on our necks, and bawls like a baby.

"No! Impossible!" We snatch the paper out of her hand.

"Attempt on the Fuehrer's life . . . DNB . . . July 20. First official bulletin." It's a galley proof from the shop.

"How did that get here?"

"Hollner was here," Heike bubbles over. "It happened at

one o'clock this afternoon—an infernal machine. They say he's still alive . . . I bet they're lying." Again she falls upon our necks, laughs, cries, stammers and babbles, until you can't hear yourself speak.

Finally we succeed in reading the slip. "An attempt on the Fuehrer's life has been made with explosives," it says, in black and white. "Those among his entourage who were severely injured are: Lieutenant General Schmundt, Colonel Brandt, Mr. Berger, a civilian adviser. Slighter injuries were sustained by Colonel General Jodl, Generals Korten, Buhle, Bodenschatz, Heusinger, Scherff, Admirals Voss, von Puttkammer, Captain Assmann, G.N., and Lieutenant Colonel Borgmann.

"The Fuehrer himself suffered no injury except for slight burns and contusions. He resumed work immediately, and received the Duce for an extended conference, as planned.

"The Reichsmarshal arrived to see the Fuehrer soon after the attack."

Andrik stares at the paper, aghast. "My God, if that's true . . . That he's alive, I mean!"

"He isn't alive! Everyone says he must be dead!"

As if at a signal we reach for the switch of the radio. Music —the *Badenweiler March,* Hitler's favorite tune; its playing has been forbidden for some time "to prevent its being artistically worn out." That doesn't sound like death; it sounds damnably like his being alive. The march dies away. "The Fuehrer has been speaking," says the announcer. We look at one another, stunned.

"His double," Heike reassures us.

But Andrik shakes his head. "I'm afraid . . ." He breaks off. We know what he's afraid of.

We wait, we tremble, we hope.

Extras all over town! "Failure of attempted assassination. Small clique of traitors was to eliminate the Fuehrer on behalf of world Jewry." The Jews, of course. The old scapegoats. "Conspiracy completely foiled. Address by the Fuehrer. Congratulations from Gauleiter Murr. Congratulations from Dönitz. Congratulations from Goering." The congratulations are enough to turn your stomach.

Hitler actually did speak over the radio at one in the morning. "So that you may hear my voice, and know that I am in good health and quite uninjured; and in addition so that you may hear the details of a crime unparalleled in German history." And then he lets go on the "crime."

"A conspiracy was hatched by a tiny clique of ambitious, conscienceless, and at the same time stupid and criminal officers. The bomb, planted by Colonel Count von Stauffenberg, exploded six feet to my right." A stab in the back . . . Usurpers . . . Confirmation of his mission from Providence.

The press cheers on order, outdoes itself in abject ovations. Since the Jew doesn't pull, they're starting to blame it on the Secret Service. In their zeal to display the greatness of Providence along with the insignificance of the attack, the editorial writers turn positive handsprings of acrobatic word twisting.

The DNB reports in boldface, "As the German News Bureau has learned, the conspiracy of the criminal officer clique has completely collapsed. Upon the failure of their attempt, the ringleaders in part did away with themselves, and in part were shot by battalions of the army. Among those shot is the perpetrator of the outrage, Colonel Count von Stauffenberg. No untoward incidents have taken place. The others whose behavior renders them guilty of the crime will be called to account."

Why army battalions for such a tiny clique? For a handful of officers—some of the papers mention just three. There's something fishy about it after all. And all the sycophancy, the whole outpouring of *holy wrath* and *immeasurable rage*, of *sworn allegiance* and *profound emotion*, the most savage abuse of the "scoundrels forgetful of honor," the "tools of international conspiracy." All these still leave a gap somewhere—a gap for rumors and blind searching after truth. Himmler has been appointed commander of the Home Army, and he celebrates his assumption of office with large-scale arrests.

If only we knew whom they had arrested. Moltke, thank God, is safe in a concentration camp. For the first time that fact is something to be glad of. But how about Hinrichs and his whole circle, Adam von Trott, Canaris, Goerdeler, Popitz, Dr. Kühn, and all the others who we know are opposed? Hundreds of names are in the air, mentioned as involved, denied, mentioned again. Moltke is not one of them. No, Moltke isn't in it anywhere; we shall take good care not so much as to think his name.

Saturday, July 22, 1944.

The city remains uneasy. Tanks rattle through the streets; the faces of the men who ride them are as cold as ice. By evening we can no longer conceal from ourselves that the attack has failed.

"Europe thanks Providence," the papers say, quoting Italy, Croatia, Prague, Hungary, Norway, and Finland. The Quislings of all nations are sitting up on their hind legs and begging.

And a Major Remer, commander of the Berlin guard battalion, is waiting for decorations and promotion.

Slowly the details of what happened begin to emerge from the welter of rumors. Stauffenberg takes the bomb to Hitler's headquarters, and puts it down in his courier's brief case beside the conference table. He leaves; a few minutes later the thing explodes.

Stauffenberg, thinking he has wholly succeeded, flies to Berlin, and informs his faithful followers in the Bendlerstrasse. They order the guard battalion to occupy the government part of town.

The guard battalion marches—and Major Remer gives away the whole show. He rushes posthaste to inform Mr. Goebbels.

Goebbels foams at the mouth; Goebbels raves. He telephones instantly to headquarters.

The guard battalion does an about-face. A few shots in the Bendlerstrasse; a brief scuffle, whose faint echo scarcely reaches the nearest streets.

Himmler takes care of the rest. And Goebbels beats the propaganda drum for his blood court. He is very discreet about it, mentioning no names. Except for Count Stauffenberg, not a single name has reached the public so far. They still stick to collective abuse, referring to cliques of traitors, abysmally evil and corrupt men, criminal creatures of ambition, conscienceless soldiers of fortune and gamblers.

Only the opponents of the regime whisper honored names —Field Marshal von Witzleben, General von Hase, Colonel General Beck, Colonel General Höppner, Count Yorck von Wartenburg.

Many others are being mentioned. Moltke is not among them; neither is Hinrichs, nor Adam von Trott. If only we had word from Hinrichs! He's been on detached duty for days, beyond reach of our anxiety—beyond reach, God willing, of Heinrich Himmler's thugs.

Tuesday, July 25, 1944.

In his capacity of "senior officer of the armed forces" Goering has improved the opportunity to impose the Hitler salute on all units of the army. "All components of the Wehrmacht, in consequence of their fortunate escape, have requested my permission to introduce the German greeting in the Wehrmacht as a symbol of steadfast devotion to the Leader and close communion between Wehrmacht and Party," he reports to his superior, "so visibly favored by Providence."

That certainly stinks to heaven of rigging. It's the finishing touch to the enslavement of the German army. The NSDAP is enthroned; the years of struggle between State soldiers and Party soldiers are finished. Roehm started it, and lost. Himmler continued it—first against Blomberg, then against Fritsch, finally against Canaris and Witzleben. Himmler won. As of yesterday, the German soldier says, "Heil Hitler!" He waves his arm, and doesn't snap his hand to his cap. Saluting at your cap is high treason. Anyone who has had this repugnant habit for decades must now break himself of it before the mirror.

"Heil Hitler! The symbol and expression of a definite way of thinking," the press observes. Certainly it's a way of thinking; only it isn't natural to the people on whom it is being compulsorily "voluntarily" imposed.

Nevertheless, the army remains silent; the German greeting produces no rebellion—at most, a secret growl. Himmler's arresting machine works with too terrible an efficiency. Is it worth risking your neck for? Worth making your exit from the stage of life anonymously, without benefit to anyone?

"The Fuehrer has acceded to the desire of the army, and given his assent." How too obliging of him!

Meanwhile the Russians have taken Lublin, and are advancing on East Prussia. The six weeks that Hinrichs predicted it would take to consolidate the landing in France are past, and apparently the break-through won't be long in coming.

Thursday, July 27, 1944.

At last Goebbels has opened his mouth—for a "comprehensive report to the German people." It's odd, though, that even this "sober and unadorned statement of fact" bashfully withholds the names of the culprits. Stauffenberg is free to be denounced. According to Goebbels, those grouped around Stauffenberg are, "A general whose sole distinction in the conduct of the war so far has been his habit of sabotaging every great decision; a colonel general who was retired and pensioned off years ago because under the slightest strain he had nervous breakdowns and hysterics; another colonel general who was dismissed from the army some time ago for a cowardly retreat on the eastern front; and a few insignificant functionaries. . . ." That's all.

Otherwise, the Reich Minister of Propaganda outdoes himself in assiduously painting the details of the intended *coup de main*. He threatens summary punishment, brandishes the knout, and almost bursts into tears as he speaks of the "deeply moving impression" when a "young officer of the German army [*read* Remer] has the honor to receive direct instructions from the lips of his Leader and Supreme Commander in Chief." This is the result of the hasty conversation with headquarters during the afternoon. "A platoon of the guard battalion immediately undertook the executions. The perjured criminals suffered a well-deserved death in the courtyard of the Bendlerstrasse. And with that the entire action is concluded," says Goebbels.

If so, why is Himmler making arrests on a mass-production scale? Why do we hear nothing of Trott, nothing of Dr. Kühn, Canaris, Popitz, and many others?

Andrik doesn't even speak these days. Frank goes around as if he had a burning dagger in his flesh. Heike weeps. Ursula Reuber is distracted. We keep the radio going all day. No names, no names, no names.

The English get their information by way of Sweden, Switzerland, or some other neutral country. Are the Swedes correct? Have the Swiss got reliable information?

Hitler proclaims total war; he appoints Goebbels Reich plenipotentiary for total war effort. They're using the attempted assassination as a suitable garnish to dish up unpopular government measures. Heaven knows the ruffians manage to kill a lot of birds with one stone! Even the new V weapons are brought up again.

We ignore all that. We're waiting for the names—the names of those involved.

We realize more clearly from hour to hour that Hitler is using the same old trick that he did after the Roehm affair. Disagreeable incidents that can't be kept from the public are used as an excuse to deal with all countertendencies that might possibly be dangerous sometime, somehow, somewhere. That was why Schleicher died, that was why Klausner died in 1934. That's why we tremble today for hundreds of people whom Count Stauffenberg may not even have known by

name. Terror is on the march. Duck your head, and say
nothing! When reapers are reaping, the grass can't rebel—
not even if it has reached the level of a flower.

Monday, July 31, 1944.

Someone has reported me to the Gestapo—because allegedly
I made a remark "derogatory to the Fuehrer" in a café during the radio announcement of the total war effort. A Party
Comrade sitting with his back to me fifteen feet from my
table claims he noticed my seditious behavior. The very next
day he reported it to the Gestapo. I'm ordered to the Prinz-
Albrechtstrasse for questioning today.

On the principle that attack is the best defense, I expose
the assiduous Party Comrade as a contemptible informer,
weave the names of exalted government authorities into my
talk, and juggle big shots, Reich Literature Chamber, complaint to the Press Authority of the Reich government, keeping them all in the air at once like Rastelli the juggler. I make
such a frightful fuss that the functionary who is questioning
me grows more and more subdued. Finally he almost begs
my pardon. What a wretched subaltern mentality it is, turning in a flash from bloodhound to rabbit the moment the name
of some superior looms on the horizon! Nevertheless I heave
a sigh of relief when the door of the palace of sighs slams
behind me.

Andrik is waiting at the next street corner. "They've broken
through in France," he greets me. "Just watch—it'll go fast
now. They'll be at Paris in less than three weeks."

"God grant they may," I sigh. "If only they'd been there
by the twentieth of July!"

Word from Hinrichs! He's all right. He says, in an army-mail letter, "After some days with a severe throat and stomach infection, I am now on the road to recovery."

"Throat" means in danger of his life. "Stomach" means anxiety, worry, uneasiness. In other words, he, too, had counted on being arrested. But the danger is past. Thank God for that! I'm still struggling to "translate" the letter when Andrik comes into the room.

"Kühn is arrested," he says tonelessly. "It was on the nineteenth of July."

"How did you find out?" I look him in the face with dismay, and my newborn joy dies away like a flame blown out by the wind.

"His girl friend told me. A message smuggled out of the jail where they hold them for questioning. He's in a very bad fix, the poor devil; they accuse him of preparing high treason." There goes another candidate for death. They're dying faster and faster in Germany; and death is eating ever deeper into our own ranks, too. My heart is like lead.

Poor Wolfgang Kühn! Now you needn't worry your head about the Fourth Reich any more; your head itself is the only subject of concern. And I'm afraid it's loose on your shoulders!

Hinrichs is free, though; and these days we must be grateful for each one that's still alive and at large.

Heinrich Himmler's men are digging away underground like moles, bringing death in terrifying secrecy. No names mentioned. But hour by hour we can feel the circle of those arrested growing—Catholics and Social Democrats, union men, army men, Communists, former German Nationalists.

Hitler acts as if nothing had happened; he confers with Mussolini, distributes Knight's Crosses and Oak Leaves, travels here, travels there, and vaunts his good health by daily picture stories. The "miracle of Providence" is being displayed as a showpiece, and the name of Heaven is taken in vain to bear witness to the historic mission of Mr. Adolf Hitler, alias Schicklgruber.

Saturday, August 5, 1944.

"Thirty-six thousand gross registered tons sunk, fifty-six thousand GRT torpedoed. Heaviest blow so far to the invasion fleet," the army communiqué gloats.

If only they'd lay off with their gross registered tons! Not a soul in Germany believes that nonsense any more—quite aside from the fact that there are very few to whom gross registered tons convey anything at all, and fewer still to whom it conveys the right thing. The skeptics have maintained for a long time that we've sunk more GRT during the war than the entire Allied navies possessed. Gross registered tons are the victory stuffing for slack days in the fighting. Like the Jews in foreign politics, they carry the entr'acte in the army communiqué.

Ten thousand a day! A hundred thousand a day! What is one cipher more or less in distracting sixty million Germans from the discovery that fighting is going on in Warsaw, the Russians are west of Reichshof and west of Baranow, and the break-through in France is growing alarmingly? Is it worth buying a paper at all just for the stupid old registered tons?

We buy it anyhow. And when we open it up, we find our burning concern of the past seventeen days: for the first time, the names of those who fought on July 20.

"Fuehrer's Headquarters, August 4. The army has informed the Fuehrer that it is desirous of immediately rehabilitating its honor by clearing ruthlessly out of its ranks the very last criminals implicated in the outrage of July 20, 1944. The Fuehrer, acceding to this request, has appointed a court of honor of field marshals and generals to dismiss the culprits from the army. The court of honor, consisting of Field Marshal General von Keitel, Field Marshal General von Rundstedt, Colonel General Guderian, General of the Infantry Schroth, and Lieutenant General Specht, convened on August 4, and dismissed from the army: (a) the following, who are under arrest: Field Marshal General von Witzleben, General of the Signal Corps Fellgiebel, Lieutenant General von Hase, Major General Stieff, Major General von Tresckow, Colonel Hansen (G.S.C.), Lieutenant Colonel Bernardis (G.S.C.), Major Hayessen (G.S.C.), Captain Klausing, Reserve First Lieutenant Count von der Schulenburg, Reserve First Lieutenant von Hagen, Reserve First Lieutenant Yorck von Wartenburg; (b) those who were court-martialed and shot on July 20: General of the Infantry Olbricht, Colonel Count von Stauffenberg (G.S.C.), Colonel Merz von Quirnheim (G.S.C.), Reserve First Lieutenant von Haeften; (c) the traitors who confessed their guilt by suicide: Colonel General Beck (Ret.), General of Artillery Wagner, Colonel von Freytag-Loringhoven (G.S.C.), Lieutenant Colonel Schrader; (d) the deserters: General of Artillery Lindemann, Major Kuhn (G.S.C.) (deserted to the Bolsheviks); (e) a motion for dismissal of former Colonel General Höppner is superfluous, as Höppner, having been dismissed in 1942, no longer belongs to the armed forces. Those dismissed from the army are being turned over to the People's Court for sentence. Proceedings against the culprits before the People's Court will take place shortly." Full stop, dash. Not a word of comment, before or after.

The tiny clique of three officers has swelled into twenty-three main ringleaders—twenty-three heads of the German army command.

By secret instructions the press has been informed that it must "give especial attention to the film of the trial, which will occupy a very prominent place in the next newsreel." So they're even going to make a movie of the ghastly show trial! "Circuses for the people!"

Wednesday, August 9, 1944.

The movie men are busily at work. The curtain has already fallen on the bloody spectacle—trial, sentence, execution. It was all done in forty-eight hours. What the papers print to-day is only a retrospect, a ghostly dance of horror that already belongs to the past. Our noble editors and managing editors have done themselves proud; even the most carping critic must admit that. The way they worked their imaginations overtime to invent headlines should satisfy even Mr. Hitler's thirst for vengeance. "Ambitious dishonorables condemned to death by People's Court for national and high treason. Sentence executed by hanging. Treason would have betrayed all branches of German people to foe," the provincial papers slaver.

And while the good old fellow Germans are at breakfast, chewing rolls and margarine and drinking malt coffee, they read what happened on the twentieth of July—some with tears, some with indignation. And most of them with the same avid satisfaction they get from reading an exciting murder story, which will just about spice up the breakfast hour for jaded brain and nerves. For shame!

During the trial Freisler outdoes himself in meanness. The cameramen are grinding. Spotlight on the chief defendant, Erwin von Witzleben. They have taken away his general's uniform, and given him a civilian suit from the textile remnants of gassed Jews. The suit doesn't fit; it sags over his shoulders; it flaps around his hips, for the man who originally wore it weighed far more than he. Persons guilty of high treason are not allowed suspenders and belts. It is painful for a former field marshal general to have his trousers fall down around his shoes. So General Witzleben has no choice but to hold up his trousers with his hand.

"Don't keep tugging at your trousers, Witzleben," Freisler interrupts the trial, exasperated. "It's disgusting. Can't you fasten them?"

He knows Witzleben can't fasten them. "No," says the defendant, and the audience bursts into loud laughter.

Spotlight on Major General Hellmuth Stieff. He wears a cardigan sweater, and looks as if he could hardly stay on his feet. "His back is one great wound," the audience whispers. "They beat him up so badly."

"Yes," says Stieff. "Yes indeed." And again, "Yes indeed." Yes, he knew of the planned attempt. And had the audacity not to report it to the Fuehrer.

Spotlight up, spotlight down. Flashbulbs; grinding crank. The camera pivots. It shines again on Field Marshal General von Witzleben.

Freisler has him in a forked stick. Every question is a trap, every question a hit with the audience. "Defendant, just how had you intended to carry out your plan of inducing the Fuehrer to retire, allowing you and Beck to play Commander in Chief and Reich Chancellor?"

"I know nothing whatever about politics and domestic

political affairs," replies Witzleben simply. "Chiefly, of course, we wanted to get control over the Fuehrer, but not by way of assassination. We were of opinion that a surviving Fuehrer would be more useful to us than one who was not alive."

Freisler looks him piercingly in the face. "It strikes me that in merely preparing for your attempted assassination you burned a great deal of gasoline, defendant," he says severely.

"That doesn't count in a case like this," Witzleben murmurs.

The audience laughs, and the presiding justice may congratulate himself on making a special hit with the illegal excess gasoline consumption.

The camera moves, then pauses on Colonel General Erich Höppner.

"When Stauffenberg arrived at the airport in Rangsdorf with word of Hitler's death, Beck came to Olbricht, and made me chief of the government," Höppner says. "I asked for an appointment in writing as Commander in Chief of the Home Army. I received it, called together the group leaders of the Home Command, and asked them to continue working as faithfully as they had done hitherto."

Silence at the judges' table. This disclosure is embarrassing, and might be misinterpreted. The best way is to pay no attention. Accordingly the official report sums up the situation as follows: "This observation by the accused aroused the spectators to such an extent that the presiding judge found no comment necessary upon these shameless words."

Lights down, lights up. Erich Höppner moves into the background. From the shadowy realm of death comes Colonel General Beck. His former housekeeper summons him up; she is forced to testify, but certainly not in exoneration.

Triumphantly Freisler the prosecutor records in his case that "for two weeks before the attempt, the burly Beck broke out every night in a sweat of terror, so that his bed was soaked, and had to be remade every morning." A telling touch indeed in this telling trail—a general with nocturnal attacks of perspiration. A general struggling with his conscience, his soul weighed down every night with the monstrous responsibility he is about to assume, with his plans, his daring, his love for his cheated and misguided people. But that aspect of the question is not touched on. The audience's sense of martial honor is satisfied merely to have a Prussian colonel general breaking out in a sweat every night for two weeks. That's enough to condemn him; it suffices to make him contemptible. With satisfaction the soldierly housekeeper goes back to her seat.

Höppner has the floor again. "I allowed myself to be arrested," he explains, "because I did not feel that I was a swine."

"What zoological description *do* you consider appropriate for yourself, then?" inquires Freisler, grinning.

"A donkey," replies Höppner. "A donkey," he thinks, "that could suppose more than ten per cent of the people understand the disaster hanging over them through Hitler. A donkey that could forget that men must be led like little children."

Höppner thinks all this and a thousand times more, and says, "I was a donkey."

Freisler takes it differently. "No, my dear sir," he protests, "you are and will always be a swine." He clears his throat significantly, and turns to the remaining defendants. The newsreel men grind away.

First Lieutenant Count Yorck von Wartenburg. He is disposed of in a few words as a "presumptuous reactionary." It would be too trying to remark at length upon his bold replies during the preliminary interrogation, and his unswerving enmity to Hitler. Count Yorck is Moltke's friend. Even Freisler, senior judge of the People's Court, has a hard time depriving this upright man of his honor.

Captain Klausing, "the supine tool of the chief criminals."

Lieutenant Colonel Bernardis, Lieutenant General Paul von Hase, army commandant of Berlin.

That is the end of the "moral execution." Again there is reference to "God's blessing," which graciously averted the intended blow from "our beloved Fuehrer."

A brief concluding word from the defense counsel. They dare do no more than stammer; they know what will happen if they speak too vigorously for their clients. "The utterance of fate and the voice of the German people have already pronounced sentence for the twentieth of July," they declare.

Two hours after the public announcement, sentence is executed upon all eight defendants by hanging in the yard at Plötzensee. The military revolt is put down. Now for the civilian revolt.

On August 8, 1944, a warrant is published in all the papers for "the fugitive retired mayor, Dr. Karl Goerdeler, suspected of complicity in the outrage of July 20." A million reichsmarks is offered for his apprehension. How many among sixty million have the strength of character to resist such a sum?

Saturday, August 12, 1944.

The camera people cranked for nothing. The disgrace-to-civilization movie of July 20 has been cut out of the newsreel. Goebbels does not think it convincing enough; the lens caught Mr. Freisler's malicious leer too truthfully, and Erwin von Witzleben's wrinkled, sorrowing face. Not even the cutter's shears can cure such a miscarriage of propaganda as that. Accordingly the secret instructions for "most emphatic notice in the press" go down-trap without even the trouble of a cancellation. We heave a sigh; at least this one cup of poison has passed us by.

Monday, August 14, 1944.

The prisons are filling up, with men, women, children. Whole families are under lock and key. All a man's relatives pay for his personal misdeeds. Trott is arrested; so are Ambassador von Hassell, Lukaschek the lawyer, and the former Hessian Minister of the Interior, Leuschner. Two days ago they found Goerdeler, too. By the eleventh of August more than a dozen Goerdelers had been reported to the criminal police. More than a dozen claimants were waiting avidly for payment of the million. They waited in vain; they had reported the wrong man.

At seven in the morning on August 12 the real Goerdeler is stopped and arrested in the woods of West Prussia by two paymasters of the Air Force. A female staff assistant from Leipzig recognized him, informed her associates, and (as the press observed admiringly) "made possible by her alertness the arrest of former Mayor Goerdeler, who was implicated in the attempted assassination of the Fuehrer!"

The dramatic scene is re-enacted for the benefit of the nation. Adendorf, the SS reporter, takes a picture of it, which appears in the new number of the *Illustrierte* under the caption, "A million for alertness."

Goerdeler vanishes into the torture chambers of the Gestapo. Poor mayor of Leipzig! Can you withstand their horrors until the Allies arrive to release you?

163

The waves of invasion are washing like a rip tide through France. Chartres has been taken. Only eleven more kilometers, and American troops will be in Paris.

Each report of a withdrawal is countered with some new forced decree. Writers and press restricted, all vacations called off, sixty-hour week, closing of all theaters and places of public amusement. The rising generation of film and movie people are assigned in a body to munitions making.

Heike wrings her hands. Now it's her neck, too. If we don't pull every wire we know, she'll have to start turning out hand grenades on September 1.

Andrik writes "on behalf of the absent father of the minor, Heike Burghoff, dramatic student" to the Berlin Labor Office: "As foster father of Heike Burghoff I undertake the responsibility toward State and Party of rendering my foster daughter a completely productive member of the national community. As the greatest possible care alone will suffice to prevent permanent damage to her heart, which would unfit her for the theatrical profession, and whereas on the other hand the State attaches great importance to employing artistic talents where they will be of most use to the entire nation, I emphatically protest against the intended labor duty, and request appropriate assistance on the part of the Labor Office." The endless German "tapeworm sentence" turns the trick. Heike is indefinitely relieved of compulsory labor duty, and allowed to concentrate on taking care of her heart.

"Congratulations," Frank grins when she comes back with the news. "I wouldn't ever have thought the Nazis would be so generous—letting you follow the call of your heart unmolested in the fifth year of war."

Heike rubs her hands cheerfully: "You can bet your boots it won't call 'Heil Hitler!'"

Friday, August 25, 1944.

Two pieces of glad news in one day: Paris taken; Rumania has dropped out!

"King Michael has ordered the army to cease fighting against Russia," the English radio reports.

"Court Camarilla and King striving to betray the country to Moscow. Marshal Antonescu eliminated by a cowardly ambush of the king and a traitorous clique made up of Anglophile politicians and reactionary bootlickers," says the German radio. The greater the worry, the more scurrilous the tone. What will our official language be like when the Allies are at the Brandenburg Gate? Just now they're marching through the Arc de Triomphe.

And our army communiqué keeps getting more and more *// cheap propaganda* involved in the tangle of its excuses. "The enemy, after a break-through, has been forced farther to the eastward by our counterattack from his original eastward course," it announces proudly on August 20. Surely a dubious success to drive the enemy in the very direction in which he is aiming.

Tuesday, August 29, 1944.

But there are still plenty of believers; and among them, more zealots and madmen than we like to see. Frank Matthis' "legitimate existence" is at an end. Boiling with rage, he is striding up and down the room. "One thing I can tell you: I won't let them lock me up! Not me! They'll have to go some to do that, those fellows, those . . . those . . ." Anger chokes him. He brandishes his fists menacingly. "East Wall duty—marking people fit for service who are on crutches—sending dying

165

men to the ramparts—processing cannon fodder! Am I knacker of human beings? They want me to stamp 'fit for combat duty' on everything, do they? Can they force me to go against my own conscience?" Once again he races like a caged tiger among the couch, table, and chairs in the little room. Wild animals should not be provoked. Andrik cautiously moves everything breakable out of the way.

"Why, who's forcing you?" he inquires gently.

"Who's forcing me? The Health Service is forcing me. Orders to report for duty, my dear fellow. As of September 1, 1944. Frank Matthis, a handyman for total war effort. And that's what I took my degree for!" He broods somberly for several minutes. Then he yanks up his head resolutely. "No, it wasn't for that! Not if they swear out a hundred warrants for me. They can count me out. I'm drawing my own conclusions, and acting on them."

He does so that very evening. After a noisy quarrel with his official superiors, he vanishes for good.

Wednesday, September 6, 1944.

Frank is a wanted man. The criminal police have inquired of us three times already.

We don't know anything. Why, we've lost sight of him for several weeks. Andrik maintains this with the most angelic innocence. Do they believe him?

Meanwhile the vanished man is living more or less merrily as a subtenant, ostensibly checked in with the police, in the apartment of an evacuated standard leader's widow. Kufsteinerstrasse, Schöneberg. He's wrestling with the initial fits or depression incident to a fugitive existence, intermittently rejoicing that he isn't on East Wall duty, and creeping to us to get the latest news.

"He's taken care of," sighs Andrik, relieved and a little envious. Trott's fate is weighing him down heavily. All we know is that he is arrested. What more has happened to him we cannot find out for sure, despite all inquiries. Further show trials are being avoided, and what happens behind the scenes doesn't leak out; only now and then we learn from surreptitious whispered messages that the terror is continuing, claiming more and more victims, in ever-widening circles.

Hinrichs has been declared unworthy of the honor of belonging to the Air Force staff. He's not up to serving in a central office, the Security Service confidentially informs his superiors. He gracefully submits to being transferred to Hamburg. A transfer is better than arrest; his getting off so lightly at all is almost a miracle.

Monday, September 11, 1944.

Dead! They're all dead! Hassell and Leuschner, Wirmer and Helldorf, Lejeune-Jung, Dr. Goerdeler, Adam von Trott. "Rubbed out of the national community!" Strung up on the gallows like common criminals. The public is merely informed of the accomplished fact; where the court convened, who summoned it, when and at what shameful spot the martyrs breathed their last—all this and much more important matters are withheld by the official report. It merely exposes the seven "politicians involved in the occurrences of July 20" to contempt as "political ignoramuses, unscrupulous playthings of ambition, discredited Party politicians, reactionaries to whom honor meant nothing." Which of the seven falls in one category, and which in another, is not specified. The insults are offered en masse in eighteen lines of print; then, squeezed into a very small space, accusation, trial, confession, and sentence. Ten lines of print for each human tragedy.

Andrik has locked himself in his room, and will speak to nobody. When I listen at his door, I hear him pacing to and fro, restlessly, unceasingly, hour after hour after hour—like Ahasuerus, the eternal wanderer.

Shan't we have had enough of horror soon? Is not the measure pressed down and running over by now, too full for another drop?

Wednesday, September 13, 1944.

It is not full. If we had never known before what horror, vileness, and diabolical corruption mean, today we found out. We found out so that our hair stood on end and our throats were dry with utter loathing. But let me try to be calm, and record things in order.

Andrik, Frank, Heike, Dagmar, Ursula, and I are sitting together. As we do almost every evening, when the door opens, and Konrad Bauer totters in. He looks as if he has had a severe illness, or has just heard some terrible news.

"Konrad!" we cry with one voice.

He stares as if he didn't see us.

"Boy! Konrad!" With two bounds Frank is shaking his shoulder. "What ails you? Tell us! Who did anything to you?"

Ursula pushes him into a chair, holds a glass of tea to his lips, and brushes his hair out of his eyes. "Let him alone. He'll tell us. But first he's got to pull himself together."

We wait until he recovers himself. We wait a long time. The room is as silent as a tomb.

Finally Konrad opens his mouth, and tells us things awful

168

to think, yet more awful to write down. "Hitler gave orders to take moving pictures of the execution of the eight men from the twentieth of July. The film of the death of Witzleben, Höppner, Stieff, and the rest was run off at a closed showing. An officer from Karlsbad told me," says Konrad. "He saw it; he was there, and heard the spectators catch their breath—with horror, shame, and secret lustfulness. With his own ears he heard gold-braided brownshirts slapping their knees and murmuring approval: 'That's right. I hope the same thing happens to Goerdeler.'" Konrad distractedly wipes the sweat from his brow. We sit crouching, as if crushed by a leaden weight.

"The morning before," he goes on in a low voice, "the lighting men and mechanics arrived at Plötzensee. They laid the cables for the spotlights, and turned the execution shed into a passable film studio. Six operators were detailed for the job; two of them are supposed to have volunteered. The eight condemned men are marched out in wooden clogs and smocks. Then the film ground on to the terrible finale. A scaffolding stands in the glare of the floodlights. Long, ghostly, hidden behind a billowing black cloth down to about knee-high. The condemned men are lined up in front of it. The first one goes behind the cloth. The others wait. Behind the cloth lurks death. Behind the cloth . . ." Konrad breaks off. ". . . living men are being garroted. Do you know what *garroting* means?" he shouts aloud. "It means choking. Letting them dangle so that they can still get a little bit of air—so that the wretched victims shan't on any account die too quickly. They swing them in the noose—seven minutes—eight minutes—*twelve minutes.*" His voice fails him. He struggles for air, and his hands tremble. "That's why they didn't have the cloth go all the way down to the ground; that's why Himmler or

Goebbels or Hitler thought up that piece of vileness. So that the others could see and yet not see what went on behind the curtain; so that the kicking of the legs would frighten them and bring the sweat of death out on their brows. Close-up! Death agonies as a sexual stimulus. They're supposed to have squandered two hundred thousand feet of film on that outrage. Sixty kilometers. That's an hour by express train—the distance from Berlin to Brandenburg. The film has been shown to Hitler three times already. And I swear to you, if it were shown to ten thousand Nazi men and women in a movie house, nine thousand of them would go back home, feeling not shame but pleasure—pleasure, like the circus crowds watching Christian martyrs, the knitting women around the guillotines in the Revolution, the gaping throngs before the piled faggots of the Inquisition."

Seven minutes, eight minutes, twelve minutes!

"Garroting is the execution of the death sentence by strangulation," murmurs Frank mechanically. He sounds as if he were reading from an encyclopedia.

Silence. . . . Our thoughts are racing in circles.

"No!" Andrik roars suddenly. "No!" He yells so loud that we jump. "No, no, no! We can't go on with this. And we mustn't. If we do, we're all guilty. We'll stand guilty before the world, and guilty before our own consciences. I have ceased to be a German. As of this hour and minute I solemnly withdraw from the community of my nation, and emigrate to the everywhere that is home to a citizen of the world." He leaps up and stands before us, glowing with wrath, like Moses as he broke the tables of the law.

We have all stood up. You can't sit when you're settling accounts with your conscience; you can only stand or kneel. So the seven of us stand in a circle, and our hands seem to join of their own accord. "The Rütli oath," I think fleetingly. "We will be free as our fathers were, and have no fear of the power of men." Astonishing how a truth suits all ages in the same way.

Now I see why Hitler forbade *Wilhelm Tell* years ago.

Tuesday, October 3, 1944.

Konrad disappears out of Berlin. It's getting too hot to hold him. Three days ago, while he was sitting reading in the subway, he glanced up into the eyes of his warden from the Hamburger Strasse.

"Come with me," the man beckons to him at the next stop. They both get out.

"Farewell, beloved freedom," thinks Konrad. Before his somber eye are visions of prison bars, electrified barbed-wire fences, dog whips, and gas chambers.

But it doesn't turn out that way. The man pulls him into a corner, grabs him by a coat button, and shakes his finger at him. "Man alive," he whispers, "get out of here! What devil has got into you, hanging around right in the very city where they're hunting for you like a needle in a haystack? You'd better thank God it was only me that caught you. And now you beat it—preferably for keeps." And with that he turns and disappears in the crowd.

Konrad slinks home with his tail between his legs. So there's a human heart occasionally even in a Jewish Gestapo employee. We make a note of the man.

Ursula undertakes to get in touch with him. "I know him," she says. "He was the only decent one among the Jewish overseers in the Hamburger Strasse. As for the others . . ." She

171

looks at us unhappily, ". . . What can you expect of people for whom stool-pigeoning is the only escape from ghetto and gas chamber?"

The following day Konrad misses by a hair bumping into his examining magistrate, outside the Brandenburg Gate. We don't want to wait for a triple coincidence. There's a girl in Homburg that loves him—one of his colleagues on the army entertainment tour. She is ready to take him in.

Now all we need is traveling papers. Dr. Tegel looks after that. Zweidorf sends one messenger to the Music Chamber, another to the office of the State Opera. Second-class ticket, sleeping car; with a prominent name and prominent requirements, suspicions are considerably lulled. Impudence has won again. And when we send off the prominent concert artist by sleeping car for Frankfort, amply equipped with traveling ration stamps and rubber-stamped vouchers, not one of his fellow travelers suspects that it is only our friend Konrad Bauer after all. He waves casually from the window.

Friday, October 20, 1944.

Scarcely a day passes that we do not talk about final victory. "Final victory" in reverse. Will it come this year? Will it be next?

Hinrichs bets on November. But Churchill has announced that the three heads of states will meet shortly to discuss the final blow at Germany. In other words, he isn't expecting any collapse before this final blow. The western front seems to be having a breathing spell. We mark time, frantic with impatience.

Himmler, on the other hand, is using the breathing spell to prepare as best he can for the next blow. Two days ago he spoke over the German radio in the name of the Fuehrer, calling up all able-bodied men from sixteen to sixty for the *Volkssturm,* the Home Guard.

Once again there was a "historic scene." "After five years' fiercest struggle, owing to the failure of all our European allies, the enemy at certain fronts is near or on German borders. Against the recognized will to total destruction on the part of our Jewish-international enemies, we set the total effort of all Germans. I therefore decree that the German Home Guard shall be formed in the provinces of the Greater German Reich out of all able-bodied men from the age of sixteen to sixty. It will defend the home soil with all weapons and means, insofar as they appear appropriate."

Thus far the official announcement. The unofficial supplement is an order to the press: "Effective immediately, all discrediting of civilian fighters in enemy foreign countries is prohibited. Expressions such as 'bushwhackers,' 'partisans,' 'bandits,' etc. will cease to be used in news stories."

Now we know what's what; we can figure out for ourselves when our own turn will come.

A further disaster is threatened. Now that all but a tiny remnant of the star bearers have vanished into ghettos, concentration camps, or the gas ovens of Auschwitz, they are starting to think about removing even the privileged ones. That means forced dissolution of mixed marriages, a torrent of new misery for thousands.

We confer for a long time with Ursula Reuber. We must organize a warning service before it's too late. So far, those who have learned in time that they were to be taken away have almost always managed to escape. Ursula talks things over with her Gestapo acquaintance, and settles with him that we are to have word the moment the question is decided. The honest fellow promises her even more; in the future he will inform her by telephone when he receives orders to take away a Jew. He will be very slow about the job; he will dawdle on the way, look in show windows, and gape at the clouds. Ursula has a bicycle. Bicycles are the fastest transportation these days. When Gestapo Agent Lewisohn arrives to take away the Cohns, the Levys, or the Abrahams, imagine how he will curse, roar, and rave on finding that the bird has flown!

Heaven reward you for those outbursts of rage, Gestapo Agent Lewisohn! We know your own neck is at stake.

"Dr. Tegel has got to be informed at once," says Frank. With his extensive "clientele," he needs the warning service more than anyone. We go out that afternoon.

He has word from Moltke—that he's all right, and treated relatively well. A smuggled note has been got out of the Fürstenberg concentration camp—several pages of it, a whole book. He's in there with Planck, Schacht, and Popitz. "The only ones here aside from me that aren't beaten," he reports. The negative exception makes the positive rule all the more terrible.

Dr. Tegel looks grave and worn out. Having almost daily to accompany to the scaffold somebody whom one respects or even loves is more than one man can bear. The fact that he does bear it, that he doesn't lose his reason, but uses every spare moment to care for the wives of the condemned, to establish communication between them and their imprisoned husbands, to help those who have gone underground, to shelter fugitives—this is a miracle that makes us look up to the man almost as a saint. And we're half ashamed to burden him with yet another case.

But the matter is important, and Dr. Tegel's ears are never closed to anything important. Wolfgang Kühn is in Moabit prison. He's hungry, and ill. Some weeks back they brought him before the People's Court—him and a few of his friends. A clever attorney managed to reduce the six years in the penitentiary that the prosecution demanded to four years' ordinary imprisonment. But even those four years have to be served without letting the felon starve to death. An occasional package, a few cigarettes now and then are more consolation than anyone outside can imagine. Often and often we've heard this from the ghettos. Dr. Tegel promises; and what he promises he usually does. Starting today, Wolfgang Kühn will be included in his weekly pastoral visits to Moabit. That's a great load off our minds.

Thursday, November 9, 1944.

At last things are stirring again in the west. The war is apparently starting to move on the Lorraine front. Germany replies by launching the much-whispered-about Retribution Weapon No. 2. But still the British Isles don't go sky high. Even now the Allies will scarcely whine for mercy, as our propaganda has been promising for months. Many times the explosive power of V-1—all well and good. But that won't win the war. And the Allied bombs aren't getting smaller month by month, either, but considerably more explosive.

"I think it's getting about time for you to be preparing for the Home Guard," says Frank to Andrik. "Better to have things ready in good time, and then when the moment comes they won't look too new."

Andrik goes to the doctor, and picks up a predated weak heart and alarmingly high blood pressure.

"There," says Frank, gratified. "You can put that on ice. The day is coming when you'll want it badly."

Berlin, Sunday, November 12, 1944.

Word comes secretly from Theresienstadt. Heinrich Muehsam is no more. He stuck it out bravely for months, and then a strange disease took hold of him—infantile paralysis, the doctors diagnosed it. Thereupon he was shipped off to Auschwitz. At Auschwitz they put him in the gas oven.

Friday, November 17, 1944.

The offensive is rolling. Maybe Hinrichs will be right about November, after all. The offensive has spread all along the western front today.

Wednesday, November 22, 1944.

There is a break-through in Alsace.

Something dreadful has happened. They've dragged Count Moltke into the Goerdeler affair. We learned yesterday quite by chance. Some people Andrik knows came to see us, and asked if we could do something for their friend Haubach, who's been arrested. Haubach was in the press department of the Prussian provincial government under Severing. A smart, decent sort of fellow, and an enemy of the Nazis. We knew they had arrested him; after all, who hasn't been arrested among the little handful of our best?

"We bribed a man at the People's Court," his friends confide. "He was squirming with terror, but finally he did let us look at the files—at the charges against Moltke, Haubach, and associates."

"Moltke?" I stammer, horrified. "What Moltke?"

"Why, the Count. The man in the Kiep business."

I go cold all over. There can hardly be any mistake.

"We'll do what we can," Andrik promises. "We're interested in that ourselves."

During the night we call up Hinrichs. He confirms the news: Count Moltke is coming before the People's Court. And anyone who comes before the People's Court. . . . Subornation of high treason, overthrow of the government, and abolition of the Nazi regime. Conspiracy with Goerdeler. Things couldn't look worse. It's unnecessary to imagine what penalties are provided. If they hang him . . . If they garrote . . . I remember the film—the movie of the Witzleben execution. Great God! It mustn't be. No matter what happens, we've got to prevent that.

"We'd better go and see Dr. Tegel," Andrik advises. Half an hour later we're in the subway; change at the middle of town; change at the Seestrasse; endless streetcar journey.

Dr. Tegel is at home. "At the moment there's very little to be done," he says miserably. "We'll have to get people interested. Try to get at Freisler. The higher the authority, the better the chance of success. But don't forget that it's a twentieth-of-July affair. Nobody wants to burn his fingers on that. And as for Hitler, he sees red whenever he's reminded of it."

Moltke and associates. Haubach and associates. The deadly rhythm keeps running through my head. Freisler is as cold as ice. To touch him as a human being seems almost impossible. "I'm the man who condemns everybody to death," he introduced himself recently to a society lady, grinning as if he had made a capital joke.

Nevertheless we must try to get at Freisler. Or Himmler. Or some other bigwig. It's a shame we have so few connections in that particular quarter.

We inform the clique. The clique is ready. So let's get going —we've got to try!

Thursday, November 30, 1944.

Heike has undertaken to attend a session of the People's Court. "We've got to see clearly what goes on there," she says. "No matter how abominable it is."

She comes back in the afternoon, her face white, her eyes distracted.

"Tell us about it!" We hang on her words.

She shakes her head; tears run down her cheeks. "It isn't a thing you can tell. It's a farce—a prearranged affair. Seven defendants, seven death sentences. The audience sits there as if it were a circus—laughing, shivering, feeling a pleasant tingle in their stomachs. During intermission they chew on apples and sandwiches. Ugh!" Heike blows her nose loudly.

"Nobody was guilty," she goes on. "Not a one among the seven. Neither the old greengrocer, who didn't understand what was going on at all, and just kept saying, 'I ask your mercy,' nor the young girl music student who was accused of having sheltered Communists. 'See here, Miss, you'll hardly just have slept with one,' said the presiding justice, wittily. The spectators giggled, and were much entertained. In five minutes she was sentenced. Sentenced to death. She wept. So did the old greengrocer." Heike falls silent.

"Go on," says Andrik, and his voice has a strange sound.

"If anyone speaks the truth, they overlook it. If anyone tries to defend himself, they slap his mouth. I swear to you, every sentence is all filled out before the session begins. All they do there is give the masses some entertainment." She shakes herself. "Bread and games. But a person shouldn't sit and watch it. It's bad enough to stand outside a lion's cage when you're a free person; but it's a thousand times worse— no, it's vile, unspeakably vile, to sit idly by when they make public sport of human beings living and dying. I'm ashamed that I was there. I'm ashamed. . . . I tell you, you have no idea how much ashamed I am."

We look at one another in dismay. "But you didn't do it for fun," Andrik comforts her.

Heike, however, is not to be comforted. "To think there are people who go to every session, the way they would to the theater or a murder movie. And they do it of their own accord. . . ."

Saturday, December 9, 1944.

Hinrichs calls up from Hamburg almost every night between two and three. Is there any news, have we made progress, any new connections? We convey our meaning in a thousand roundabout ways, by hints and code words of our own. If anyone is listening in on our conversations, and understands what they mean, we'll be arrested tomorrow morning.

The press maintains silence on the Moltke case. The Witzleben trial made too bad an impression; so now they don't shout things from the housetops. Whoever dies, dies anonymously. Only now and then, when it seems pedagogically advisable, do the masses hear something of sentence and execution.

"Five radio criminals condemned to death for listening to foreign stations. Sentence already executed"—that means the B.B.C. is disclosing dangerous truths again, and it seems wise to frighten people by firing a few blind shots in the papers. What are five human lives by comparison? Less than nothing!

Time is marching on. Our chances grow worse and worse. We rush from one man to another; we are sent away, left cooling our heels in waiting rooms, or at best received with hollow phrases.

Tegel is right: nobody wants to burn his fingers. Anything to do with the twentieth of July is red-hot iron, pestilence, leprosy, and deadly peril.

And still the work goes on, piling up from week to week, brooking no delay. At the office we are secretly getting ready the first peace edition. Call-ups to the Home Guard multiply daily. Every day new men wait to be made invalids by affidavit, medication, and quackery. Frank is writing his fingers to the bone. "Mr. X is suffering from a marked circulatory insufficiency. The electrocardiogram accordingly shows unmistakable signs of muscular damage to the heart." Another doctor friend fakes the electrocardiograms, reinterprets them, twists them to fit; it all looks imposingly professional.

We ransack the drugstores for Atabrine, the artificial jaundice medicine. Sold out all over town. The men have to take to bed with grippe until a new shipment arrives. Frank, underground as he is, and our five medical allies are enjoying a practice as good as the best in peacetime.

The so-called "privileged Jews" are worrying us too. New rumors are current about the dissolution of mixed marriages. People say the Jewish members are to be shipped to Theresienstadt. Flamm was here to see us today, desperately worried about his numerous protégés. Should they "submerge" right away? The "submarine" market is already overcrowded; the harsh rule of the moment is that no one must "dive" who isn't in acute peril of his life.

Our hands are overfull—conferences, arrangements, prescriptions, food supplies. And encouragement! Consolation and encouragement all the time. For the war is dragging on; the fronts come to a standstill. There's no chance now that it will end this year.

The Germans have launched an offensive against Aachen and Liège; they take back in one sweep what the enemy strove for weeks to capture. The people who know say that our army command flung together 120,000 men. Why don't the Allies fling any together? Why does Hitler keep pulling off one surprise blow after another? Each German victory prolongs the war. That's why we keep hoping for our own defeat.

At eleven tonight Countess Moltke is coming to see us. The results of our three weeks' struggles are a poor enough offering.

The day passes with work and worry. Two people need Atabrine prescriptions. Konrad calls up from Homburg, begging desperately for more identification papers.

Flamm is supposed to be drafted—into the newly established half-breed battalions (penal battalions to you) of the Todt Organization. There are ghastly rumors about them—barbed wire, starvation diet, maltreatment. Are they founded on fact?

Evening comes, then night. At eleven o'clock the phone rings. "This is Freya. I'm at South End Station; I'll be there in ten minutes." Countess Moltke. Andrik runs downstairs to open the door for her.

We greet one another as if we had been acquainted for years. When life is at stake, social ceremonies drop off.

I look into her face. Seldom have I seen a purer reflection of the soul in human features. We don't talk much about feelings, about our fear and our anxiety. We talk of what has been done, what can and must be done.

The trial is to take place early in January. If Freisler hasn't been reached by then. . . . Of course Hinrichs has known him for a long time, but he has already gone to see him once, about Wachsmann. If he goes again now, it may do more harm than good. No; until we've exhausted every other resource, Hinrichs is not to be thought of. There must be other ways. We discuss at great length. And when she leaves at two in the morning, we know that we can go on working.

Sunday, December 24, 1944.

Still no approach to Freisler; still no mercy in the quarters that we have appealed to. A sad Christmas Eve indeed.

Dr. Tegel preached today at St. Anne's Church in Dahlem. Heike took communion. "For the martyrs of the twentieth," she said when she came back. I wonder whether Dr. Tegel understood.

Sunday, December 31, 1944.

The trial of Moltke and associates before the People's Court has been set for January 8 and 9. Freisler must finish his Christmas holidays, and sleep off his New Year's hang-over.

If only a miracle would happen! But no miracles do happen in this unbelieving age. We must hope, work, and pray. Perhaps we don't pray enough; perhaps we don't hope enough. There's some religious denomination that maintains anything can be done if you tackle it with the proper confidence. Is confidence what we lack? Probably our fear is too much for us—our absorbing anxiety for that precious life.

Today was the first time that they haven't played the *Lied an die Freunde* over the radio at midnight. When the New Year begins, Andrik and I go out on the balcony and gaze into the night. There are many stars above us. The city lies dark, with a thousand curtained windows.

"I wish he may live, and we may live," says Andrik softly. He kisses me, and looks immeasurably sad.

Tuesday, January 2, 1945.

We have penetrated far into the Nazi camp. Andrik has described the Moltke case to a prominent SS spy. "You know," he says, "this must all be a mistake. Moltke is no politician; he's a dreamer—a real German. Goerdeler was his opponent, and never his friend. Only some wretched misunderstanding could possibly have implicated him in the affair."

The prominent spy proves to be well disposed. Andrik has to drink a lot of whisky with him. It would really be nicer if you didn't have to drink whisky at moments like that.

Thursday, January 4, 1945.

I've been on the go all day. Hinrichs claimed there was a Dr. Lenz who had once been Freisler's assistant and his personal confidant, and wasn't a Nazi. I should try to track him down.

Tracking down is hard work when the houses are bombed to pieces, government offices have moved, and the telephone service is disrupted. From Zehlendorf they send me downtown; from downtown to the Fehrbelliner Platz; at the Fehrbelliner Platz they shrug, and give me an address in Babelsberg; in Babelsberg they send me to Potsdam; from Potsdam back downtown.

"Dr. Lenz?" they say there. "Dr. Lenz hasn't been working here for a long time."

"All right, but where does he work?"

The clerk in charge casts down his eyes. "He's away," he mumbles. "Indefinitely."

Now I know. He's been arrested too. Now Hans Hinrichs is all we have left; he'll have to risk it, no matter what.

I go home, crushed. Ursula Reuber is waiting for me there. She has word from her Gestapo connection that the mixed-marriage drive has been temporarily laid aside, and we have nothing to fear in that quarter for the moment. Some consolation, anyway.

"Only I'm not doing so well," sighs Ursula, her sweet face falling into sorrowful lines. "They nabbed me. Starting Monday I have to sweep the streets."

"What?"

"Yes, or break stones, or scrub busses. I think you can mend soldiers' trousers, too."

"But you've got a job."

"I had. Until day before yesterday; then they bounced me out because half-breeds are not employable for the exacting job of a typist any more. They gave me my choice; so I took the broom."

"And what did Dr. Tegel say?"

"He can't help either. The regulation is in effect all over the Reich. And anyway. . . ." She looks thoughtful. "Maybe sweeping streets isn't the worst that could happen. Not fulfilling your destiny is bad. Not approving of yourself is bad. You see, I want to fulfill my destiny, even if it's a broom and sweepings."

Touched, I fold her in my arms. "You're the best of the lot of us, after all. And if you *should* need a certificate—just in passing, for a couple of days' vacation. . . ."

Friday, January 5, 1945.

We've telephoned Hinrichs three times today, imploring him to come and work on Freisler. And of course yesterday they *would* put an embargo on official travel for a week. There seems to be a positive conspiracy against us. Hinrichs will do what can be done. But he can hardly get here before the eighth. And on the eighth at 8 A.M. . . .

Saturday, January 6, 1945.

On the ninth at 8 A.M.! Freya Moltke comes during the night: the trial has been postponed a day—twenty-four hours' grace. If there aren't air-raid alarms, and the trains aren't endlessly delayed, Hinrichs should make it. We sit together for a long time, talking about things near and far, transitory and abiding.

The siren howls; together we move down cellar, together we come up again. Our thoughts are far away from war and alarms.

"We must carry the spark through time," says Freya Moltke. "If one carries the spark, everything takes on meaning—living and dying. Yes, even dying. I've thought about it often. Perhaps that's the miracle of the Deluge story, and the secret of the Wise Men from the East."

Andrik nods. "That they save the Ark above the waters, and carry gold through the desert—the Wise Men of the old civilization to the Child of the new civilization; gold, frankincense, and myrrh, the choicest treasures of their people."

Freya looks him earnestly in the face. "Yes, the choicest—Gothic enchantment, the abundance of Hölderlin, Bach and

185

Mozart, Dürer and Goethe. It's a blessing to be allowed to carry the spark, and a sacred duty. Let us take it as our duty. Somewhere, beyond the desert, the Child is waiting for us." She falls silent. Her clear eyes are like stars in her face.

I think of Aaron's blessing: "The Lord make his face shine upon thee, and be gracious unto thee," I think tenderly. "The Lord lift up his countenance upon thee, and give thee peace."

Tuesday, January 9, 1945.

Heike and I get up early. The trial in the People's Court begins at eight. At seven is the last morning mass.

"We ought to go to church tomorrow," Heike said yesterday. "Almost all the people of the twentieth are devout Christians. Moltke is a devout Christian too."

So we attend mass, and arrange to have a requiem said at seven on the morning of the tenth. "For fifteen souls that will be leaving this world at that time without the consolation of the sacrament."

The chaplain looks at us. "Fifteen souls," he murmurs. We feel that he is thinking of the right men.

Hinrichs comes in at noon, exhausted, harried, and beaten. Freisler wouldn't see him; sent word he was out, and pretended to be swamped with work. Now all we can put our faith in is the "blessing."

Early in the evening Count von Moltke is brought back by police car to the house of correction. His case is bad. The presiding justice of the People's Court is in an ungracious mood; even the borderline cases are considered worthy of death. He saves up the most important for tomorrow, like a greedy child with its best tidbit.

"Try to attend the trial," Freya von Moltke requests.

I try. I pull all the strings I can: press identification, press card, the highest quarters in the Reich Government Press Office. I butter people up, act disgustingly familiar.

"Secret government trial," they tell me. Only fifteen or twenty dependable Party Comrades. "Incidentally—" they freeze—"what leads you in particular to . . . ?"

All I can do is say nothing, and then mumble some nonsense or other.

Count Moltke's case is bad. But when he comes back from the People's Court to his cell, he sits down and writes. Six pages, seven, eight—the whole course of the proceedings, word for word. Dr. Tegel smuggles the letter out. Freya types it, with a lot of carbons. And that night the wife or fiancée of each man on trial for his life bakes a little cake. An egg, a hundred grams of sugar, fifty grams of butter, half a pound of flour. The letter is in each cake—the letter and everything it says. On the morning of the tenth Dr. Tegel takes the cakes to the jail cells, to eight men who are awaiting sentence that day. Now they know what they may say; they know what the others have said.

Wednesday, January 10, 1945.

The morning is dull and damp. Not a soul on the streets. Heike and I go in silence to the church. Just once she speaks. "Do you think it's sacrilegious to order a requiem when you don't belong to the same denomination?"

I shake my head. "Not in this case. And certainly not when you're filled with reverence and good will."

The chapel fades away in the tiny gleam of the few candles.

Only the eternal light on the altar shines like a consoling eye. Not many people are praying at this hour of the day. Moltke and associates; Haubach and associates. The incense burns smokily. The monstrance glitters in the priest's hand. "Let him live, let us live," I whisper softly. I feel that I have joined the circle of those who suffer throughout the world, of those who have gone before, and those who are yet to go—Witzleben and Schulenburg, Reichwein and Yorck, who carried the spark through the desert, and the gold across the sea.

"Forever and ever, Amen," the priest finishes. The church empties. An old man carefully snuffs out the candles. Only the eternal light on the altar shines like a consoling eye.

"We must go," whispers Heike, tugging at my coat. The clock says eight. At this moment the trial of Count Helmuth von Moltke is beginning in the People's Court. Its beginning is ugly, and so is its ending. Before evening, the death sentence has been demanded for three of the nine defendants. Their names are Moltke, Delp, and Sperr. They have carried the spark—and believed in the spark. They are among the best men that Germany has had to give to the world.

Three of their companions are sentenced to long penitentiary terms: Reisert, five years, Gerstenmaier, seven years, Fugger, three years. Haubach, Steltzer, and Gross have been separated from the "Moltke case" as "not appertaining to it."

Freya tells us. Her voice is clear and firm. "Now we must do everything to get the petition for clemency through."

Two hours later I hear the details. A newspaper colleague from the SS has been at the trial. "A strange sort of fellow, Moltke," he says, rubbing his forehead in bewilderment. "He doesn't say a word, he just looks at him. Just looks at Freisler with those huge dark eyes of his. Do you know what it seemed like to me? It was like Christ before Pilate. Only when they charged the others—Gerstenmaier and Reisert—he went to work. He actually wiggled them out of it. He's a queer stick!" He frowns.

Even Freisler could feel it. "Count," he says, when everything is over, "Count Moltke, Christianity and National Socialism have only one thing in common. They both demand the whole man."

The whole man. The man Moltke, the man Delp, and the man Sperr. Perhaps the privilege of living is not the important thing after all. Perhaps the privilege of dying is a thousand times more important—of dying for an honest faith. And it's only because we're shortsighted that we sometimes pray for very much the wrong thing. When Andrik and I are alone this evening, mortal sadness comes over us.

The tension is over now. Sentence is being pronounced tomorrow afternoon at four.

Thursday, January 11, 1945.

Everyday living comes into its own again, no matter how much we may wish to concentrate on the one thing. Our apartment is buzzing like a beehive again.

A friend of Andrik's turns up, dismayed, scared, and helpless. "I need a father for my child," he says, "an Aryan father. My girl friend . . . We've been living together for ten years. . . . Nothing ever happened before. . . . And now, of all times! You see, the girl's an Aryan. For me as a Jew. . . ."

We see it all. It's hardly possible to misunderstand. Law for the Protection of German Blood and German Honor, Aryan section. Extramarital intercourse between Jews and citizens of German or racially related blood is prohibited, says Paragraph 2. Race pollution is punishable by imprisonment. Or worse. If Andrik doesn't go to the registrar's office. . . .

"I'll do it," he sighs resignedly, and firmly drills himself in the unexpected new role of fatherhood.

Shortly Ursula Reuber calls up. "SOS for chocolate cookies," she pronounces. "Let me know just as quick as ever you can." This means, in everyday language, that the mixed marriages are in danger again; all those involved must be warned at once. Heike goes out to carry messages. Hardly has she gone when word comes that Frank has been given away by one of his colleagues. Well, this is enough for an ordinary weekday. If he isn't triply careful, the catastrophe will be past imagining.

Nine o'clock at night.

There is no more hope for Moltke. They have announced the sentence: death by the noose. In two, or at most three, weeks the period of grace will be up.

Monday, January 15, 1945.

Now only Himmler can save us. From morning to night we ask everyone the same question: "Do you know Himmler? Do you know any way to reach the SS Reichsfuehrer?"

People shake their heads; they shrug their shoulders. Well, of course, if it were for themselves. . . . But for the life of a stranger? Compassion as an end in itself is not highly rated.

Freya Moltke writes a letter to the Ministry of the Interior and SS Reichsfuehrer Heinrich Himmler. The letter would wring tears from a stone. It does not beg or complain; it radiates dignity and nobility. If Himmler should actually see it. . . .

"Do you know Himmler? Do you know any way to reach the SS Reichsfuehrer?" We ask and search, search and ask. Every hour is precious. Two weeks—three at most. Four days of that scanty period are already gone.

"Do you know Himmler? Do you know any way to reach the SS Reichsfuehrer?" I am talking to my publisher.

He looks me searchingly in the face. "I do know a way," he says slowly.

I feel as if the sun were rising. "Really—you do?"

The man is marvelous. He spins his web like a king; he uses it like a human being—the web stretches upward, the help downward. Even Party bigwigs are only means to his ends. "It isn't my own connection; but anyhow, the man does have something to say. An adjutant of the Reichsfuehrer. Better the valet than the boss in person. Only valets know when their royal majesties are in a good humor."

"Then you really will?" I look at him gratefully.

He smiles. "Why else do you think I joined the Party? Let me have the letter. As long as I have any cognac, Himmler's adjutants will continue to come here with pleasure."

Friday, January 19, 1945.

Is the whole universe conspiring against us? Himmler's right-hand man is not presentable at the moment. An accident has tied him to his bed for the past fortnight. The story is that in the excitement of New Year's Eve he put his foot on a hot stove. He burned the sole, got blisters, and then an infection that wouldn't heal. Is Freya Moltke's petition for clemency really to depend on a drunkenly burned foot?

Meanwhile Haubach too has been condemned to death. Sometimes the utter senselessness of the world would drive you to despair.

Ursula Reuber comes over during a breathing spell between two strokes of her broom. On January 15 the Jewish spouses in privileged marriages were to be taken away to the Jew camp at Theresienstadt. The trucks were ready; gasoline was available. Gasoline is always available when Jewish matters are involved. Then, supposedly, the Foreign Office put its oar in—under pressure from the Allies people are whispering. The lives of ten German POWs for each Jewish life. At last even the other side seems to have seen the light. So it's been called off again; and Heike goes out to spread the word.

Sunday, January 21, 1945.

We pray for the recovery of Himmler's adjutant; a hundred times over we ask the same questions. Is he better? Has his wound healed? Can he hobble around yet? And wouldn't cognac be the most effective remedy? Every day I telephone my publisher; no fever chart was ever more passionately watched.

Two days ago they assembled the Home Guard. One hears that the first battalions have already gone off, in civilian coats and spiral puttees. Many of them had never had a rifle in their hands, we hear. People are already talking about eighty per cent casualties, ninety per cent casualties: they are simply thrown in to fill up gaps, walls of corpses against Allied tanks —anything so that they hold out until relief arrives, a day, an hour, no matter how long. The breaches are filled with torn human flesh. And again we ask ourselves, what does a single life weigh against this? A great deal—many tons, when it's as precious as this one.

Monday, January 22, 1945.

The offensive is rolling on in the east: Gnesen falls, Insterburg, Allenstein. They're advancing on Posen, Breslau, and Koenigsberg by forced marches. There is an immediate embargo on the shipping of food to Berlin. The gas supply is cut off; express trains no longer run. We are racing against history. Time, time, time. We have only to gain four weeks. Already events are rushing with giant strides toward catastrophe. Time, time, time. And a healed foot for Himmler's adjutant. The first refugee trains are arriving from Silesia. An open car of frozen children has arrived at the Silesian Station. They stood in the cold for ninety-six hours, packed like sardines in a can. The wind blew on them, the snow covered them up; they froze and wept; they stood on their feet and died, jammed into a wooden coal car. Who can tell meaning from senselessness any more?

Tuesday, January 23, 1945.

Endlessly the refugee trains keep coming, heavy, slow, overcrowded. "Owing to the situation at the front, a few counties to the right of the Oder have received a loosening order, in accordance with which women, girls, and children are being withdrawn from the area. The loosening has now been extended to the entire provincial capital. Young girls and women with grown children are urged, however, to leave the city on foot, taking a southerly and westerly direction, in order to save hours of useless waiting at the stations," say the Silesian newspapers. On foot, in a southerly and westerly direction. The thermometer stands at seventeen above. It's a long way to Tipperary, it's a long way to go!

But Himmler's adjutant has recovered. Tomorrow afternoon at two he'll be having breakfast with my publisher, and reading Freya Moltke's letter over cognac and real coffee. Then he can pass it on to Himmler.

Wednesday, January 24, 1945.

Andrik has been called up for the Home Guard. Within an hour he packs his toothbrush and shaving kit. For the time being he's to get out of the apartment.

I write a polite letter to the appropriate official quarters, saying that Andrik Krassnow is at present away, and cannot be reached by letter. Delay is everything! At two o'clock in the afternoon they'll be breakfasting in Dahlem, with cognac and real coffee, and tomorrow all Russians living here on a Soviet passport are to be arrested. Another wave of submersions. Our hair stands on end at the prospect; how can we ever keep up?

The last busses have been pulled off the streets; trams henceforth will run only until 10 P.M., at endless intervals. Bicycles are trumps. People in town are predicting periodic cutting off of current, and stoppage of all traffic.

But Himmler's adjutant has read the letter, and promised to hand it on. Late that evening I telephone to Dr. Tegel. "We did it. Freya's letter will get to Himmler tomorrow. The petition for clemency—and the clemency."

Why is Dr. Tegel so strange? Why isn't he pleased? Why does he scarcely answer?

Yesterday noon they took Count Moltke to be executed—at the very time when Himmler's adjutant was reading the petition. By four o'clock he was dead. It all happened suddenly and unexpectedly.

At one o'clock Dr. Tegel left his cell. "Well, until tomorrow," he said.

Shortly before two they took them away, Helmuth von Moltke and some others. "For proceedings at Plötzensee," was the laconic explanation. In the shed at Plötzensee stand Adolf Hitler's gallows.

In the shed at Plötzensee prison . . . The Lord be with you, Count Helmuth von Moltke. The Lord make his face shine upon thee, and be gracious unto thee.

Because Himmler's adjutant stepped on a hot stove. Because Thierack, the Minister of Justice, came back from vacation yesterday, and gave orders to clean up at once all "unfinished business." Because the Russians aren't in Berlin yet, and the English aren't in Potsdam. Because . . . Because . . . Why do we cudgel our brains? The world is tumbling about our ears, and we can't halt the collapse.

Wednesday, January 31, 1945.

All Berlin is unhinged. Russian tanks are supposed to be in Straussberg. Highest state of readiness for the Home Guard. The men are disappearing in droves. I meet Andrik on a remote street corner. He looks nervous and downcast.

"They're looking for you," I say unhappily. "A man was at

our place, a messenger from the Home Guard. Ready to march in one hour, the order said."

Andrik pinches his lips. "And what did you say?"

"That you were away. That I didn't know your address. That you had kidney trouble, and couldn't be called up anyway."

Gloomily we watch the troops of soldiers hurrying by. "This can't go on much longer," Andrik sighs.

That evening he comes back home—a man with kidney trouble who simply must keep to his bed until Friday, February 9, when he will prove to the doctor on duty at "pick-and-shovel fortification headquarters" that he's not fit to serve in the Home Guard.

Every part of the city is teeming with fugitives. They are cursing these damned times, some loudly, some softly. No one minds what he says. A man who has lost everything loses even his fear, and doesn't care whether he dies here or yonder. The police are deaf. For twenty-four hours every fellow German may vent his distress, his despair, and his mortal terror unmolested. After that Goebbels is master of the situation again.

Friday, February 2, 1945.

The panic was premature; everything has quieted down overnight. The front is still clustered along the Oder. And instead of winking now, the police are making new arrests. If something doesn't happen soon, they'll catch Hinrichs too. He came today to say good-by. The news he brings is not at all encouraging: Roesch, the Jesuit provincial of Munich, is arrested; Delp's execution has been delayed.

Everyone knows what such delays mean. They mean torture and martyrdom—beatings day in and day out until the required confession has been squeezed out of the tormented flesh.

Roesch belongs to Moltke's circle. He and Hinrichs both attended the Kreisau sessions. And anyone who attended the Kreisau sessions—!

Hinrichs is packing. "If I'm lucky, I'll get through to Hamburg," he says, smiling a bit hopelessly. Hamburg is far from the shooting. By the time they can fetch him back from there, the noose will probably be drawn around Berlin. Again a man is racing time for his life.

Twenty kilometers outside Stettin, twenty kilometers outside Frankfort, say the latest official bulletins. "Come faster, come faster!" we beg in secret.

We accompany our friend of twelve fighting years to the nearest subway. He pushes into the crowded train. He waves back twice, and then we're alone on the platform.

"Another man less," says Andrik, looking somberly after the taillights fading in the distance. We start our gloomy way home.

On the Lauenburger Platz we meet Fabian—Fabian Trooth, a friend and fellow student of Heike's. He's an actor, poet, exhibition horseman, passionate smoker, passionate *bon vivant,* and has reached the ripe old age of twenty-five. We have suspected for some time that he's quite fond of Heike.

He beams at us as if he had just won the sweepstakes. "Have you heard the latest?" he asks, laughing. "They threw me out on my ear, bang, right out of my room. Officially, so to speak—because I let a man who had been in a concentration camp spend the night on my sofa. That wasn't suitable for a decent German, they told me. All right, I thought, then I'm not one, and I packed up and left."

"Well, and now what?" I inquire anxiously.

He makes a magnificent gesture. "Heike's looked after that. Subtenant number eleven in the bachelor's paradise—second door to the right, if you should want to call." Fabian Trooth kisses my hand, bows, and disappears around the corner.

In spite of all our sorrows I can't help laughing. "Well, *he* certainly fits into the crowd!"

Late that evening we have our first drink together—to Hitler's downfall and to our being good neighbors. So there isn't one man less, after all.

Saturday, February 3, 1945.

Heavy daylight attack on Berlin. The city is frightfully damaged. I fight my way through smoke, soot, and grime to the office. It's pouring rain; the water beats down the smoke, and turns the ground into sticky paste that clings to your feet. Walking is painful—painful and dismal.

"Hey," cries a passer-by to his neighbor, "hey, the People's Court is on fire! They say Freisler's underneath!"

For a moment I waver between horror and joy. Freisler—the man who condemns everyone to death? He has died two months too late; and how many weeks too early for accounting and retribution? Truly, this hangman's death did not come aright for us.

At the office the walls are on the desks, the windows on the floor. And word has arrived by the morning mail that we have definitely got to close up on the fifteenth of March. What comes after that is only the windup—a windup that will have to be stretched out like a rubber band as long as possible, on account of the men's essential classification, and to keep the women out of forced duty on fortifications, armaments, or army auxiliary detail.

"It's hardly worth cleaning up any more," Hollner grumbles. But he has a hammer in his hand already, and within two minutes the whole building is banging away like a smithy.

I get out of there. I'm worried about Frank. We hear that the Bavarian quarter was very hard hit; the Bayerischer Platz subway station has been hit, too. More than a hundred dead are in the ruins. As I pass by the spot, I pause in surprise. What an odd gathering of people—men, women, children, crowding close together, bowing their heads, saying nothing. They hardly speak or move for a long time together. Grave, mute, and solemn, they are waiting for their dead to be dug out—sisters, brothers, mothers—out of the thirty-foot crater that an aerial mine blasted in the subway shaft at eleven this morning.

I gasp. Could Frank be . . . ? I hurry on. Thank God, his house is still standing.

But he isn't at home. Where can the lad be? Five times before evening I go to the nearest pay station. Gas, water, electricity, and telephone have gone to hell again for days to come. Only the postal telephone lines are still working. A wall of humanity stands outside each red booth. The rain is still coming down. It falls on my coat, on my shoes. I wait till my turn comes to drop my coin in the slot.

"Frank! Hello, Frank! Is it really you . . . ? Yes, but where were you?"

"In the air-raid cellar, with three stories of ruins over my head. They didn't dig us out until an hour ago."

"And . . . and you're . . . still alive?" I stammer.

"As you can hear!" Frank laughs. Imagine his still being able to laugh!

"Dear, good boy!" I can't think of anything more to say.

"Dear, good boy." I'd like to put all my sympathy into those three words, all my friendship and anxiety. But Frank isn't in favor of sentimentalities, and still less of extended telephone conversations. So I shall have to save up my sympathy, curiosity, and joy until tomorrow.

Sunday, February 4, 1945.

Frank spent nine hours in the shelter, along with twenty-six women who screamed with terror, wept copiously the whole time, sat frozen with fright, or kept praying desperately. Ten seconds before the bombs hit the Bavarian quarter, he ran into a strange building. The blast from the first hit knocked him down the basement stairs. The next one was a direct hit; it tore the building apart down to the ground floor. But the basement roof held. For nine hours it carried the weight of the three stories of ruins, until finally the rescuers broke through the fire wall.

Frank is still alive—reason enough to celebrate. Andrik, Dagmar, Ursula, Wald, Fabian, Flamm, Frank Matthis, and I gather in Heike's room. Someone has "organized" a bottle of red wine. Its precious contents are divided into nine mathematically equal parts with the measuring cup. There's just enough for everyone to drink a toast.

As we are in the very act of making our modest libation, there is a knock at the door. Some man by the name of Eckardt wants Fabian.

"God Almighty, good old Eckardt!" he yells, dragging the stranger into the room.

He's a blond man of about forty, with sharp blue eyes and the kind of face you often see on boxers. He looks frankly at us all, one after another, and then nods his approval. "Yes,

I've come to the right spot. I guess I can talk plain German to you people." He draws up an armchair and sinks back in it comfortably. Within a few minutes we are all listening to his story—how he's a Social Democrat, how when he was a child he used to arrange a boys' demonstration at the grave of the fighters of '48, how he would like personally to kick in the teeth of all Nazis, and never lets a day go by without giving them something to remember him by. All this and much more Kurt Eckardt tells us. We've known him for half an hour, and within the first five minutes we realize that he's a man of action and a natural-born revolutionist. We don't break up until late at night. He, too, belongs to us.

Thursday, February 8, 1945.

"What are we to do with you?" says Frank anxiously, looking at Andrik, who has been lying around at home for a week now. He's half in bed, half not in bed, one of the thousands of "Home Guard cases" that Berlin is full of at the moment.

"All right, Wald can print a Home Guard certificate in his night-shift printing shop. Flamm can furnish the rubber stamp to go on it. But what good is that to you? After all, you haven't submerged. They aren't looking for you—they merely have you. On their damned muster rolls, that is."

Andrik doesn't answer; he stares dismally at the ceiling.

"So you get sick," Frank continues his soliloquy. "Well and good. But it's got to be something special—something that will keep you with us, and not just let you rot uselessly in some hospital." He ponders intensively. For five minutes we say nothing. For ten minutes we say nothing. Then Frank lifts his head.

"Have you got it?"

"Got it! Wait half a minute; I'll be right back." He bestrides his bicycle and disappears toward the Kufsteinerstrasse. In an hour he's back, laden with vials, little nickel-plated boxes, instruments, and test tubes. In a trice Andrik's desk is transformed into a chemical laboratory.

"It seems you have kidney trouble," Frank sets forth in a professorial tone. "People with kidney trouble have albumen in their urine. A definite percentage, which can be exactly measured. Weeks ago they certified that your heart wasn't good, and your blood pressure was too high. Heart, blood pressure, kidneys—the combination is alarming, extremely alarming to any medical man. Shrinking of the kidneys. See? You're at death's door, more or less. With that kind of thing threatening, they send a man home, or to a dietary sanitarium for a cure; certainly not to pick-and-shovel duty."

A sigh of relief is heard from Andrik's bed. Frank works busily with tubes and bottles.

"Take your electrocardiogram along. Now all we've got to do is get the albumen." He screws together a hypodermic needle. "Let's see your arm," he says to me, handing me a test tube, and swiftly winding a rolled handkerchief around my left upper arm. A jab. "Let go!" The blood flows dark red into the fat glass barrel of the hypodermic.

"That's that," says Frank with satisfaction, carefully squeezing the liquid out into the test tube. "Now listen here. By tomorrow morning the stuff will have settled—clot on the bottom, serum on top. In the serum is the albumen. Pure albumen, the dosage of which can be exactly calculated. If we pour the albumen into your specimen bottle, not even the Wise Men of Zion would ever guess it had got in there anorganically." He juggles his mixture like a wizard. "And if they should happen to want you to . . . that is, right there . . . I mean, without bothering with the bottle . . . just tell them that you're sorry, at the moment you simply aren't able. Then we'll dry the preparation, and give it to you. . . . Oh, well, we'll see what to do then. I hardly think it'll be necessary."

Friday, February 9, 1945.

It wasn't necessary. The electrocardiogram, benevolently interpreted by Frank's colleague, the ominous contents of the bottle, and three Pervitins to raise the blood pressure, are enough to make the Home Guard doctor certify that Andrik Krassnow is unfit for a period of six weeks. Six weeks starting with his admission to a dietary sanitarium. Until he can get in there, he can go right on working with us. Time, time, time! Maybe we'll have luck, and they'll be here first—the Russians, the English, or the Americans.

Yesterday, the Canadian and English offensive in the west began. The Russians are preparing frantically on the Oder for their last blow.

Roosevelt, Churchill, and Stalin have met in the Crimea to discuss the capitulation of Germany, the downfall of Hitler, and everything that will come after.

There isn't much choice of dietary sanitariums any more. We take our time about making inquiries.

Monday, February 19, 1945.

Every day we go down cellar, in the morning after we get up, and at night before we go to bed. The Americans are softening up central Germany for the invasion. The English are taking care that we don't get any rest at night. Last Tuesday they devastated Dresden most terribly. Three times in twenty-four hours they unloaded ton after ton of bombs, until there was hardly a whole house left in the city, and all the splendor of a centuries-old civilization had gone up in smoke. Thousands of people met their deaths; they ran like burning torches through the streets, stuck fast in the red-hot asphalt, flung themselves into the waters of the Elbe. They screamed for coolness; they screamed for mercy.

Death is mercy. Death is good when you are burning like a torch.

Dresden was a glorious city, and it's a little hard getting used to the idea that Dresden, too, no longer exists. I almost feel like crying.

But Andrik puts his arm around me, smiles, and says, "Never you mind, little one. However it happens is right. Idols are perishable, says Plato. Only the ideals remain. The 'idea of civilization.' "

The "idea" is the goal—gold, frankincense, and myrrh, carried through the desert by three old men. What does it matter if the "image" perishes? I ponder for a long time. Is he right? Is he wrong?

And I think of Helmuth von Moltke, Reichwein, Delp, and Roesch, of Dresden, Weimar, and the faggots that were lit outside Berlin University in 1933, upon which they burned Germany's cultural heritage in less than ninety minutes. And I realize he's right—that only one thing matters in this final stage of Gothic civilization: to carry the spark through deluge and desert; gold, frankincense, and myrrh; the "ideal" of our creative power.

And yet it isn't easy to think about the "ideal" when you learn that Hitler has resolved to defend Berlin itself, "tooth and nail." If army and Home Guard are not reliable enough, the SS will have to be mobilized for the task. Four divisions move up, hastily assembled from all the fronts. Among them is the Frundsberg Group, notorious for its striking power, cruelty, and unshakable devotion to the Fuehrer.

Saturday, March 3, 1945.

Andrik has found a sanitarium, at Braunsdorf, eighty kilometers from Berlin. He leaves tomorrow; heaven knows when he can come back.

Thursday, March 8, 1945.

What's the good of their capturing Cologne, attacking Bonn, and crossing the Rhine by a piece of reckless daring? Somehow everything comes too late—the Rhine crossing, the preparations on the Oder, the daily bombings, and the rising uneasiness of the Nazi bigwigs. By the time we've really got there, we shall all be too tired. Too tired to act, too tired for reconstruction, too tired for the one thing that is true: the offering of gold, frankincense, and myrrh.

Karli Gennert came to see me today, the son of my school friend Freda. Adolf Hitler's dicing with human beings landed Karli in Pomerania. From there he came to see us, during a brief furlough from the Hitler Youth.

"My father's in jail," he says. "Has been since Christmas. He's perfectly innocent, and he's in the Gestapo prison at Lehrterstrasse, simply because he knows Goerdeler, and my little brother was Goerdeler's godchild. There's no heating at the Lehrterstrasse. He'll simply freeze to death, my father will." The boy looks at us like a grief-stricken old man. "That mustn't happen—when he's perfectly innocent all the time!"

Many are innocent; many are freezing to death, burning, being tortured, dying. Oh gold, oh frankincense, oh myrrh!

Friday, March 9, 1945.

Heike goes all the way across Berlin, with a blanket over her arm, and a food package in her hand. It's a long way to the Lehrterstrasse. The siren wails. The trains are stopped. Take cover. Change trains, stumbling over the rails; preliminary all-clear.

A lot of people are crowding around the reception window at Lehrterstrasse. "Countess Bergstein," says a lady, blushing, pushing a basket with a pint aluminum soup can through the half-opened window.

"Baroness Drewitz," whispers another. She weeps as she hands up her package to the Gestapo man. Her brother, she says, has been there for six months, forgotten by Adolf Hitler and the People's Court Council on Charges; he's sitting there dying.

The elite of society have a daily rendezvous at the Lehrter-strasse. Heike hands in her little pot, her blanket, and her package of zwieback. "For Dr. Gennert," she stammers un-comfortably. Dr. Gennert is freezing to death behind the bars, because he's a friend of Goerdeler's, and his child was bap-tized with Goerdeler's name.

Monday, March 12, 1945.

The "broom girls" are sweeping in Zehlendorf. Half-breeds by birth, tried by fate, they sweep the streets, ten hours a day, and sometimes eleven.

"It's not easy," says Ursula Reuber. "Because the brooms are so heavy. And besides . . . Well, one isn't used to it." She sits in our midst, a little weary, a little downcast. "Oh, by the way," her voice rises a little, "I've got someone living with me. Eva Gerichter—a half-breed, like me. She was bound for Theresienstadt, because with her Jewish faith she's one of the official Jews. So I took her in in the Ihnestrasse, as a U-boat; didn't check her in. You know what I mean."

We know it all. So the new member of our crowd is named Eva Gerichter.

Another major raid on Berlin. "The heaviest of the war," say the English broadcasts.

I lug a parcel to the Lehrterstrasse. Change trains, stumble over the rails. Preliminary all-clear. Around the reception window stand many great ladies. Years ago people used to kiss their hands; today hardly anyone knows anything about them. They stand and wait, until the Gestapo functionary condescends to receive their little pot of food. Cell No. 95: one set of clean laundry, six rolls, a letter, a dish of vegetables. I hope Cell 95 enjoys them.

Sunday, March 18, 1945.

Frank Matthis is living with us for a few days. It's better for him not to be seen too often in his own air-raid shelter. The Mosquitoes have been coming every night for three and a half weeks, and sometimes twice. That's what we get for our silly V-1 bombardment, for the boastful statement in every army communiqué, "Retributional fire upon London is being continued."

Once again we're at breakfast when the siren howls. Full warning! After the first few waves we see that they aren't aiming at us. They fly over us, indeed, but their load is destined for other parts of town. We stand outside the front door, staring up at the sky. In the cloudless blue, like little knots of wool, hang the enemy sky markers. Now they unroll —white threads of cloud, growing longer and ever longer until they reach almost to the ground. The wind comes along, sweeps them into arcs, tangles them into graceful scrollwork.

"If you didn't know that there was death behind it, you'd be all excited at anything so beautiful." Frank is completely carried away. Then the bombers come roaring over, great, silver birds—birds of peril. We pull our heads in. One hit after another crashes down where the white markers are. Clouds of smoke go up, spread a black blanket across the city, hang like a pall over death, horror, and destruction. Squadron after squadron follows.

"Aren't they ever going to get through today?" Heike asks impatiently.

I give her a severe look. "Better too long in the cellar than too soon into eternity! Spit three times, child, and stop tempting the gods!" Major raids make me superstitious, and I don't like to hear people passing frivolous remarks.

At last, after two hours, comes the preliminary all-clear. We rush upstairs as fast as our legs will carry us. If we're lucky, we'll get lunch finished before they cut off the current. There's ten minutes until the final all-clear. Fried potatoes, water for the coffee, a poached egg apiece from the last ration. All the pots are bubbling; it's a race against time, against current, against the Berlin Electrical Company. You don't cook when you're hungry any more, but when the current is on. You'd rather chance a bomb on your head than the prospect of sitting around for four hours with your stomach grumbling. You get hardened even to dying.

One minute after the wire news has stopped, the radio

also goes off. The current has stopped. Final all-clear. But we've done it; our lunch is saved.

At three o'clock Ursula Reuber comes. Despite all the traffic interruptions, she has made her way through fire and ruin to see us. Her clothes smell as if she had been on a hook in the smoke chamber for a week. Under her arm she carries a big package—vegetables for our "U-boats."

"I've got something much better yet," she boasts, extracting her wallet from her jacket. "Sixteen ounces of bread stamps, fresh stolen from the stamp box in the bakery."

"But how did you do it?"

"Perfectly simple. There wasn't a soul in the shop; I called a couple of times; nobody showed up. Then my eye happened to fall on the box on the counter. The lid was half open. There was no time to argue. St. Crispin, friend of all thieves, be good to me! I thought, and dipped in."

Frank beams. We all beam, just as if this were not theft but a heroic achievement of human decency.

"This is all extra," says Ursula radiantly. "Eva has had her own stamps for two weeks now." She proudly unfolds a police check-in sheet. "Helga Seidler, fugitive from Guben, checked in with Mrs. Gerichter, 46 Bleibtreustrasse," we read.

"Naturally this Helga doesn't exist at all. I checked in at Eva's mother's place under a phony name as a fugitive, and then drew my whole month's allowance from the ration office. It was as easy as one-two-three."

An idea dawns on me. "I'll do that next month myself. If you can just get me the check-in paper. I'll look after the police and ration office. Then we'll have two complete sets of cards, anyway."

Fabian strokes Ursula's hair. "You really are quite a girl," he says admiringly.

Then we discuss the plan of campaign for the coming weeks. Frank undertakes the assignment of duties. "I'll furnish certificates, prescriptions, and take care of all sick 'U-boats,'" he says crisply. "Ursula, you look after food supply, and keep touch with the Gestapo through your Jewish warden friend. Fabian will organize scarce goods. Eckardt is our sabotage expert. Wald will print any passes we may need. Eva and Heike can run messages on their bikes. Flamm will give legal advice, Hinrichs the news from the scene of war. Dr. Tegel will continue to act as employment center."

"And what job had you planned for me?" I venture to put in modestly.

"The honorary post of Jack-of-all-trades," Frank laughs merrily. As always when politics and future plans are involved, he is in a radiant humor.

"Now make sure they don't nab you," I warn him anxiously. "Himmler is making damn short work of people, and what goes on at courts-martial is no fun at all."

As a matter of fact, executions are being carried on by conveyor belt again, and daily new raids bring in a constant stream of fresh victims.

Only yesterday they "combed" Berlin, and arrested fifteen deserters in one block of houses—fifteen poor devils who didn't feel like fighting the war for Hitler any longer. Thank goodness we got word in time; Ursula's Gestapo man was on the job. Two hours before the affair began, all of our connections had been informed, and got safely into hiding.

Ursula looks at the clock. "Gosh, I've got to get home. Our subtenant has guests. That means Eva can't show herself in the apartment; she's hiding in the broom closet. If I stay away long, the poor girl will starve to death."

Frank takes me to see a friend of his sister's. Her name is Ulrike Weitzen, and she's a newspaperwoman, just like me. She's been hiding a July 20 fugitive in her apartment in the back building of a big apartment house for six months. No one knows about it except the two girls she lives with. These three women have protected a man about whom they had scarcely heard up to the moment of his flight, simply because they knew he was in trouble, simply because reliable friends had recommended him to them. Now this man has spent more than twenty-five weeks within the four walls of the tiny back room, which he never leaves except to sneak to the nearest shelter after dark.

We climb the gloomy back stairs—of course, as usual, there's no electricity—give the agreed number of knocks, and a moment later confront the man who has been working since 1938 to destroy the Hitler regime. He has a noble, sharply chiseled face, grizzled hair, and around his eyes a look of painful sorrow that doesn't leave his face even when he smiles.

"Colonel Hartmann," he introduces himself. We know that isn't his real name, but it's better so. What you don't know no one can get out of you.

As we drink tea, he tells us his story. Professional officer; regimental commander; transferred in disgrace for refusing to shoot Croatian civilians; restored to favor; invited by Admiral Canaris to join the Counter Intelligence. "—and what went on in the Counter Intelligence of the German army, you know yourselves," he adds with a smile. "For six years we labored to remove the Fuehrer. For six years we devised one plan after another. It was supposed to be done back in '38, at Munich. But the generals were against it. Actually the generals were always against it, no matter how much they pretended otherwise. Halder held back, and Kluge held back. For six years they talked, and did nothing. 'I'll set the time,' Halder said, and waited until they chucked him out. 'I'm in command; it's your business to obey,' said Kluge. It's the generals' fault. The generals were quite simply too stupid. Well, finally I decided it was too stupid of me to go on wearing out my tongue. I applied for a transfer, and was put in command of the Berlin patrol detachment." He looks at us. "A disagreeable job considering my present situation, by the way, because every patrol knows me as a superior officer.

"When they took away Canaris, they arrested me too. Two days later they had to let me go for want of evidence. Then in October they found the admiral's safe. It was broken open; all the papers with our plans came to light. When they sent out orders over the radio to arrest me again, a regimental friend warned me.

"I said to my wife, 'There are three possibilities open. I can surrender, and let them hang me; take my own life; or submerge.' 'Naturally you've got to disappear,' she decided. I was off within an hour. Two days later she was arrested. And you see, that's what I simply can't bear—her being in prison on my account. It's six months now; she doesn't know how I am, and not a soul cares a straw about her. I've got hold of some poison. I'm cudgeling my brains. Did I do what was right? Wouldn't it be more decent to surrender to the authorities even now?"

"It would be madness—sheer madness," Frank bursts in passionately. "Do you think your wife would feel better if you were on the gallows? Do you think they'd turn her loose just because they got hold of you? Man alive, don't lose your nerve at the eleventh hour and fifty-ninth minute!"

"But the bombs," the colonel groans. "They don't let her into the shelter. And how do I know whether she won't have starved or died of exhaustion or maltreatment before we can get her out?"

"Where is she?" I ask matter-of-factly. It seems to me that the main thing at the moment is to turn the discussion from emotional to practical subjects.

"In the Dirksenstrasse women's prison."

"They don't maltreat people there, so far as I know. And besides, I understand interviews are allowed, and food can be sent in. That can certainly be arranged."

Gradually the colonel regains his self-control. When we leave him, we've carefully discussed all the steps to be taken for the present. Frank is to see that we get hold of a red Home Guard certificate. Wald will have to print it. Flamm has his connection with the stamp counterfeiter. That's at least something by way of identification for patrols. We may also manage to prepare a blank such as the army district commands send out: "You are hereby instructed to send in your army pass to us without delay." After that, all you need is a postal registry receipt, which you clip to the blank, and the business is done. Many a diver has founded his existence on one of these blanks. The letter to the army district command is sent off right enough, only the army pass is not enclosed, but a blank sheet, which the sender signs not with his real name but with his newly chosen "diving name." A very simple plan indeed— all you have to do is hit on it. Certainly Wald's typographical skill will be equal to this, as to so much else.

It's my job to get myself introduced to Hartmann's wife as a friend. Dr. Tegel is to go and see her. As a clergyman, he has access to most of the prisons, and also a chance to speak to the inmates in private. He must warn Mrs. Hartmann that henceforth she has a friend by my name, who will visit her, bring food, and deal with the lawyer for her. If we don't tell her beforehand, she may think I'm a spy. Accordingly I undertake the trip to Dr. Tegel's, the lawyer's, and the weekly visit in the Dirksenstrasse.

On the way home we begin meeting the people with the folding chairs on their way to the public air-raid shelters.

"Looks ominous," I say to Frank. "The shelter crowds are coasting in." They spend hours and hours there, morning, noon, night. For a good many women it's a sort of *Kaffeeklatsch* substitute. You sit at ease, gossip, gab, and discuss the latest rationing—whether there is anything, and where it is. And once you've sat out your time (in fifty cases out of a hundred without a single enemy plane's crossing the city limits) you go and line up in front of the shops. A line in front of the dairy for butter, a line in front of the butcher, a line in front of the shelter. Lines, lines, lines, from the time you get up until the time you go to bed.

This evening there's a lot of shooting again. It's the thirtieth Mosquito attack on Berlin in the last thirty nights. At half past three we're yanked out of bed again.

Thursday, March 22, 1945.

Yes, they dropped them. But they hit the wrong people. At nine o'clock I'm called to the telephone. A lady wants to speak to me. I hear a girl's faltering voice. "Are you Ursula Reuber's friend?"

"Yes, what is it?"

Silence. Then a sobbing at the other end of the line. "Her house got a direct hit. She's . . . I think she's under the ruins."

"It isn't true! It's preposterous." The shock almost knocks the receiver out of my hand. "I'll be there right away," is all I can say.

To help dig . . . Help dig . . . Every moment is precious. Maybe she wasn't at home at all. But what about Eva? Good God, Eva! Why, she . . . And the check-in form . . . And Eva's mother . . . It can't be—no, no—it mustn't be! The thoughts flutter through my head like scared birds; tell Heike; warn Frank.

Five minutes later we're racing down the Schloss Strasse on our wheels. Our tongues are hanging out. Good God, there's even a head wind!

We turn down the Ihnestrasse. Number 20, 22, 24. Not a window broken. No rubble, no clouds of smoke. The street is peaceful, as if deserted. One more block . . . The street closed off. People. A few policemen and the gray cars of the rescue detachment.

So it's true after all. We jump off our bicycles. Distracted faces turn toward us. They make way for us as if they could feel that we were part of it. Number 40 Ihnestrasse. We stare at a mountain of ruins. Crumpled beams, window frames, rubble, mortar. A ghastly jumble. In the branches of the old elm that formerly flanked the front door, a scrap of colored curtain bellies in the wind. Eight soldiers are silently busy removing the hill of rubble piece by piece.

I turn to the nearest policeman. "Are there any people still under there?"

"There's supposed to have been two young ladies in the house. But there was only one checked in with the police." He shrugs. "We can't get in there. We've been digging since four o'clock in the morning. It keeps sliding down again. Even the places they broke through have filled up again."

"Do you think they're still alive?"

"Possible, but not probable. We tried tapping. No answer. The hit must have gone straight into the air-raid cellar."

"May we help dig? We're friends of Miss Reuber's."

The policeman looks at us for a moment, half appraising, half sympathetic. Then he shakes his head. "Strictly prohibited for civilians. You have to know how to do it; otherwise it just makes things worse."

"But we can't just leave them under there!" Heike is almost crying with impatience and excitement. "When do you think . . ."

"Not before tomorrow at the earliest," the man says. "Possibly the day after."

We stand and watch—we and the strangers—as timber after timber, stone after stone is removed from the crushing weight that lies upon the shoulders of Ursula Reuber and Eva Gerichter. Stone after stone. Timber after timber. Carefully, and horribly slowly.

Now one of the soldiers reaches deep into the rubble; he pulls something out, and tosses it aside. A book (half torn to bits)—the poems of Rilke. Ursula's favorite poet.

Heike sobs aloud. "I can't go on," she wails despairingly.

Frank goes over to the pile of furnishings, dirty scraps of cloth, and rubbish that they have flung together in one corner of the garden. "Look at this," he calls to me. In his hand he has a round alarm clock of purple tin, the kind you used to buy by the hundred for four marks fifty at the Kaufhaus des Westens. The hands are stopped at 3:40. Forty minutes and seventeen seconds after three. The moment when Ursula and Eva ceased to breathe. The alarm is set for quarter past five —time for Ursula to get up so as to be on duty promptly.

"Put it in your pocket," I beg Frank. Then we turn to go.

As we pedal down the Ihnestrasse, a troop of young girls comes toward us, shabbily dressed, their shoes dusty, each of them carrying a huge twig broom over her shoulder. Ursula's fellow workers in the street-sweeping detail at Zehlendorf.

We accost them: "Are you going to Ursula Reuber's?"

They nod. Tears run down their faces. "We're just coming from work. We wanted to help dig. Surely we must be able to do something."

"We can't do anything, and they won't let us. It probably wouldn't do any good, anyhow. All you can do is go and show her that you're fond of her." We shake their hands—six little half-Jewesses, officially declared unworthy to do anything but sweep streets or clean busses. They have come to help—after ten hours' hard work; they have come to weep, because they have hearts that are still capable of weeping.

Saturday, March 24, 1945.

The criminal police have called up. Would I please come at once to the scene of the damage? One of the casualties has been extricated. At half past four this afternoon, please.

I set off by wheel. "Be brave," Frank calls after me.

There's plenty of need to be. Under the old elm lies a pitiful little heap, covered with corrugated cardboard. I turn back the cardboard. I see a tangle of dark hair, two hands over the face as if in fright. The face itself is an unrecognizable mass of blood, dust, silt, and mud.

"They found a handbag beside the dead woman," says a man next to me. "A leather handbag. The criminal police

217

confiscated it. There was a check-in form in it. Helga Seidler, fugitive from Guben, checked in with Mrs. Gerichter, Bleibtreustrasse 46."

The fat's in the fire!

"Do you know this Helga Seidler?" the man asks. "There are some pictures—twenty-five photographs. Possibly they would show. . . ."

It makes me ill to think of what they would show. "I have no idea," I say. "I don't know Miss Reuber's friend. And I don't know what her name is, or where she was checked in, either."

But the man won't let go. "The neighbors say her name was Miss Dohm. And the check-in says Helga Seidler. There's something funny about that. Something that isn't as it should be. Well, we'll find it out all right." In the grandeur of his own importance he struts off. A Gestapo spy, I think. Thank God he's such a fool!

At the cemetery office I meet a second mourner, Ursula's father. He's been summoned in from out of town. Now he stands beside me.

"We must give her a beautiful funeral. We want it so she'd be pleased if she knew."

I nod. "She'll be pleased. We won't let her down. If only they've found the other girl, too."

"That's right, the other girl," he sighs. "Until today I didn't even know she existed. I don't know anything at all. And I don't want to know."

"But surely you'll let them be buried together?" I ask hesitantly.

"Certainly I will. And perhaps—" he hesitates, "—my son?"

I look at him, speechless. "Your son? Why, your son wasn't there at all."

The white-haired man suddenly looks like a guilty school-boy.

"I know the story." I try to help him out of his embarrassment. "He's submerged. Three weeks ago—hiding somewhere here in Berlin, because they wanted to pull him into the Todt Organization as a half-breed. Ursula confessed that to me."

He turns his head uneasily, then bends down to me. "I thought . . . One more or less might not make any difference, I thought. If the police thinks he's under the ruins . . . ?"

I begin to see. "So you told the police you knew . . . ?"

"Suspected, suspected," he contradicts. "I thought I was doing him a favor."

I have a hard time suppressing a smile. What times these are, when a father pretends his own son is under the ruins of his house, so that the dead boy can be an alibi for the living one!

They don't give us much news at the cemetery office. No, the second body has not been found yet. The first casualty will be ready for the coffin on Sunday.

"How about getting a coffin?" Ursula's father asks. We both know that coffins are hard to get. After air raids you often have to wait weeks for delivery.

The cemetery official looks uncomfortably away. "That'll be taken care of through us," he mumbles hastily. "You'll get a coffin certificate." I remember rumors I've heard that on account of the timber scarcity coffins are only lent. They take the dead to the grave, lower them into it with due ceremony, and the moment the mourners have left, they unpack them, and bury them up with no wooden covering. People claim that only Party Comrades enjoy the honor of going to the grave in their own coffins.

"I'd be glad to contribute a nightgown," I say shyly. "For her to be put in the coffin in. A lovely nightgown."

The functionary objects. "It isn't allowed—textile regulations. We'll dress the deceased in the garments in which she was found."

So it *is* a borrowed coffin, I reflect. But I consider it better not to voice my thought.

When I come home, a strange lady is sitting in my room, sobbing. "I'm Eva's mother," she introduces herself. "Mrs. Gerichter—from the Fashion Shop on the Kurfürstendamm. I've been to see Dr. Tegel. He sent me to you. Oh, it's all so dreadful."

"I know, I know," I say softly. Mrs. Gerichter dries her eyes. "They sent for me at the criminal police. On account of Helga Seidler. They want to show me pictures—want to find out if the two are the same. What am I to say? After all, she was my only child."

"You just have to deny the whole thing," I suggest. "A person might have lots of pictures; there's no reason why it has to be Helga Seidler."

Eva's mother shakes her head. "If that were all . . ." she sighs. "But Eva's real passport picture, with photograph and signature, is in her handbag, and so are a diary with a thousand nasty remarks about the Nazis, a satirical poem against Hitler, and Jewish stars that the girls forehandedly got in preparation for the Fourth Reich. Oh, if they find that handbag! Suppose they've found it already! She always carried it with her."

That, indeed, is a disaster. One more complication in this cruel snarl. "You mustn't turn up at the criminal police on any account before the body has been uncovered," I declare positively. "Get sick, go away, think up anything you like. On

Monday we'll go to the cemetery together; we can plan the rest after that."

Mrs. Gerichter looks at me dubiously. "Do you really think so?"

"Yes, I think so! You mustn't go there as a mother. Favoring an official Jewess—you know how that goes down."

At that moment the siren goes. We say hasty good-by's. "Unfortunately I can't recommend my cellar," I apologize. "You can hear the enemy pilots coughing. But five minutes away from here is a shelter with a seven-foot concrete ceiling. If you run, you can make it all right."

Eva's mother runs, and makes it.

Monday, March 26, 1945.

Thank goodness! The second body has been found. It has just come in when I meet Eva's mother outside the Uncle Tom Cemetery at ten in the morning.

"Viewing is strictly prohibited," says the cemetery official.

"But surely we can go to see Miss Reuber."

He nods. I take Eva's mother by the arm. She has flowers in her hand—vivid yellow coltsfoot. We go down to the basement where the bodies are kept. The door is locked. An old woman opens to our knock, and shuffles ahead of us into the darkness.

"The current's off at this hour," she says. "Just a minute, and I'll get a candle." She vanishes, to return in a few moments with a lighted stump, obviously the remnant of an altar candle. The flame casts leaping shadows over the walls of the vault.

We look at each other in dismay. There are fifteen coffins side by side.

"You'll have to look for the name," the old woman explains. Sure enough, each of the black, tarred wooden boxes has a long tag hanging from it, like a baggage label.

In the candlelight we stoop over the coffins, painfully deciphering, *Friedrich von Schrick* . . . *Anna Geber* . . . and finally, the last one, *Ursula Reuber.*

We stand a long time before the wretched box. "And even this trash is only borrowed," I think bitterly.

The coltsfoot shines like yellow stars in the darkness.

Next to the coffin, shoved way off in the corner, stands a wooden bench, covered with black crepe paper such as is used for blackouts.

"The second body from the Ihnestrasse," says the old woman, holding her candle a little higher. I cast a glance over. There seem to be remarkably few outlines under the black covering. Eva's mother squeezes my arm. "I must see her!"

"Please don't. . . ."

She pulls away, and one step carries her to the head end of the trestle. Slowly she turns back the paper, then screams, and staggers back into my arms.

Five lumps of charred flesh, five nondescript masses. Nothing more. An intolerable odor spreads all through the room.

I lead Eva's mother out. "You shouldn't have!"

But she makes no answer. She's as white as chalk, crying. "My only child," she says. "My only child!"

I can understand her grief; but at the same time I consider that she mustn't show it—not here, not before these people. And I am thinking even more of the fact that when a person has been charred to a cinder, no handbag can survive. And a monstrous load is off my mind.

Tomorrow the two are to be burried—tomorrow at two in the afternoon. Dr. Tegel is to hold the funeral service. And we will make every effort to give it a worthy setting.

"It's a point of honor," Heike declares, "for us to get together a monstrous lot of mourners. And flowers enough to cover the whole chapel." The others agree. Our whole view of life is involved here; we have something to prove.

The "thieves' gang" go to work; the "thieves' gang" will let no grass grow under their feet. Heike has gone out at crack of dawn to Wannsee after greenery and boxwood. If we bribe the gardener with a few cigarettes, he'll make them into wreaths, and possibly even put in a few flowers. These days you can trade anything for cigarettes—even funeral wreaths.

Frank hangs on the telephone half the day, drumming up our crowd. It isn't easy to telephone—a matter of luck if you ever get your number. Only defense plants with a registered special number have the privilege of hanging on the wire early and late. Common mortals have hours when they're disconnected. If one only knew when! At the office they claim it depends on the last digit of your number: even numbers are disconnected during the hours that are free for odd numbers, and vice versa. But there must be some other secret behind it, too—a secret that changes incessantly, for the telephone system brings us some new surprise every day. But Frank refuses to give up; he spins the dial until his fingers are ready to drop off.

"Listen," he says emphatically, "everyone's got to be there. The Zehlendorf broom girls are coming in a body. Only our 'submariners' have got to stay away. Why? Obvious—because

there'll be somebody there with field glasses. All right, now—
everybody on time! The cemetery won't allow us more than
fifteen minutes, on account of the crowd. And bring flowers
—be sure to bring flowers!" He rubs his hands. "I think it'll
come off all right. And the spy that the criminal police have
detailed for tomorrow can just see what he gets!"

Heike brings mountains of evergreens and greenery. "The
shops were all empty," she reports. "There wasn't much left
outdoors, either. So I just took a loan from the Wannsee
cemetery. I don't think the dead will hold it against me."

Wednesday, March 28, 1945.

The sky is a radiant blue. Ursula would be happy about the
day. At eleven o'clock the siren goes. If we're lucky, disaster
will pass us by.

It doesn't pass us by. While we crouch in the basement,
streams of heavy bomber formations roar over us. The sky
turns black in the direction of Charlottenburg, and downtown. The walls tremble. As each wave of bombs drops, the
iron front door crashes open and shut. I look at my watch.
Good God! The funeral! It's out of the question for the subway to be running after such an attack. And Dr. Tegel! From
the Afrikanische Strasse to the cemetery is several hours' walk.

The all-clear goes at half past twelve. Heike charges out
of the cellar to get the wreaths from the gardener. We at
least will try to be punctual.

"Don't forget the flowers," Frank reminds us. Sure enough,
the wreaths. They aren't adapted to bicycle transportation.
The best we can do is to hang them around our necks.

224

And so off we go, like six-day racers before the last spurt. We're decorated as if the finish were already behind us.

Just before quarter of two we jump off our wheels outside the cemetery gate. Mrs. Gerichter appears from a side path; she has come from Charlottenburg, thanks to successive lifts by kindly truck drivers.

Gradually the others also arrive, even the bespectacled criminal-police spy, in a preposterous getup.

Only our pastor is missing. Six hours to the cemetery is too much. Out of the question; he can't make it.

But he does make it. Eyes reddened with smoke, gown and bands in his knapsack, he pushes his bicycle through the gate at five minutes before two. "Here I am," he smiles. "And now we can begin."

More than fifty people have gathered outside the chapel. Many of them I don't know; many of them don't know Ursula, nor Eva Gerichter either. They have simply come because the "thieves' gang" summoned them. The two tarred boxes, standing in sisterly fashion together before the altar, are quite covered with wreaths. The organ is playing Handel's *Largo*. Candles flicker gently among green box trees.

"You who were on the way," says Dr. Tegel. "You who struggled and endured a harsh fate. . . ."

He that has ears to hear, let him hear. Mrs. Gerichter is crying beside me. It's hard to be a mother, and yet not allowed to be a mother. It's really almost too much to bear.

When the pastor lifts his hands in the benediction, a time bomb goes off near by. "Not a blade of grass grows on earth," sing violin and cello. That's Ursula's song.

Eight pallbearers come and lift the coffins. The coltsfoot shines yellow on the black boxes.

As we stand by the graves, a second time bomb roars. Then

the dead glide downward. "In the name of God," the pall-bearers repeat mechanically.

A third time bomb. "The English are firing salutes," I think.

Good-by Ursula, good-by Eva! The gravediggers are in a hurry. "Faster, faster!" Even the casting of earth is timed. The next mourners are already gathered outside the funeral chapel. They're waiting for the organ to play for them, and the pallbearers to start marching. I wonder if you have to wait in line in Heaven.

Saturday, March 31, 1945.

I've pulled off a coup, and brought home magnificent plunder. Yesterday evening I went to see a colleague who has a sub-let from a fairly high Nazi bigwig, and I found the building shattered by blasts from the last bombing. The usual scene—doors stove in, window frames out, roller curtains dangling askew, mountains of broken glass, plaster, mortar, and torn blackout paper. The other side of the street is on fire from cellar to roof. My colleague has gone out.

"Is your telephone working?" I ask the Nazi cook. "Then perhaps you won't mind if I make a short call."

She shows me into her master's study. I stumble over the litter on my way to the desk. Through the gaping window hole shines the somber red of the conflagration. In its flickering gleam I recognize the instrument, and also recognize right beside it a bowl of writing instruments and a lot of rubber stamps.

An idea flashes through my head. Might one of those stamps be . . . ? I whip out my flashlight. The cook is far away; I hear her pounding and banging somewhere in the distance. She's covering the windows with cardboard—the endlessly recurring business after each bombing.

I shade the flashlight with my hand, and carefully examine the contents of the bowl. Rectangular stamps; oval stamps. No, none of that. *Special Delivery. File. Sample, No Value.*

At last! There *is* one! A round, red knob. The gray stamp a perfect circle. A "birdie"! Actually, a birdie! The eagle emblem of the Party—a priceless possession for anyone who needs passes.

Out with some paper—an old envelope: I pound the stamp pad as if I were beating kettledrums. "Foreign Organization of the NSDAP, Reich Headquarters," says the circle of words around the eagle. It couldn't have been better.

With one swift motion this jewel of great price is hidden in the wide hem of my stocking. Another motion: two or three stamps go out of the window, followed by a few pencils. The remaining contents of the bowl are strewn on the floor among broken glass and plaster. Bombed out! Carried off by the blast waves, everything on the desk. Let them hunt for traces of *that!*

"Swiping for others makes stealing a pleasure," Ursula Reuber said. I'm enjoying every minute of this—enjoying it so much that my heart pounds in my throat for sheer pleasure.

At home Frank is awaiting me. "Hey!" he cries. "The Russians have taken Küstrin! Danzig has fallen! They've reached Paderborn in the west. Duisburg is captured, and thousands of prisoners. You watch—in three weeks they'll make it."

"And who'll be here first?"

"No telling yet. But no matter who comes. . . ." He hugs me ecstatically.

More and more people feel that way now. You see fewer

227

and fewer Party emblems in buttonholes, and hear fewer and fewer fanatical Party Comrades driveling about final victory. Final victory is when the Allies come marching through the Brandenburg Gate.

Then we discuss the matter of the birdie. Frank is all on fire; he convenes the crowd this very evening. We are all sitting together.

"We'd have had to buckle down about now anyway," says Fabian. "The customary method of begging stamps is done with; they won't take points that have been separated from the cards any more. Starting next month, our U-boats will be stranded, if we don't . . . Well . . . If we don't . . ." He looks dubiously at Frank, the foolhardy adventurer of the crowd.

". . . make up our minds to stage a little burglary at the ration office," Frank finishes for him. "That was what you meant, wasn't it?"

For a moment we look at one another in dismay. We have a choking sensation. Burglary! Why must we start right off with burglary? After all, none of us was bred to that trade; and somewhere underneath we still have a very lively conventional conscience. But once you get into a thing, there's no backing out.

Frank explains his plan. "I'll go tomorrow to Ration Office No. 9, out at Tempelhof. It's quartered in a bombed-out school, very temporarily. Nothing but cardboard over the windows, and wooden doors. The police are in the basement, along with a Home Guard draft office. It sounds rather dangerous, but when you come to look at it, it's an advantage. They wouldn't expect anybody to have so much gall. I'll reconnoiter. Two people will do for the rest of the job—you and I, Fabian. You other people can just knock on wood for us."

At night I dream I'm hanging by a thin rope over a dizzy abyss. Beside me hangs Frank, saying, "Let yourself drop! It's quite nice below, too." I wake up bathed in sweat. The clock says ten, and Frank is gone long since. Bells are ringing outside—ringing loud and long. Has the upheaval begun? I jump out of bed and rush to the window. Good God, if we've missed that. . . .

People are walking in the Bismarckstrasse as usual.

No, it's merely Easter, I suddenly remember. One even forgets holidays. For us the conventional measurement of time has ceased to exist so completely that we live only for the moment, happy and grateful to give each minute its due.

There's a thundering knock at the front door. Three times repeated—the signal for "a friend" when the current's cut off and the bells don't work. I rush down. "Thank God you're back!"

He laughs all over. "And I'm not alone; I've got the key to the ration office, right here in my pocket. This afternoon we'll turn the trick."

"But how can you, on Easter Sunday?" I stare at him foolishly.

"That's just it—Easter Sunday. Now don't stand there and gape, sweetheart, get on your horse! Fetch Heike and Fabian over. The privy council is going to meet."

Frank discusses the situation like a general. "You'll go first, Fabian. I'll watch for the cops, and cover you until I know you're inside. The outer door just has a wooden bar—you can lift that up with your pocketknife like nothing at all. Then there's a flight of stairs—six steps. Then down the corridor

229

to the right, third door. Here's the key. As soon as the coast is clear, I'll follow. If we get caught, we'll jump out the window."

"What magic did you work on the key?" Heike asks admiringly.

"No magic at all. It was right there—simply sticking in the lock. Two girls were in the room, putting in a little overtime. I politely inquired whether this was the Home Guard draft office. 'No, that's on the other side,' they said. While I was noisily thanking them, covering the doorknob with my back, the key slipped into my pocket."

At four the two leave the place. Heike sacrifices her cheese allowance, and gets up a marvelous burglar's breakfast. "After all, we can't let them go off on an empty stomach," she says. And our amateur second-story workers fall to as if they had been starving for a month.

"Do you suppose burglary always gives you that kind of an appetite?" Heike and I have been huddling in our chairs for three hours, not daring to stir. Twilight is already falling. Then it grows quite dark.

Long—short—short. The bell jingles! "There they are! At last!"

A glance at their faces: they did it! We go silently into the room; silently they empty their pockets. Bomb-damage certificates. More bomb-damage certificates. Still more bomb-damage certificates. Piles of yellow blanks tower on the table.

"Is that all?" I ask, disappointed.

Frank nods. "The burglary was a success; the loot is not so good. They had evidently taken the best stuff into the basement."

"And how did it go?"

"Just as we had planned. We waited twenty minutes until

the coast was clear. That was what took the most nerve. Then Fabian started off. The bar was no trouble. Nothing stirring at the police station downstairs. They had shoved two school benches in front of the door, obviously because of the missing key. Fabian went through the cabinet, I took the desk. We didn't find any food cards anywhere. So we just stuffed our pockets with what was around. Now it's the birdie's turn."

"And you're sure nobody saw you?" I'm still a little scared.

"Not a soul." Fabian piles the last bomb-damage certificates on the table. "All right, up and at 'em!" he encourages us. "Let's strike while the iron is hot. Blank forms butter no parsnips—let alone a month's allowance of bread. Hand over the stamp!" He rubs his hands.

"We'll get three families ready—three families of three each. Nine sets—nine sets of provisions for the unprovided." The two men go to work with stamp and ruler as if they were draftsmen by trade.

"Has anyone got any gummed paper or tape? We've got to make the lower edge of the stamp illegible. 'Foreign Organization' doesn't look right. The Foreign Organization must be blurred."

It is blurred. Now everyone can interpret the illegible lettering on the lower half of the stamp as whatever is momentarily official and suitable.

"Now, good people, for God's sake learn your names. And your birthdays," Frank warns us. "For nine people—you'll have to concentrate."

Finally it's all ready—green bomb-damage certificates, carefully prepared, with all the official entries that are required. Mrs. Berg and children; Mrs. Kühn and children; Mrs. Helfer and children.

"The girls can go to Potsdam on Tuesday," Frank decides.

Long before eight Heike and I are at the Steglitz Station, dressed in sweat shirt and trousers and beret, as befits the bombed-out.

"Lore Berg, born May 17, 1921," Heike mumbles to herself.

"Else Kühn, born September 13, 1912," I retort. We are mechanically learning our descriptions by heart.

No streetcars are running in Potsdam. "Not until four, when business traffic begins," they explain to us. Four o'clock is no good to us; so we hoof it, all the way through town.

"It might be a good idea to have a look at the house we're moving into," Heike suggests. "After all, we should know a little something about it."

New residence, 12 Mirbachstrasse. We walk and walk. How *can* people live so far out of town?

At the police station there's a sleepy girl, on compulsory duty, and obviously resentful of her new job. She scarcely looks at our forms, but dully stamps what she's been told to stamp. Our spirits rise. Now all we have left is the ration office.

Thousands of fugitives have moved into Potsdam; we take our place in line.

"If they get suspicious, act as if you had to go to the toilet, and beat it," I whisper in Heike's ear.

She nods. "And we've got to take care of the papers for Mrs. Helfer and children, too, because she's in bed and can't come," she whispers back.

We have no need of the toilet. They hand us everything without batting an eye—nine months' food cards, household identification, vegetable card, Potsdam purchase identification for special rations, smoked-food card, and milk card. My handbag is too small to hold all these riches. "Thank very much," I say by mistake. "Oh, thank you very much!"

Joy lends wings to our feet, as we race back through Potsdam. We can hardly wait for the train to start.

"We've got 'em, we've got 'em!" Heike rejoices, falling into Fabian's arms.

Ten minutes later the men start off on their wheels to "distribute."

Hartmann gets one set, Wald the second, Flamm is taken care of, and so are the two fugitives from the Jewish redistribution camp. We feel like Santa Claus.

As we sit catching our breath in our room, our work accomplished, Fabian says, "Funny how you can be a criminal without feeling like one. My conscience is as pure as the driven snow."

"So's mine," Frank replies. "Robbing the Nazis isn't robbing at all. Only we must be careful to draw the line. And when . . ." he hesitates, ". . . when I think of those tobacco cards. . . ."

Three pairs of eyes are cast down guiltily. Frank is the only one of us who doesn't smoke. And the shortage of tobacco is growing more acute every day. Our protégés don't smoke either; so we thought. . . .

"Here are the tobacco cards." Fabian, crushed, rummages in his wallet. "Three women's, two men's. The ones from Potsdam. Truly, I didn't mean to do anything rotten."

"Of course you didn't." Now Frank in turn looks aside uncomfortably. "Only it all hinges on the principle of the thing. Anyone who expects to justify the means by the end needs a doubly tender conscience. Otherwise end and means will run away from us. And if we ever sink to the level of ordinary black marketers—"

"—we *deserve* to have forfeited our lives," Fabian finishes for him softly. "I hope we'll be living for a long time yet."

The siren screeches at eleven. "Ladies and gentlemen of the radio audience, the customary evening air-raid alarm," flutes the voice of the wire-news announcer from the loud-speaker.

"Stupid cracks," growls Frank. "Now he's getting coy about it."

I'm in no cheerful mood myself. "Did anyone ever die from sleep starvation?" I inquire as we go downstairs, groaning under our daily multiplying air-raid baggage.

We crouch endlessly in the basement. We doze fitfully.

Fabian growls, "If they keep on with this business of chopping up their attacks into individual installments, we'll still be here a month from now. Besides, my leg has gone to sleep."

Nobody says anything. Only Heike gives the sleeping limb a sympathetic glance. Somewhere we hear the howl of a bomb. We pull in our heads. Thank heaven, it passed over. We swallow down a little flying dust.

Long after midnight we slink up the stairs in single file. There is fire in the direction of Schöneberg.

"Now there's nothing but off to bed," Heike sighs.

She sighs in vain; we haven't been in bed ten minutes before the siren howls again.

"This sort of thing ought to be prohibited, downright prohibited," we grumble.

Wednesday, April 4, 1945.

I start from bed early—another alarm. Now that the German frontier is in Thuringia, they've given up any attempt to time enemy flights. The current is turned off before the final all-clear.

So once again there won't be any breakfast, or presumably lunch either. Sometimes you feel like giving up altogether. How is a person expected to work with this sort of thing going on?

Looking for consolation, I go over to see Heike. Her room is full of thick black smoke. From the balcony I hear assiduous bustle and the rattle of pots and pans. "Have you started a lampblack factory?" I ask.

She pokes her sooty face in at the door. "No," she beams, "just a coffee kitchen for malcontents. Homemade, if you must know. From the ruins of the house next door."

I admire her handiwork—thirty-five bricks, skillfully piled to make an open fireplace; two iron rods as a grill, and on top our old teakettle.

"For the moment I'm using my love letters to stoke with," Heike explains. "They do smoke some, but they give a lot of heat." She pours me the first cup of coffee. It's hot, and smells like a sausage shop.

We haven't finished our combined morning and noon meal when Wald appears, brandishing a newspaper, and simply raving.

"This is the end! The nails are in all our coffins."

We jump up. "Who's given us away?" asks Heike, turning pale to the lips.

"Given us away?" Wald stops. "No one so far. But just you wait. This is long-range talebearing. This . . . this is . . . It's the dirtiest trick of the century, that's what it is." He points fiercely to the boldface headline: "Werewolf German Freedom Movement."

"Well?" I ask tensely.

"Well? Just listen to this damned stuff!"

He reads: "A will to resist is breaking out, beyond any organization, from the simple passion of hatred that threatens to become a fearful menace to any invading enemy."

He stops to remark, "Surely you can see which way the hatred is running—straight to outlaw warfare. Here it is, word for word: 'The forces gathered in the werewolf proclaim their firm and unshakable determination, sealed by a solemn oath, never to give way to the enemy. To offer him resistance upon resistance; to confront him proudly and persistently; and to avenge every misdeed that he commits against a member of our people by his own death.' " Wald is sweating with fury.

"Now do you believe me? Here's some more: 'Any means is good enough. The werewolf has its own courts, which will adjudge the life and death of the enemy as well as of the traitor among our own people. Let it be known that wherever the German army, after hard and fierce struggles, has been forced to yield German territory, the enemy will now have an adversary whose resistance he had not counted on, who will be the more dangerous to him inasmuch as he need not consider the antiquated notions of so-called legal warfare. Hatred is our prayer, revenge our battle cry.'

"Damn them and their prayer; I spit on their battle cry. They're saying around town that the first volunteers have already been trained. All schooled for this delightful gang of theirs—hand-to-hand fighting without arms. Lassoing with piano wire; neck breaking by jiujitsu. Sneak killing, you might say. If the Allies stand for this. . . ."

We, too, gradually begin to realize the full implications of the new Nazi invention. Military defeat will not be enough now. Resistance is to be kept up to the very last attic chamber.

For what? So that Mr. Hitler can hug life for another week; so that Mr. Goering can go on stuffing his potbelly with *pâté de foie gras.* What a trifling gain for so tremendous a state!

"Do you think people are actually volunteering?"

"Any who don't come of their own accord will be compelled. I guess we know that line. Forty reliable Party Comrades in each local group is what I heard confidentially from an intermediary. The number alone speaks for itself. Forty fanatics in each borough; forty spies by passionate conviction. If we can hang on after all that . . . !"

Misfortunes seldom come singly. Frank arrives with the news that all transportation is to be discontinued as of Monday. Only wage earners with passes will be allowed to ride back and forth to their places of employment. And what about our "divers"? There isn't enough shoe leather in the world to cover those distances.

So we've got to start counterfeiting again, and there's no time to be lost.

I happen to remember that as long ago as February some list or other was going around the various business houses, asking whether people used subway or streetcar. Possibly one's employer is the answer.

But when I ask at the office, they can't tell me anything definite. Requests are in; final decisions have to be awaited; nothing hasty must be done on any account—the usual policy of spineless timidity.

Saturday, April 7, 1945.

The paper hasn't been allowed any traffic passes. Neither the green ones, grade III, nor the yellow ones, grade II, nor yet the red ones, grade I. We aren't important enough to the war effort, they tell us. Not important enough to the war effort to get any of the pitiful remnants of coal over whose distribu-

237

tion Goebbels and Speer have been squabbling for weeks.

Current for the people to cook with, or industrial current for war materials? You can't have both any more. Now the authorities are quarreling over who shall squeeze out the last drop.

We're shelved, anyway.

Before the transit passes go into effect, the green grade will already have been withdrawn, and the yellow will be on the edge of it. That leaves the red: rapid-transit travel on vital war business. So the red's what we've got to counterfeit. Red's the thing.

The crowd gathers for a conference. Wald assigns the jobs. "This time we're playing for keeps," he says. "If we really want to pull a fast one on Speer, we'll have to go into large-scale counterfeiting. At least a thousand passes, perfectly printed, and put to work in the right places."

"We'll do it! We'll do it!" Frank is pawing like a race horse before the barrier goes up.

"All right, you can crank up your bicycles. Point one, get a copy of the pass. Heike can do that; where she swaps, steals, or organizes it from is her business. Point two, each special letter of the type heading will have to be engraved separately. My engraver was bombed out yesterday; I believe he moved to Britz somewhere—Gärtnerweg, or something like that." Fabian is already taking notes. "Point three, we need boxwood to engrave on. There's a batch still waiting for me at Friedrichshagen. Eckardt can take care of Friedrichshagen. Meanwhile, Frank can bike over to Neukölln, and pick up the right colored paper from Leitmann & Krause. The shade is what counts; we can't afford any wrong shades. He'd better talk to Heike first. I'll take care of the printing. If everything goes right, and they don't run a night shift at the shop again on account of the current's being cut off, I can be ready in five days."

Fifteen minutes later we are swarming out in all directions like district messenger boys—Britz, Friedrichshagen, Neukölln, Grunewald, Schöneberg, Adlershorst.

Sirens. Preliminary warning; take cover. Preliminary allclear; all clear. Really, they don't make it easy for us.

I cook over Heike's brick fireplace for those who return exhausted. It smokes, and makes soot, and it takes an awful time. But we've got everything—the genuine copy, the boxwood, the engraver, the right shade of paper.

"Do you know how I got the red pass?" Heike asks, brandishing her trophy triumphantly. "Swapped it for three liters of milk stamps. To an SS man. They're all swapping like crazy; every office does its own special business; they've even been known to demand flowers in trade."

"Aha, the language of flowers!" Fabian jeers. "The government krauts are growing lyrical. Ugh! For God's sake!"

To put himself in a better humor he turns on the radio. "This is England; this is England," the loud-speaker shouts.

"Hey, for God's sake put a pillow over it," whispers Frank, horrified. "They'll hear you all the way to the Reich Chancellery."

"But just the same, you wanted to know that the Russians are in Vienna, the English are marching on Hannover, Brunswick, Leipzig, and Bremen," Fabian growls after five minutes of silent communion with the cushion-muted radio. Our weariness evaporates. Four weeks at the most! We'll have to hurry with the transit passes.

Late that evening I sit down and write post cards to the four corners of the earth—cards that I've been hoarding, for the government supply even of these is failing, and you can

239

get only a few at any one post office. "The Fuehrer knows nothing but struggle, toil, and care. We will take from his shoulders what can be taken," is printed in verse form next to the space for address. "You never talk about anything that goes without saying," my father once remarked. "Anything that has to be emphasized too much is always suspicious."

Of course it's suspicious. Particularly the lack of sleep, which not only Hitler, but Goebbels and Goering mention imploringly at every opportunity, good or bad. Whoever heard anything about how Churchill sleeps? Or Stalin? Who knows when Mr. Roosevelt goes to bed and gets up? Yet they keep rubbing our noses in the fact that Adolf Hitler sacrifices his night's sleep year in and year out for the German people. But at the moment Hitler's sleep isn't so important as the fact that presumably the mail service throughout the Reich will soon stop. So, under the smoking oil lamp, I write cards to Stuttgart and Hamburg, to Munich and Sigmaringen.

"Dear friends: Probably we shan't be hearing from one another now for a long time. If this card reaches you, I want you to know that we're alive, in good health, and hoping confidently to surmount all difficulties. We'll try to get in touch again as soon as possible. Take care of yourselves, and think of us. Don't forget us."

My eyes fall shut as I put the last card on the mountain of those already written. The lamp smolders; the room is almost dark. Do our dear ones abroad know how hard it is for us to endure the struggle to the end?

Monday, April 9, 1945.

"We've got to see to Hartmann," says Frank. "For three weeks now he's been waiting for that red Home Guard certificate. Remember, the man has no identification at all. It's irrespon-

240

sible of us to leave him in such peril for an hour longer than necessary."

"But Flamm didn't deliver the stuff until yesterday!"

"Just because he delivered it yesterday, we've got to go to Hartmann today. When will you be back from the office?"

"At five."

"All right, let's meet in the Eisenacherstrasse at half past."

They're raising hell at the office again. "We might just as well shut up shop unless we can get some passes," wails our personnel manager.

"How many do you need?"

"At least a hundred and twenty—red ones, of course. The yellow ones are shaky already."

"You can get them," I say casually.

Our personnel manager gapes. "When . . . how . . . how do you mean?" he stammers.

"That's my business. But you shall have them—in four days at latest. And if you wanted to do a little something in return, you might shoot a thousand-mark note. Even outlaws have to live."

He nods silently. "In four days, then. Discretion guaranteed!"

"I certainly hope so," I think.

Five minutes after half past five I knock at Ulrike Weitzen's door—long-short-short, the prearranged signal. Frank is already on the sofa. Hartmann huddles as always beside the radio.

"You feel as if it were going faster when you listen more often," he smiles apologetically. "But I'm afraid I can't make it."

"You will make it. Just these few weeks? What an idea!"

"But these 'few weeks' are deciding the life and death of

hundreds of thousands. And after this last piece of villainy—"

"You mean the Werewolf?"

"Yes, the Werewolf too, of course. But not just that. I'm much more troubled about the business with the prisoners of war."

We look at him inquiringly.

"Hadn't you heard? Well, Hitler's planning a murder that's really in the grand manner—shooting all the English and American prisoners of war."

It takes our breath away. "What about the laws of war— the Hague Convention?"

"No longer exists in his mind. This is really his last gamble. Not the murder of the prisoners, you understand, but the Allied reprisals. Murder for murder. He wants the other side to butcher the Germans; then no German soldier will get any fancy ideas about deserting to the enemy. They've been surrendering in droves these last few weeks. He wants to put a stop to it—a policy of terrorization to save the Fuehrer's life. Loathsome!"

"But that's a madman's plan!"

"Well, he *is* a madman. Or did you think normal people nibbled on curtains and ate carpets for breakfast?"

"What about the generals—the heads of the army?" Frank stammers. His cheerful, boyish face is pale and sunken with agitation.

"They're still balking at carrying out the order. But how long will they balk? How long can they? Anyone who won't play gets lopped off. Whether it's Kesselring or Kluge, Brauchitsch or Dönitz, what's the difference? As long as there are still marshals who will obey, the wagon will keep going."

No one ventures a reply. We stare dumbly into space.

"By the way, we brought you a red Home Guard certificate," I finally dare to break the silence after a long pause. "All beautifully stamped, by your very own borough authority."

Hartmann's eyes light up. "Give it here! Quick! Thank God, thank God. Now I can. . . . Now I'll. . . ." A new man suddenly seems to be before us—self-assured, liberated.

We go home through ruined Schöneberg in the dusk. The plaster dust clutches at our throats. The sunset shines beyond the ruins of the Schöneberg town hall.

"Look at those clouds," says Frank. "Magnificent! If they take everything away, we've still got the clouds."

His bicycle crashes down into a bomb crater. "It's still the most important thing," he repeats defiantly. But the front tire is gone, and we both have to push our wheels.

Wednesday, April 11, 1945.

"If I don't get out just once, I simply can't stand this nonsense any longer!"

It's a brilliant spring day, and Frank and I have spent the morning sweeping up rubble, repairing bicycles, and getting the brick fireplace going.

"All right," I agree, "as far as I'm concerned, we can slip in an hour's creative pause."

Ten minutes later we're off.

In town people are hurrying through the streets as usual; but out along the canal it is still. Among dark evergreens stands a solitary bench, framed by a hedge of blossoming forsythia.

"Let's sit down for a while," Frank suggests. Through the bright twigs we look at the sky. "How can there be so much spring?" I think, squinting into yellow-and-blue space. "So incredibly much spring . . ."

"Look, they've moved a gun in over there to the left. Take a good look—just next to that big evergreen."

I turn my head to the left, and see a field-gray cannon barrel, holes in the ground, ammunition cases. Like a needle it pierces my brain: there the war is, right there—directly beside us. It'll catch us in a moment! It'll shake and throttle us —me, Frank, all of us. Today we're behind the lines. But tomorrow we'll be at the front—the Berlin front! Complete with tanks, shells, and the shouts of battle. Who can tell what will survive?

That evening the crowd girds itself for a new achievement. This time the project and point of attack is our old water tower. It used to be the borough water reservoir. Then the Nazis turned it into a monument, with swastika, eagle, and flags, red-ribboned wreaths and pompous inscriptions. "For the fallen of the Movement." From the Nazi fighters to the Nazi fighters. British bombs struck the tower, killed some people, and did a good deal of damage. But the flags were left; they've been an eyesore to us for some time.

Hanging, drawing, and quartering is the least of the penalties for sacrilege to Nazi emblems. Reason enough for us to proceed with the utmost caution.

"We'd better wait for the alarm," Fabian suggests. "When the planes are buzzing over, everybody'll be in the cellar."

It's dark outside—so dark that you can't see your hand in front of your face. Our steps echo across the asphalt. Sure enough, there isn't a soul in the streets anywhere. All you hear is now and then a cough from inside a cellar door; you may see the glowing dot of a cigarette for a moment or two.

We clamber like cats over the high wire fence that surrounds the water tower at some distance. We creep forward on tiptoe. The planes are roaring overhead.

"Listen, there's actually a night bird singing over yonder," Frank whispers in my ear.

I stop and listen. "Ki-ri-witt, ki-ri-witt" comes quite clearly from somewhere. The cool wind stirs the trees; they stand in the blackness of space like yet blacker shadows.

A twig snaps loudly under my feet.

"Don't make such a row," Heike snarls at me. "Do you want to fetch in the Gestapo?"

No, I don't want to; I certainly don't. But nobody can be responsible for twigs lying across paths in the pitch dark.

Now we're standing below the high dome of the water tower. "Out with the shears," Frank orders. "We've got to be done in five minutes."

"I can't get at it," Heike whispers despairingly.

Neither can I. We bounce up and down uselessly like rubber balls.

"What's the matter—got St. Vitus's dance?" Wald is beside me. "Get on my shoulders, quick." He makes a stirrup of his hands. The shears squeak; the planes still hum.

Down comes the first flag; down comes the second.

Heike's working at the other end of the building, her legs around Fabian's neck like a horsewoman. Third flag, fourth flag, fifth flag. There are still two left.

Then the preliminary all-clear siren goes.

"Hurry, hurry!" We cut and snip till our arms ache.

"Where's Frank?"

"Here" his voice comes mysteriously from above us. A flapping something descends slowly from the middle of the vaulting. It dangles like a black jumping jack above the head of the Nazi eagle. A moment later Frank is beside us.

"Let's get going," he urges. "It's high time."

In mad haste we cram the flags under our coats; they smell of dust and some sort of acid.

"Where the hell were you?"

"Up on the second floor. I was hanging Hitler."

"Whom?" I ask, stumbling over dry twigs again.

"Unfortunately only his paper effigy. With a piece of string around his neck. But anyway . . ."

The long-drawn clamor of the all-clear swallows up his last words. As we go on, the first shelter dwellers come toward us, chattering like magpies, and filling the night with bustle. Baby carriages squeak along the sidewalk.

"Time to be coming home," says Heike disdainfully.

At home Dagmar Meyerowitz is waiting for us. "Did everything go all right?"

Proudly we draw the swastika'd trophies from the depths of our bosoms.

"Well, I guess that deserves a cognac!"

"Cognac, you call that fusel oil they distributed last time?" asks Frank sarcastically. But he has the corkscrew in his hand. And once again it's morning before we get to bed.

At five o'clock Fabian considers the moment ripe to perpetuate our night's experience in poetry. He writes on the wall with Heike's lipstick.

> "Seven loathsome Nazi rags
> Drooped from posts like flour bags
> When they caught our practiced eye,
> We knew that we must steal or die.
>
> "Seven rags torn from above
> Briskly fly into the stove.

When freedom is the goal we'd gain,
We gladly hazard any pain."

"And I'm the one who's got to wash that off tomorrow," Heike sighs resignedly. But the sympathy of the house is not forthcoming; we are much too weary to get excited about such trifles.

Friday, April 13, 1945.

Roosevelt has died, quite suddenly, of a stroke. "Warmonger Roosevelt dead," the papers say. Once again Hitler sees it as a signal from Providence because not he but the American has been laid low. He even dares to say that this is a plain proof of our inevitable final victory.

Too bad, people say. Too bad; still, it won't change anything now. The avalanche will come, no matter whether Mr. Roosevelt is under the sod or walking on it.

Saturday, April 14, 1945.

Eckardt arrives at six in the afternoon, sweaty, his cap on the back of his head, jacket and boots covered with dust. "I fixed their wagon," he says contentedly, flinging himself on the couch. "I always say you can't beat wire cutters!" He's cut eight cables on the way from Nauen to Berlin. Eight important cables that were supposed to carry orders for the defense of the capital. "And not just the plain wires," he declares triumphantly. "Kurt Eckardt isn't that much of a fool. The cable shoes are what count. You have to take away the cable shoes. No matter how they hunt, they'll be a long time getting those together again." In his enthusiasm he quite forgets his weariness. "What I always say is, talking is nonsense. You've got to act. Or don't you think it's anything to run five hundred liters of gas down the drain? Five hundred liters—put aside for four Nazi bigwigs to run away on."

"How did you ever do that?"

He beams at us proudly. "I got them to lock me inside, in the factory garage—at closing time the day before yesterday. That was when I spied it out—the hiding place, and the gasoline. The rest was nothing at all. Roll the drums over to the drain, out with the plug, and down the sewer with it. And I can tell you it stank. Boy, how it stank!"

"Dirty business always stinks," Frank laughs.

The siren interrupts our conversation. This time it isn't the usual night-flying Mosquitoes, but regular bomber units flying in from the west. Disagreeable—very disagreeable indeed.

To raise our fallen spirits, Heike sings in time to our steps going down:

"The Chancellery is a glorious sight:
Bigwigs are hanging from every street light.
They've got the Fuehrer up there too
What a clever thing to do!
But doesn't he look an awful fright!"

"You must be tired of living," Frank scolds. "You have to start singing like the trumpets of Jericho right out on the stairway, with all this echo, and the windows broken. If an air-raid warden happens. . . ."

But the air-raid warden is far away; he has left Berlin, bag and baggage. Heading west—heading out of danger. Delightful people, these Nazis.

"If you just knew what I pulled off last week," Eckardt, undisturbed by bombs and air raids, picks up the interrupted conversation. "Do you know what emery is? Have you any idea what happens when you dump it into high-grade lubricating oil? I spoiled our whole supply. It's perfectly useless —a dead loss to the war economy." He grins so that you can see his horse teeth clear to the gums. "Those devils . . . those devils," he murmurs. Then our saboteur squats down in the corner, and sleeps the sleep of the just for an hour.

"There's a lad with steady nerves," says Fabian.

Sunday, April 15, 1945.

So the bombers were heading for Potsdam—the marvelous, haughty city that boasted until yesterday of being the only one left undestroyed in Germany. Pride goeth before a fall. Now Potsdam and all its beauty are in ruins. An irrevocable loss to civilization, but—possibly—a gain to humaneness. Last night the people of Potsdam joined the fellowship of sufferers.

Late in the morning comes a messenger from Hollner, who was called up for the Home Guard four weeks ago. The man brings a letter, and insists on waiting for an answer.

"Here on furlough for two days," is hastily scrawled in pencil. "Send me the doctor. I can't go on."

"Well, let's go," Frank growls, already half into his overcoat.

"I'll go with you. Don't forget your prescription pad."

Fat Hollner looks pale and frightened. "I've got to be back with my company by six tomorrow morning. I don't want any more of it. I can't stand it. I just can't keep going any longer." He looks at us helplessly with the blue eyes of a child. "If something doesn't happen, I'll turn on the gas."

Another man who's really in earnest at last.

"Atabrine?" Frank looks at me inquiringly.

"If you can still get any."

All at once Frank is no longer the submerged Mr. Unknown, but a doctor, professional man, and fellow of the university. Bending over the table, he writes swiftly and silently. He scrawls an illegible signature.

"You go to bed right away. Severe attack of bilious colic. Wet compresses on your liver. If you take five sleeping tablets, even the staff doctor will believe you're in a stupor. Act a little—you can surely do that. Let out a yell if they touch you under the ribs on the right side. Here are four prescriptions, each for one box of Atabrine, containing fifteen tablets. Take two, six times a day, for five days running. Eat as much fat as you can. In three days you'll turn yellow. You'll show every symptom of infectious jaundice."

"You don't die of it?" asks Hollner dubiously.

"It's horse medicine, but it's better than being in the Home Guard during the last fight for Berlin."

"How many Germans," says Frank on the way home, "do you suppose have taken to their beds and turned olive color by this moment, just to be out of it? There must be thousands. Atabrine, Pervitin, contagious jaundice, heart murmur, kidney complaint—everyone does what he can. 'Oh, to be sickly!' is the wish-dream of every able-bodied German these days."

At home we find Andrik. He couldn't stand it any longer in Braunsdorf, out to pasture on a diet for his kidneys. "I don't care if everything goes to hell, I'll chance it!" he declares firmly. "I guess they won't catch me in these last few days."

"Oh, just to have you here!" I'm quite weak with joy. Within an hour we have drummed up the crowd to welcome him.

"Important news, good people," Andrik reports. "They're saying that the final Russian offensive is starting near Küstrin. The United Nations are at Halle and Tangermünde. On the way here I met a new man—I should say the best connection we've made yet. His name is Gregor Schulz. I have no idea whether that's his real name, and anyway, what's the difference? Well, this new man . . ." he hesitates, and gives us a searching look. "They're preparing for action—gathering all opposition groups. Do we want in?"

"You bet we want in. What's it to be?"

"A great big No to Hitler's policies—war, resistance, Werewolf, the whole crazy business. I'm supposed to hear the details tomorrow."

Toward evening Rita and Ralph arrive—Dr. Tegel's protégés from the Jewish redistribution camp. "We can't sleep at the doctor's all the time; the neighbors have been getting leery." The two have come on foot to Wilmersdorf.

Heike prepares a shakedown—rather haphazard, cushions and mattresses on the floor; but it will do.

We don't get much sleep, anyway—three Mosquito attacks. They are so carefully timed that arrival of one and departure of another never coincide.

Monday, April 16, 1945.

"The day of lone wolves is past," Frank said once. One can afford individualism only so long as the state is in balance. In times of stress, terror, and collapse, the individual is forced to grow into a part of the community. Everyone needs the support of kindred spirits; each man must take his neighbor's part. We live and breathe for a common goal, so we can't pull

251

in different directions to reach it. None of us ever used to be much interested in politics; none of us ever belonged to a political party. All we wanted was to be human beings. But because we wanted that, we had to take up the heritage of those who perished in the struggle for their humanity. They handed on their mission to us; now we are bound to it, whether we will or no. Moltke and the Scholls, Witzleben and Trott, Ursula Reuber, Eva Gerichter, Dr. Muehsam and the Bernsteins, Anna Lehmann and Margot Rosenthal—they have made us the executors of their unfinished human tasks.

As I am taking my thoughts for a stroll, Andrik comes into the room, and claps me on the shoulder. "A new U-boat has surfaced; how about going over and looking after him?"

Over the way, that is, in Andrik's room, is a young man, about thirty, with the black hair of an Indian, and grave brown eyes. He wears the uniform of a captain in the medical corps. "I'm Johannes Thäler," he introduces himself, "Frank Matthis' friend."

"Welcome, Mr. Thäler," I say. "We've been expecting you for weeks."

The young man hesitates. "I've just got in from Schwerin, with faked orders."

"Have you got a place to stay? Passes? Ration cards?"

He nods. "All prepared long in advance. I didn't make the decision yesterday, as you probably know. Frank thought they'd be needing me here."

"Everyone's needed. It's good to see you, Mr. Thäler."

For seconds there is the barest hint of a smile on his lips. "My name is Joe, if you . . . if you want to call me that."

"All right, Joe!" We shake hands cordially. "The crowd is meeting today, at nine o'clock, here in the colony. The front door will be open."

Andrik looks at the clock. "It's high time to be off to the Uhlandstrasse."

"What are we doing in the Uhlandstrasse?"

"Saying No! Come on; we've got to pick up Frank on the way."

At five minutes after seven we turn off the Kurfürstendamm into the Uhlandstrasse.

I am posted behind a projection in the wall to guard our locked bicycles, and keep a lookout for cops. It's a day of wind and rain; hardly a soul on the streets. Only now and then a cyclist whisks past, head hunched between shoulders, with wet cap and wet clothes. I shiver, turn up my coat collar, bury my hands in my pockets, and stand first on one foot, then on the other.

Does anything look suspicious? Is there a man leaning against a corner somewhere, inconspicuously watching the door of the building? Is that curtain moving over yonder?

The rain drips monotonously; I look up the street and down.

At that moment Frank stands before me. "It's all right. You can come up."

A narrow rear courtyard; in the right corner, an iron door. "To Air-raid Shelter," says a yellowish-red sign in luminous letters. The winding stair is dark and narrow.

"Haven't you got a flashlight? We'll break our necks here," I whisper to Frank. I hear the scraping of matches, and suppressed curses.

"The damn things won't light." At last a faint spark gleams.

We halt at the third floor, and fumble for the bell push. One, two, three, four. Each man has a different ring, but they all have some signal.

Shortly the door is opened from the inside. In the darkness I can scarcely make out the silhouette of a slim male figure.

"Do come in," says an amiable voice. "There'll be more light in a moment."

A long passage, a white door at the end, and then we are in an ordinary living room. The man who showed us in turns to me.

"How do you do again," he says, holding out his hand. "I'm Gregor Schulz. These people here—" a quick gesture includes everyone in the room—"are Berthold, Reinhard, and Emil."

Three men get up, and make a brief, silent bow. A little to one side stands Andrik.

"Do sit down," says Gregor Schulz. We seat ourselves in silence. One of the men takes out a cigarette case.

"May I really?"

"Please do!" The case makes the rounds. When you smoke, everything is much cozier. For two or three minutes we pull thoughtfully at our cigarettes.

Spread out on the floor is a huge map of Berlin, covered with a great many square bits of cardboard.

"You know what we're doing?" Gregor Schulz tosses his cigarette into the ash tray, and looks inquiringly at us. "In a word, we're saying *No* to Hitler's policies. The real answer to his last election referendum—the ballot with the big circle for Yes and the tiny circle for No. Do you, German man, and you, German woman, approve the policies of Adolf Hitler?

"No, we don't approve these policies. And we want to demonstrate unmistakably that we don't." The slender young man, with his faintly slitted, Japanese-looking eyes, jumps up and bends over the map. "We're planning an action to cover all Berlin—Wednesday night. The first one on this scale since 1933. The watchword is *No*. We want every wall to shout *No* at the Nazis—in chalk or paint, charcoal or whitewash. Each of us is taking over one borough of the city." He puts a finger on the square bits of cardboard. "Each of us will undertake to do his level best in his own district."

"Which district were you thinking of giving to us?" Andrik's voice is curt and matter-of-fact.

"The southwest. Steglitz and Schöneberg aren't taken yet. We have nobody in Friedenau, either. The north and east are already arranged for; so is Spandau, and the surrounding territory." Gregor Schulz pushes the bits of card around like chessmen. "Then there's Wilmersdorf—a little too much, perhaps. It depends on what your group has available."

The three of us exchange a swift glance, and mentally reckon up our forces. Dr. Tegel's group will supply at least four people. Ralph and Rita, Heike and Fabian, Dagmar, Joe Thäler, the three of us. Thirteen all told. Eckardt is away working; Wald is indispensable for counterfeiting.

"We'll take Wilmersdorf—at least the southern part. Our group will furnish twelve or fourteen people." So Andrik has reached the same total.

"Good. Then I'll give you the breakdown. The main streets are the thing; side streets don't matter so much. Cover the ground by day, and make a mental note of the most important points. The moon rises late. You'd better not begin until after the alarm." Gregor Schulz straightens up.

"Here are three boxes of chalk. You'll have to take care of the rest yourself."

It's still raining outside. Funny—you feel as if years had passed. We pedal slowly home.

Over our heads a buzzing begins. "I think we're going to have an alarm!" Hardly have I spoken when the siren goes. We pedal away like sprint racers. It isn't far to the water tower. Perhaps we can use the current during the wire-news period to cook with.

"Flights from the east," the announcer says after five minutes of the false triad note of the intermission signal. The first time Russian combat planes have been over Berlin.

To celebrate this event we don't bother going down cellar. There'll be opportunity enough to make up for it during the night. You don't fool around with English blockbusters.

Tuesday, April 17, 1945.

It's not so easy to buy anything specific in bombed-out Berlin, particularly when you have to have it right away. The stock reply, "Try again in a couple of weeks," is beginning to get on our nerves.

Finally, in a remote side street, we find what we need. A melancholy shopgirl hands me three packages of first-quality chalk. "It's funny," she says reflectively. "I've been in the shop for five years, and never sold so much chalk the whole time as I have today. You're the seventh person that's been asking for it."

"It is queer, isn't it?" I reply, and get out in a hurry.

At home we assemble our loot. Frank has hit the bull's-eye—four tins full of glaring red oil paint. "Swiped out of the stock of a propaganda company," he explains magnificently. "I should say it was going to be used in due course for its intended purpose!"

The rest of the day is spent in manufacturing brushes. Shortly before dusk, each man covers his territory. Frank and I have taken the Albrechtstrasse district; Andrik joins on toward the south end.

"This corner is good—that wall will be splendid—we must remember that jutting wall—the NSDAP bulletin column."

Our brains work like cameras, taking in the pictures so as to project them tomorrow, no matter how dark it may be.

During the endless night alarms we exchange views in whispers.

"Do Ralph and Rita know about it? Do you think Dr. Tegel's people can be relied on?"

The clock says three as we come out of the basement.

Wednesday, April 18, 1945.

Wald brings new printed matter, and word that Dr. Tegel has to leave Berlin for a short time. Will he manage to get back? The ring is drawing closer about Berlin. If he should be among the missing at the last moment. . . . But we have no peace of mind to consider this question at length. The printed matter has to be distributed.

Travel permits from Danzig. "Valid as police check-in," it says below. And above, NSDAP, County Headquarters, Greater Danzig. Why must we always have everything "Greater"? Greater Germany. Greater Danzig. We are indeed the land of the superlative!

As the day draws to a close, each of us begins to grow restless. Nobody talks about his restlessness, but it's in the air; each of us can feel it in the others.

The alarm comes early, and lasts forever. We keep shuttling between apartments and basement. Finally it's too much for Frank. "I'm off. I just can't stand this. I can finish up the Bismarckstrasse at least."

"Good luck!" we call after him. The city is in bright moonlight.

Half an hour later Frank wheels his bicycle back into the

basement. We almost smother him with our joyful relief. "Tell us—how was it?"

"Rather too bright. Rather too few bombs. Fellow Germans were just standing outside their shelter doors in droves."

Once again we are three feet below ground, brooding and running through our night's program for the hundredth time. The last English plane departed at two. The inmates of the house lug their bags upstairs. A door slams here, another there. At last nothing more is heard.

We prepare in silence: bread bag, windbreaker, rubber-soled shoes.

"The girls had better put kerchiefs over their heads, so people won't recognize the silhouettes," Frank advises. Himself, he puts on a peaked cap.

"Are you ready?"

"Yes." We fumble down the stairs in the dark.

"Good luck!"

"Good luck!" Then our paths diverge.

The moon has set; the streets stretch before us like black tunnels. The last shelter-user has gone home. It is so still that the sound of bicycle tires on the asphalt seems like unnecessary noise.

Fifty yards from the first house on our "beat" we jump off our wheels and hide them in the ruins of a burned-out building.

"If they notice us, we'll stop and start kissing each other," Frank whispers in my ear. "Loving couples always look innocent." It's too dark for a nod, so I simply squeeze his arm. We grope slowly into the pitch blackness.

For a few seconds it seems as if we had undertaken a job that can't possibly be done. Somewhere in the distance a dog barks. My hands begin to tremble. I hear Frank breathing fast and unevenly beside me.

Don't sag now, of all times, I think. For God's sake don't give up *now*.

I take a few faltering steps to the right, and get my hands on the cold corner of a letter box.

N-E-I-N, *NO*, I mark hurriedly, with gritted teeth, on the wide flap over the slot. The chalk squeaks. This is the way blind people must feel when they write.

I turn around. "Look, it's all right," I start to whisper. But Frank has vanished from my side. A few seconds later he appears before me like a shadow, takes my arm, and pulls me ahead.

"Come on, let's get going!" Our fright has suddenly left us.

"Did you make it?" I ask. No answer is necessary; the smell of fresh paint comes at me like a cloud from the door of the neighboring bakery.

Our eyes are adapting to the darkness; the broad surfaces of walls and show windows stand out more and more clearly from the blackness.

No — No — No. Anything worth doing is worth doing well. We paint and write with fervor on window sills, telegraph poles, garden gates, poster pillars. Wherever there's a spot to catch the eye, a *No* goes on it as a colored seal.

We whisk noiselessly from building to building.

"Ssh! Quiet! Police!" We stand like statues. A returning night patrol passes us at a leisurely pace.

"Squeeze against the wall," Frank breathes. I push against the stone as if to crawl into it. It smells of dust and charred wood. If only they don't discover us! The iron-shod military heels tramp heavily on the pavement. An overcoat brushes my knee. I hold my breath. Thank God, they didn't see us! Their eyes are held blankly to the front, as if they were asleep on their feet.

Frank tugs at my sleeve. "I think the coast is clear."

On a high platform in the Rathausplatz stands the big bulletin board of the Party, screaming to the world with giant letters that "The Jews are our ruin." Four steps lead up to it. We look around cautiously—isn't it too near daylight?

"I don't care, I'm going to risk it!" says Frank. He runs up the steps; I stand guard like a bird dog. Five streets converge in the square—five danger points.

Frank, meanwhile, is at work on his airy eminence like a master painter. Much too slowly for my impatience he dips his brush in the paint pot. Now he lays on the brush; the paint drips dark red on the ground. "As if it were blood," I think.

"The Jews are our misfortune!"—and aren't they indeed? Those thousands upon thousands who have been tortured, persecuted, outraged? Will they not rise up one day and call for justice against us—against the innocent as well as the guilty? Surely vengeance for what we have done to them will make our misfortune complete.

N - O! Frank's protest glares from the wooden bulletin board in strokes as wide as your hand. He stands off to study his work like an artist.

"Come on!" I urge. "Come on!"

Just before dawn we start home. Frank's coat looks as if he had just butchered a pig. Our paint pots are empty; the last bit of chalk is barely enough to scrawl a few thin *Noes* on the barricade across the Albrechtstrasse. When we turn into the Mariendorferstrasse, we halt as if at a word of command. *No — No — No!* says a sandbox in great white letters. "Teamwork," Frank observes approvingly. "Andrik's been at work here."

He certainly has. Right and left, high and low, *Noes* are shining everywhere. "Andrik," I think, gently running my fingers over a white-scrawled lamppost.

Our wheels are damp with the dew. As we pull them out of the ruins, two rats run squeaking across the path. Hundreds of them are living among the ruins in the great dump heap of Berlin.

"Loathsome!" I shudder with disgust.

Frank laughs: "That's women for you. You risk your life with the Nazis. But if you see a mouse, you climb on the table."

I pocket this reproach in silence; five in the morning is no time to discuss women's rights.

We're beginning to be rather weary. Will the others be back yet? We meet the first early risers in the Bismarckstrasse. People on compulsory duty, pale and cross, hurrying toward the scene of their forced labors.

At home we find Andrik waiting for us. "Everything went first-rate," he reports cheerfully. "I could have painted up fifty streets more."

"And nobody saw you anywhere?"

"They saw me, I guess, but not in the character of a painter. Besides, who's to say I wasn't working for Mr. Goebbels?" He smirks. "What do you think of this?"

We gaze with admiration and astonishment at the crumpled paper: "Foreign Organization of the NSDAP, Reich Headquarters. This is to certify that Party Comrade Andrik K. is charged with a propaganda assignment under our orders on the night of April 18-19. It is requested that his work be facilitated. Signed, Illegible."

We sit down together to our tea. The fact that we've succeeded and come back intact makes us as merry as if we had drunk a great deal of wine.

"If only the others were back," I think in the midst of our restless jollity.

Suddenly the telephone rings. We jump like red-handed murderers.

"Are you home? This is Joe. I'm going to sleep now!"

Thank heaven! Another man safe.

Half an hour later Heike and Fabian arrive, daubed, dusty, infinitely content. "We aren't even going to bed at all; we'll take two Pervitins, and clean up the basement. We'll have to move down there sooner or later, anyhow."

"How was your trip?"

"Marvelous! You've simply got to admire our work tomorrow." They vanish into the basement.

At quarter of seven Dagmar arrives; now we can go to bed with a clear conscience. The birds are singing outside, and the sun shines in through the window straight on my bed.

Thursday, April 19, 1945.

Will wonders never cease? We actually catch up on our sleep. There's no alarm—either in the morning, or at noon, or in the afternoon.

The leaflet action starts tonight. Before we go to Gregor Schulz's, naturally we have to see how our *No*es look in the daylight.

The Albrechtstrasse is the scene of a big scrubbing bee. The shopkeepers are scouring away at the windows with furious energy. But oil paint withstands even the best wartime cleansers. Where the usual signs "Temporarily closed, in service" hang behind dusty windows, the *No*es stand out unimpaired.

"Well, would you look at that!" says Frank, indicating a

young lad who is busily painting away at a wall that has been daubed with red.

"Ca - pi - tu - late," I spell out as his brush advances. Sure enough, he puts a question mark after it. I look around. *Capitulate? No. Surrender? No,* I read to right and left. The nerve! They're twisting our *Noes* in their own favor.

"It took them long enough to think of it. And anyway . . . they know perfectly well it was we and not they who wrote the *Noes*," Frank comforts me. "Besides, everyone with eyes in his head can see the difference in lettering and color."

Be that as it may, it's annoying. Our exasperation does not subside until we discover that the counterfeit change is an exception, only proving the rule all the more emphatically.

We pedal along the Kaiserallee. This is where Heike and Fabian were at work. Work is the word for it; they have not been idle. In front of the Hindenburg Park stands their masterpiece. The pedestal of some monument or other rises like a marble warning from the center of a wide lawn. The monument itself has been removed. The bronze discus thrower, nymph, or naiad that used to adorn the square has long since been melted down into cannon balls by the Nazis. Only the granite pedestal remains behind, being unsuitable for war purposes. *"No!"* its wide front now shouts in eighteen-inch black letters—ineffaceably, an end in itself, visible from afar.

"Beautiful!" we say enthusiastically. "Bee*y*ootiful!" The farther we ride, the more gaily our hearts beat.

The Kurfürstendamm is the masterpiece of all. Real artists must have been at work here. Not a single show window is left out. Wherever we look, we see glaring white-painted protests.

Gregor Schulz's place is a veritable beehive. People are coming and going, all with the same bustling cheerfulness as ourselves. Nobody knows anybody else; but they say hello and shake hands as if they had been intimate friends for years. "We made it!" says every handshake. "How marvelous—we made it!"

Gregor Schulz beckons us into a corner. "Here are the leaflets. Distribute them however you think best. They might be better, though without an automatic printing press. . . . We spent three nights on them." He gives us a bundle of paper sheets the size of your hand.

In the twilight we read: "Berliners! Soldiers, men, and women! You have heard the order of the lunatic Hitler and his bloodhound Himmler to defend every city to the last. Anyone who still carries out the orders of the Nazis today is either an idiot or a scoundrel. Berliners! Do as the Viennese did! By overt and covert resistance the workmen and soldiers of Vienna prevented a blood bath in their city. Is Berlin to share the fate of Aachen, Cologne, and Koenigsberg?

"No!

"Write your *No* everywhere! Form resistance cells in barracks, shops, shelters! Throw all the pictures of Hitler and his accomplices out into the gutter! Organize armed resistance!

"Berlin Resistance Groups
"Ernst."

"How many do you think you can get rid of?" Gregor Schulz asks.

Frank considers. "I should say a thousand."

"Good. And please tell your people that we'll have to be doubly careful today. Yesterday Goebbels hadn't heard of us. Now he knows."

Frank wedges his brief case full of treason under the spring of his baggage carrier.

264

"Where do we go first?"

"The Kufsteinerstrasse." We race off.

Joe Thäler is waiting for us at Frank's hideout. He's sitting in the dark, because the current is off again. By the gleam of my cigarette lighter we count out the leaflets into his hand. Fifty, a hundred, a hundred and fifty.

"And how did you make out?" Frank asks.

Joe Thäler smiles. "The captain's uniform did miracles. German army regulations have no provision for sabotage by medical-corps captains."

We do the rest of our distributing at home. Alarm, Mosquitoes, air-raid cellar. The clock strikes one. It strikes half past, and two.

The time has arrived; we can start out. At the front door we shake hands. Danger is in the air—we know that. "Be careful now, kids!" Andrik warns us. "If it looks ticklish, take a powder. There's no sense in winding up on the gallows right at the last moment." He turns to go. I see his figure disappearing into the dark.

"Andrik," I call softly.

"Yes, what is it?"

"It's . . . it's . . . Oh, nothing, really. I just wanted to say good-by again."

"Silly girl!" He puts his arm tenderly around me. "Come back safe and sound, now! We'll meet again in three hours."

"In three hours!" I tear myself away.

"Where are you, anyhow?" Frank calls. I race after him.

Again the nocturnal streets yawn blackly at us. The leaflets rustle in my bread bag. They're carefully piled so that one motion will suffice to paste them up.

Aren't we there yet? Yesterday it didn't seem nearly so far. My thoughts roam abroad. "If I must die, I'll die with you," I hear myself humming. Goodness, how long since I last thought of that song?

"Look here, if we get hooked, just deny everything."

Frank's voice seems to be coming through cotton wool. "We won't get hooked!"

Here's the town hall; we've arrived. What a relief! The stage fright before the act is worse than the act itself. Open the bread bag, lift out the paste bottle, and loosen the cork. "Take the leaflet out with your left hand, dab on the paste with your right," I repeat to myself the motions we practiced at home.

Frank comes to a halt. "Come on, give me a kiss. And then to work."

I can't help laughing. And the kiss hits his nose instead of his mouth.

Leaflet out, dab on paste. The first leaflet is stuck up; the second; the third. They stand out like white lozenges against the black planking over a long row of show windows.

Out with the leaflets, dab on paste. Now we're coming to a cross street.

"Look out!" Frank is by my side at a bound, hastily cramming leaflets and paste pot into his pocket.

Round the corner come two soldiers, with steel helmets and carbines, chin straps made fast. Frank takes me by the arm and carries me along at a stroller's pace.

The soldiers look across at us sharply. Will they stop? Will they go on?

And if they do go on, then what? What of the leaflets sticking like white lozenges to the long row of show windows? Suppose they find the broadsides! Suppose they discover that the paste is still wet! And not a soul on the street except us.

266

Slowly we stroll on, arm in arm, like a loving couple. The bread bag dangles between our hips; frantically I clutch the bottle with my right hand.

Ten steps, fifteen steps, twenty steps. Then the darkness drinks us in.

Out with a leaflet, dab on paste. We work hastily, as if we were pursued.

"Listen—some more of them!" I whisper, startled.

Before us two shadows separate from the darkness. Steel helmet, chin strap, carbine. The next patrol. It's following the first at an interval of hardly two hundred yards. It's intentional, all right!

Again two pairs of suspicious eyes scrutinize us. Don't run now, of all times! Don't act as if you felt they meant you.

We walk as if we were wandering through a meadow in spring; and the sweat runs down our backs.

Ten yards, fifteen yards. That peril, too, is past. Out with the flier, dab on paste. . . .

"My God! The third lot!" Like ghosts the silhouettes of two domed helmets appear beyond the dimmed-out glow of a traffic light.

Walk slowly . . . walk slowly. This is a veritable gauntlet.

Frank pulls me into a side street. "It's no use. It's perfectly hopeless. They're out for us. You can bet your life on that." He raises his head and listens into the night. "There—see? The fourth patrol. Number five and number six won't be far away. Extreme state of alarm. I must say, Goebbels is trying hard."

Like mice we slip into the black hole of an arched driveway. Steel helmet, carbine, chin strap. This time they didn't notice us.

We decide on the quieter side streets. I drop the next

broadsides into a letter box. They can edify some surprised post-office employee.

In the distance we hear the rhythm of heavy military boots. The situation is growing more and more sinister. Now, on top of everything else, it begins to rain softly.

To the left of us is open country, peaceable little workers' garden houses. "Harmony Garden Colony" I read over the wooden gateway.

Out with the leaflet, dab on paste. . . .

We are in the very act of decorating the wooden fence with our proclamations when I jump in horror. From behind us comes a gentle crunch on the asphalt. So gentle that the noise of the rain almost swallows it up—as if someone were creeping along a gravel path in stocking feet.

If I turn around now—I know perfectly well—if I turn around now, I shall be terrified past endurance. My hands are icy cold.

"Frank!" I stammer, "Frank!" As if someone were pulling my head around, I turn my face toward the rear.

Almighty God! Breath-takingly slowly, with darkened lantern, a patrol is bicycling behind us on the roadway—straight toward us. Steel helmet, carbine, chin strap.

Run—run! As fast as our legs will carry us!

But they're armed. If they fire. . . .

Closer and closer creeps the soft, crunching sound. I feel as if my feet had grown fast to the ground. This is how Lot's wife must have felt when she turned into a pillar of salt.

With a superhuman effort I raise my left arm. I force it into the bread bag and clutch the packet of leaflets.

Search, arrest, court-martial, gallows—it all tumbles through my head. I feel a pricking as of needles under my skin.

The wheels crunch softly; they approach with breath-taking deliberation. My fingers grip the package. Even if I were to drop dead this moment, I can't help dropping them on the spot. They rustle to the ground between Frank and me.

Now two dark lanterns flash on; they catch us in their cone of light. We put one foot mechanically in front of the other. In a moment they'll be . . . arrest, court-martial, gallows. . . .

Great God! They've overtaken us. They're beside us—ahead of us—crowding us in as if enclosing us in a magic circle.

Frank has grabbed my arm. His hands are cold too.

If only we could think of something innocent, something commonplace such as ordinary citizens say. I rack my brain. I'd like to kick myself for being so helpless.

The wheels crunch, as if someone were creeping in stocking feet along a gravel path. The dark lanterns are still pointed at us. They grope over us from head to foot. Not another sound.

"Golly, what a cold! Can you lend me your handkerchief?" I hear Frank's voice suddenly beside me. It sounds a trifle hoarse, but infinitely reassuring. I seem to be waking from a nightmare.

"Of course, darling. Wait a minute, I'll get it." My throat, too, seems to have a severe catarrh.

We stop. I ransack my pockets with emphatic thoroughness.

A loud and long blowing of the nose, an immeasurable sigh of relief. The cone of light vanishes. Softly, like someone creeping on stocking feet along a gravel path, the bicycles crunch away.

My knees are ready to fold under me. "Look here, come on home. I just can't do any more."

Frank shakes himself. "That wasn't nice. God, that was terrible! But we're going to go on pasting anyhow!" And within half an hour we actually get rid of his last fliers. They aren't so very conspicuous, it's true, but even so! I feel as if I had just finished a mountain-climbing expedition. Mechanically I put one foot in front of the other. Search, arrest, court-martial, gallows. How can one be so close to the boundary of life? How can it be so easy to put your head in the noose?

I think of all the people who have died for us. Do you suppose they'll put up a monument someday to Count Moltke?

At five o'clock in the morning we get home. Not a soul in the place. The empty rooms stare silently at us. I plant myself beside the telephone. Suppose the others had the same sort of time. Suppose one of them. . . . Morning light seeps through the cracks in the blackout curtains. Five o'clock in the morning is when they usually take people out to execution. One hears that the passing bell rings for them even today. It rings and rings, until. . . .

"Sure enough! She's fallen asleep!" In front of me stand Heike, Andrik, and Fabian.

I stare at them, bewildered. "Haven't I got to. . . . But I was. . . ."

"You haven't got to do but one thing, namely make tea." Andrik flings himself exhausted into the armchair. "Boy, what a scare they threw into us! Crouching in the bushes for half an hour! The police on our heels—two men at a time, hardly two hundred yards apart. In the end I was crawling among the ruins on all fours."

Heike and Fabian don't look very chipper either.

"They chased us on motorcycles. Halfway down the Kaiserallee. I can't say it was much fun. Where's Dagmar?"

"She's asleep!"

270

"It's great to be young! Well, we'll let her sleep." I go into the kitchen to put the water on. The tea is hot and strong; Karla sent it from Nanking two months ago. If she knew what we were using it for, she'd surely be pleased.

Friday, April 20, 1945.

The great migration to the outer districts has begun. No one shows any special desire to be downtown during the street fighting in the capital. People say that today marks the closing of the "Fortress Berlin." No express trains are moving in or out. All transportation is at a standstill. Postal and telegraph service have ceased. We are cut off from the world, for better or for worse, at the mercy of the oncoming catastrophe. In view of such prospects, there is something uncommonly reassuring about the immediate neighborhood of parks and cemeteries. Frank has gone back to his apartment in Schöneberg. If only he were with us again!

All the streets today are full of restless bustle. Army cars flash past; heavy-laden trucks roll endlessly to westward. At the very last second the bigwigs are still trying to save whatever they can. Beyond question Berlin is in danger. You can scent it in the air, read it in the distracted faces of men called up, the scurrying of steel-helmeted policemen and couriers.

As Andrik and I are coming back from town through the Bismarckstrasse, he tugs at my sleeve. "Look over yonder. Something looks damned rotten there."

Ahead of us on the sidewalk two men are marching, jingling metallically, keeping step. Top boots, Storm Troop trousers, civilian jackets. Carefully, as if they were taking fresh eggs to market, they are lugging a box between them. It is flat, longish, mysterious.

I look inquiringly at Andrik. "Bazookas," he hisses. "Werewolves!"

The two men ahead of us hear nothing; jingling metallically, keeping step, they go on up the Bismarckstrasse with their load. I look at their faces. They have the wooden features of insatiable order-takers. Stupid but obstinate. If they once take something into their heads, no power on earth will convince them differently.

"We ought to murder such riffraff," Andrik grits spitefully. We walk on, very much out of humor.

"Heavens above! Aren't those fellows there carrying another bazooka box?" Two pairs of Storm Troop trousers, two wooden faces, civilian jackets; between the two, flat, longish, mysterious, the ugly burden of death. Behind them come four Hitler Lads, wearing over their shoulders broad leather belts of rifle ammunition.

"Not a very peaceable neighborhood, Steglitz," I observe disapprovingly.

Hitler's birthday begins and ends equally noisily. Three alarms. The attack waves are endless. First there is a crash on the right, then a roar on the left. Before, behind, everywhere. The concrete and iron apartment building rocks like a ship on a stormy sea.

We count the hours. Our wartime candle smokes gloomily. Five of us crouch on the floor in the corner. The basement is only a yard below the surface; if we were sitting in chairs, every blast from an aerial mine might be dangerous.

"I'll see what it looks like outside," says Andrik during a break in the firing.

"I'm coming too." Rather painfully I get up on my feet, which have gone to sleep. We smoke a cigarette outside the door.

"Well, it's burning quite briskly," I sigh. And indeed the horizon is red, as if blood had been poured over it. The slim silhouettes of the cemetery poplars rise black before us, rustling in the wind, swaying to and fro. Clouds race across the sky.

The city cowers like a frightened animal. You don't see the danger, but you can feel it; you seem to know it's there like poisonous breath across the roofs.

"Listen," Andrik whispers. I strain my ears through the night. From the east comes a grumbling like distant thunder.

That's no bombing, that's . . . Well, as a matter of fact, what is it?

"Artillery! They're attacking the city."

My heart stands still. "Oh, Andrik!" His hand creeps into mine. We stand like two lost children, hand in hand. Before us lies the endless city, black in the black of night, cowering as if to creep into the earth. And we're afraid.

"Come inside," I beg. "It's too awful."

The others are asleep inside, stretched out wherever there's a bit of space. From the neighboring basement comes monotonous snoring. There is an odor of soot, dust, and humanity.

Andrik looks at me. "Do you want to go upstairs?"

I shake my head. Together we lie down on two boxes that have been pushed together. I dream I'm sitting in an arbor, eating strawberries and cream.

Saturday, April 21, 1945.

At four o'clock in the morning we go upstairs—with creaking limbs, crumpled, full of kinks, and ill-humored. We don't say a word, but fling ourselves silently on our beds. Sleep, sleep! Everything else will come in due time.

It comes! Does it ever come! When I try to put on water

273

for tea at nine o'clock, not a drop comes out of the tap. I press the light switch. No current. I pick up the telephone: the line is dead. Overnight the life lines of Berlin have been cut. A grumble like distant thunder comes from the east; but it's a thunder that doesn't stop, that swells from hour to hour, implacably, fatally, insistently.

Fabian comes out of the bathroom in shirt and trousers, his face white and fluffy with shaving cream. He brandishes his dry brush. "Oh, what a beautiful morning, oh, what a beautiful day!" he sings sardonically. "It would be nice if I could finish shaving today."

I can't help laughing, although I feel very little like it. "That's a luxury you'll have to start doing without. Water is a scarce commodity."

By noon we have organized our first pump expedition—three men with two pails each. But the nearest pump is three blocks away, beside a Home Guard office. More than a hundred people are thronging about the pump. A restless bustle centers around the Home Guard office. Motorcycles come snarling up to the door. Men with the black-white-and-red brassard, in home-assembled military outfits, as shabby as tramps, pour in and out. They look as if they hadn't had any sleep for ten days, or any food for two weeks. And that's the kind of people they hope to defend Berlin with! Resignedly we paw the sandy soil beside the pump until our turn comes to start working the iron handle. Six buckets. That will barely do for cooking, washing, and tooth brushing.

But suppose there's an alarm? Suppose we have to put out a fire? People say some of the fires in Berlin have been put out with skim milk and thin beer. But where's the skim milk?

So we lug buckets. So we fill the bathtub, and all the vessels we can find in apartment and basement.

274

"It must be about time to use up our stamps," Heike suggests, looking anxiously at a queue two hundred yards long lining up outside a bakery.

After the next trip for water, we tackle this problem in earnest. Each of us dumps his remaining monthly rations and loose stamps on the table. Four pounds of meat, two pounds of butter, six pounds of prepared food, ten and a half pounds of bread, thirty rolls. An imposing collection.

"Let the girls shop," Andrik decides. "If they have to stand too long, we'll take their places."

Heike and Dagmar start off with nets and shopping bags. I mount my wheel, and go to the Kufsteinerstrasse. We must look after Frank and Joe Thäler. I must find out what they've decided about the next few days. For us not to stick together now would be insane.

I pedal through a turmoil of people and vehicles. Everything on two feet seems to be moving westward. Among the trucks and army vehicles move the safaris of fugitives. Rack wagons, pushcarts, baby carriages, doll carriages—loaded with knapsacks, bundles, and bags. Tired women pulling, exhausted children bringing up the rear, pale, hollow-cheeked, barefoot. A dismal spectacle. Lines of people at the pumps. Lines of people outside the bakeries; lines of people outside the butcher shops.

"Can you tell me where I could buy bread?" a harried-looking woman with a kerchief and shopping bag asks me. "Everything here in Schöneberg is sold out."

I don't know. Nobody knows. You buy wherever you find anything. You gather up whatever you can. The enemy artillery grumbles like distant thunder. Planes roar over our heads. But no one pays any attention; there are more vital concerns just now.

It looks like moving day in the Kufsteinerstrasse. All the bureau drawers have been pulled out; half-open bags stand around on the floor. "Time to be packing" is Frank's welcome. The impulse of the whole city toward flight has infected even him. He points proudly to a pile of bulging paper bags, packages, and cardboard boxes. "Fat, meat, bread, canned goods! We've bought everything we had coming to us. There won't be anything by tomorrow anyway."

"There isn't even today," I reply gloomily. "They've gone after all the supplies like a swarm of locusts."

"He chews best who chews last," growls Joe in the background. "I don't intend to starve for the Nazis."

"And what else are you planning to do?"

Frank shrugs. "Wait and see. What else can we do? And try to keep from being knocked off our wheels, the way I was this morning."

I did not notice before that a bleeding scratch runs across his forehead. It is very inadequately bandaged with adhesive.

"What happened to you?" All my motherly instincts are suddenly aroused.

"Nothing, except that the Russians are bombarding the Tiergarten—firing over the Brandenburg Gate and into the government section. I was riding along Unter den Linden on my wheel, when something went whizzing past my ears, and bang, straight into the sidewalk. It threw me over the handle bars before I could count three. I lay flatter than a pancake in front of the Adlon Hotel."

Artillery fire—Russian planes—English Mosquitoes. The moment night falls, the merry dance begins all over again. Heike, Dagmar, and Fabian decide to prepare for a night in the basement to begin with. I sit upstairs with Andrik beside the oil lantern, drinking cold tea, eating sausage and cheese sandwiches. I'm ready every second to grab brief case and "storm baggage" and rush down cellar likewise. We've opened the casement, so that at least the last windowpanes may withstand the blast.

The ack-ack is banging outside. And in the distance growls the thunder of the Russian artillery.

"Look out!" I cry. The teacup falls on the table; we both lie flat on the floor. Wheeeeeeeee goes a Mosquito bomb near by. Wheeeeeeeee howls another, still closer.

"Downstairs!" cries Andrik. We shoot down the steps like hunted rabbits.

The air pressure has snatched the cardboard off the lobby windows. The glow of fire lights the stairs.

"Good God, my handbag!" To rush up again would be madness. But that's the way it always is; when danger really threatens, you forget all the most important things.

Thank goodness, the house is still standing. Only a thick layer of plaster dust lies upon furniture and floor when we go back to the apartment. The rooms are icy cold. But the open casements have survived the air pressure. At least one piece of luck!

Sighing, Heike falls to with broom and dustpan. After all, you can't lie down to sleep on plaster. The familiar woodpecker hammering comes from the neighboring apartments; people are nailing up the cardboard over the windows again.

Sunday, April 22, 1945.

"The harsh spirit of the front dominates Berlin," the headlines of the Sunday papers proclaim. "We must help last out the turning point of the war. Berlin is fighting now, fighting with all the consistency that this battle for existence or non-

277

existence demands of us. It is fighting, striking a blow where-ever a foe of the people shows himself. Military command is absolute. We now cast aside every last thing that might hamper us at the front. The order of today, tomorrow, and all the days to come is no excuses, but grim passion: fight."

Starting today, death penalty for cooking by electricity.

Goebbels stops the mouth of the populace with the last special rations—a pound of meat, half a pound of rice, half a pound of legumes, a pound of sugar, a hundred grams of malt coffee, one tin of preserves, and thirty grams of real coffee. What's the good of all that if you have no way of preparing the things?

An emergency program goes into effect for the city. The courts-martial are permanently convened. Contradictory rumors are buzzing everywhere: the Russians have broken through in Pankow and Weissensee; Potsdam has surrendered to the English without a struggle; the Allies have effected a junction at Luckenwalde; Dahlewitz is taken; the last big-wigs are leaving Berlin in grasshopper planes.

And meanwhile the Nazis are behaving as if they would live another thousand years. Only the day before yesterday all the ten-year-olds were inducted into the Hitler Youth in a body, and sworn to "unconditional allegiance to the Fuehrer!" Lambs turned into werewolves—what a blood-thirsty fable!

The restless bustle in the streets has not subsided. People are moving westward, they're moving eastward; it looks as if no one really knew where or why he was moving. Today again the queues of waiting women line up before the shops. They stand for four hours, five, six, seven—just to get the preposterous handful of coffee beans with which Goebbels means to whip them into the home stretch.

Late in the morning someone bangs at the bell. Before the door stand Frank and Joe, knapsacks on their backs, a couple of battered suitcases in their hands. They look harried and worn out.

"What's new?"

Frank smiles rather forcedly. "Nothing particular—only the Gestapo is at our heels."

"Good God!" I pull them hastily into the room. "How does that happen?"

"During the alarm last night. They made a raid, and arrested forthwith everyone who couldn't identify himself. Joe was just coming in; when he tried to get into the building they stopped him."

Joe Thäler nods. "Not only stopped me, but surrounded me. All the air-raid wardens in the block felt obligated to help the Gestapo. They hemmed me in like a wall. Papers? I had none. Putting my hand in my breast pocket was only a symbolic gesture, but I made it. Just to gain a few seconds. I wanted to see Dr. Matthis, I said. Matthis? Matthis doesn't live here. The wall kept coming threateningly closer; I ransacked my wallet. I knew perfectly well that in two more minutes . . . one more . . . then there was a howl beside me, as if hell itself were showering down. I heard yells, groans, and crashes; there was so much dust and smoke that I couldn't see a thing. For one moment I stood as if I'd been hit on the head; then I beat it off into the darkness as fast as my legs would carry me. A bomb had hit right next to us; broken glass was jingling under my feet. I got back by a roundabout route to the Kufsteinerstrasse, climbed the back wall, and got in through the kitchen window."

"And how did you get out?"

"Just before daybreak," Frank said, "through the kitchen

window again, and then across the courtyard in stocking feet. As we were climbing the fire wall, we heard a car drive up at the front of the building, and commands and soldiers' boots. Someone pounded on the door and yelled, "Open up!" Joe was over, and so was the baggage. I was hanging between Heaven and earth like a monkey. This is for keeps, I thought, and swung myself over the top with a great heave. We dropped thirty feet on the other side, into what was left of the next building. We sat among the ruins until day broke. And then . . ."

"Then you came here," I finish for him. "And presumably want to stay here."

Frank laughs: "How you always do take the words out of a person's mouth!"

"Room is room, and crowded is crowded," I observe soberly. "Welcome to the sardine can!"

After some difficulties we get ourselves settled. There are now seven of us in two and a half rooms; the only way it can be divided up any more is according to sexes. The apartment looks like an army camp. As I'm getting the shakedowns ready, Andrik takes me aside.

"Somebody's got to go to Nikolassee today. Reinhard has some ammunition ready. You'd better go with Frank."

"With Frank? And the Gestapo after him?"

"That's the last place they'll look for him. The bolder you are, the safer. Besides, this is against the werewolves. Somebody's got to go who knows what he's doing."

"What about you?"

"I'm going to Gregor Schulz's."

"All right, if you think we should."

"Of course we'll go!" Frank reaches resolutely for his bicycle pump.

The farther west we go, the more the streets are jammed. There is complete turmoil—cars, walking fugitives, marching columns; faces encrusted with dust and dirt, hollow-eyed and wasted. They are marked with despair and a hopeless incomprehension.

I speak to a few of those who are moving in the other direction. "Where are you coming from?"

"From the east, from Fürstenwalde. The Russians have broken through there."

I ask the next ones I see, "Where are you going?"

"East, to Fürstenwalde. The Russians have broken through in the west."

Enemy planes roar over, zooming down and sweeping the street with their machine guns. We throw ourselves flat on the ground.

That danger is past. Into our saddles, quickly, and on we go. Reinhard is impatiently awaiting us. He rushes to the cupboard, drags out a couple of little bundles tied with string, and flings them on the table. "There's the ammunition—three hundred rounds of M 65. We've got arms; we've got two cars; we've got drivers; but I can't do it alone." Savagely he paces the room. "We've got three candidates lined up: one murderer of Dollfuss, one SS group leader, one werewolf commander. Three Nazi gangsters who have brought more than one man to the gallows. I've got them in the hollow of my hand, and I can't close my hand. I've got them. . . ."

Hysterical screeching is heard outside. The door flies open; a woman rushes in. "The Russians are in Nikolassee," she yells, looks frantically around, and rushes out.

"They've all lost their senses," says Reinhard contemptuously.

We get up; Frank puts away the ammunition in his deep

coat pockets. "I'll talk to Gregor Schulz. You'll get reinforcements. Tomorrow evening, early morning of the day after at latest. Done?"

"Done!" Reinhard shakes hands.

We hurry out of the place. The Russians aren't in Nikolassee yet, of course, but the thunder of their artillery draws alarmingly near. And it's no fun being on the street when the blast may snatch you off your wheel at any moment.

They are having a quiet, untroubled evening at home. Joe is on the kitchen stool, peeling potatoes and whistling cheerfully to himself. Andrik is in the act of enticing the British evening communiqué from Heike's People's Radio set.

"I believe you could drag the English station out of a cigar box," Frank jeers. "Where are the girls?"

"They're boiling soup."

"Soup? With the death penalty on cooking by electricity?"

"That's just why; that's what really puts the seasoning in Goebbel's short rations."

After supper Fabian takes me aside mysteriously. "Do you know what pseudarthrosis is?"

"What what is?"

"Pseudarthrosis! That's the medical term for the draft-proofing ailment with which I propose to come down indefinitely this evening at eight o'clock."

"Why, have you really got this pseuda . . . pseudar . . . whatever it's called?"

Fabian looks at me as if I had just asked the stupidest question of my entire life. "Really? I suppose you think it's nothing that I fell off a horse in '41, and broke my right foreleg in nine places? And that the bones didn't knit, and my leg wobbles around as if it were on rubber bands—I suppose that doesn't impress you at all. Joe and Frank showed more under-

282

standing. They advised a plaster cast, a plaster cast without question. Immediately. This very evening."

Artillery bombardment, strafing planes, battle planes, Mosquitoes. Until five in the morning we keep stumbling up and down the basement stairs. Joe and Frank stay up there. Is their nerve better, or has their underground experience hardened them more to such hazards? I don't know. At all events they both sleep like dormice through the infernal concert of the night.

We have to lug Fabian and his plaster cast down cellar on a stretcher.

Monday, April 23, 1945.

"I think we ought to bid our friends good-by," says Andrik at breakfast. "Tomorrow will probably be too late for calls of that kind." The cups rattle on the table. Bomb after bomb goes crashing down outside.

Frank takes out his notebook. "I've got Gregor Schulz down, to begin with. Then we'll look in on Flamm, see to Hartmann, and stop at Wald's. I suppose we shall have to console Hollner, too."

First comes the Uhlandstrasse. A strange woman opens the door, and regards us suspiciously. "I don't know any Gregor Schulz. You must be mistaken." She slams the door brusquely in our faces.

I look helplessly at Frank. "Hectorstrasse," says he laconically. "Emergency quarters." Here too, then, things seem to be getting precarious.

We make off as best we can; the Hectorstrasse is not far. There we find Gregor Schulz in an empty back room. On the floor are two bags, a telephone instrument, and a few bundles of papers tied with string.

"Reinhard sent us, on account of the reinforcements."

Gregor Schulz smiles his agreeable Japanese smile. "All taken care of. I did what I could, but I just couldn't manage any sooner. You can see for yourselves . . ." He points apologetically to the bags, the bundles of paper, and the telephone. "My hands are tied too. Each of us has got to be his own dictator now."

"How about the individual actions?"

"They've become just that—individual actions. Try to do what you can. Each werewolf less is so much to the good. Every man kept out of the Home Guard shortens the war by a few seconds. And even seconds are precious today."

"You mean you advise us—"

"Run a campaign against the Nazis in your own section. Anything else is an impossibility."

Frank nods. "I get you. All right, then, we'll be seeing you after the war. You know you can count on us."

Gregor Schulz shows us to the door. "I know I can." He pauses a moment, looks at us, and smiles. "Yes, I really do! Good-by—dear friends!"

We turn off the Kurfürstendamm into the Schlüterstrasse. "I wonder if Flamm will be at home."

At home? What was home to him is only a pile of rubbish now—a direct hit. "Everyone out alive" is written in chalk on the charred wall. Praise God! That much, at least. But where shall we find him?

I ask a woman who is searching among the ruins. "Dr. Flamm? A sort of a pale fellow with glasses? I think he moved to the Brückenallee."

The building is easily found. Since the heavy attack of November, '43, there has been almost nothing but ruins in the Brückenallee. Flamm's new domicile looks rather ruinous itself—no windows, no front door, no roof. When it rains, they have to put up an umbrella in the bedroom.

We sit with him in the kitchen for a few minutes. "How's it going? Oh, thank you, we're all alive. Only I do feel badly about my books. Five thousand volumes, and collected with such loving care." He stares into space. "Books ought never to be destroyed."

"You'll be reading again. I hear they're printing German classics in Switzerland and Sweden by the million."

"But we won't have any money to buy them."

I know he has been spending the remnants of his fortune for years to support his five Jewish protégés. "You're a marvelous person," I say.

"Take good care of yourself." I put my arms around his neck and kiss him on both cheeks. "People like you have just got to come through all right."

Frank is rummaging in his wallet. "I think he needs the rest of our bread stamps worse than he does your kisses." He puts three 1,000 stamps on the table. "Too little to live on, too much to die on. But it may help out until the beginning of May." Then we take our leave.

We go on to Hartmann's. As we turn into the Reppich-strasse, we meet four women, sobbing as if some awful sorrow had just befallen them. They look at us in fright and hastily wipe the tears from their faces. Unquestionably they're afraid to have their grief discovered.

Merciful heavens! Now we see what's happened. Long and lean, arms tied behind its back, a figure is dangling from the lamppost before us. Swaying to and fro. Two drooping military boots rattle with a ghostly sound against the iron post. The head hangs forward. Two bloodshot eyes glare emptily out of a bluish dead face at the pavement.

Those that strung him up put a sign around his neck—gray cardboard, tied with a string. It says in toppling printed letters, "I, Corporal Heinrich Lehmann, was too cowardly to defend women and children. That is why I am hanging here."

I don't dare look Frank in the eye. Didn't he die for him, too, this Heinrich Lehmann—for him and for Joe, for Wald and for Fabian, for everyone who says *No* to Hitler's war?

In front of Hartmann's house stands an army car. We are paralyzed with shock. They've got him! We creep hesitantly up the stairs and cautiously give the prearranged knock.

Ulrike Weitzen opens the door. "I'm glad you came. He's just leaving."

"Where for?"

"Potsdam. He can't keep on here any more."

"No, I can't keep on any more," Hartmann agrees, "with nothing but the fake Home Guard certificate. Two or three more days, and they'll be fighting in the streets. They'll go through the buildings with a fine-tooth comb, and pull out everyone who can crawl—to fight or be stood up against the wall. Since I don't care for either alternative, I've got to disappear." He takes a paper from his pocket.

"Identification," we read. "S.D.," and "Central Office of Reich Security." We stare at him blankly.

"Anyone who wants to save his own head these days has to stick it into the lion's mouth. Even in the S.D. there are corrupt elements—people who want to bet on the other horse at the last moment. I've made the acquaintance of one of those men. His car is downstairs. The office is near Potsdam."

Colonel Hartmann as an S.D. man! You'd think such lunacy would stand the world on its head.

While Frank is helping the colonel pack, I call Ulrike Weitzen outside for a moment. "Bad news about his children.

They did in his youngest at a lunatic asylum. Ought we to tell him?"

Ulrike Weitzen turns pale. "Not on any account—it would kill him. But how did you find out?"

"A friend of ours came from there. It happened back in February. A Nazi nurse brought him in, with convulsions. The death certificate says angina. We know all about that kind of angina—'Die faster, Comrade,' the common people call it."

Ulrike shakes herself. "Ghastly! But we've got to spare him now. He'll find out soon enough."

Wald isn't at home. We don't want to ask his fellow tenants where he may be. Who can tell what name he's going under?

That leaves us time before dark to look in on Hollner. We find him in bed, a bright canary yellow. He has dark circles under his eyes, and sunken cheeks. He's utterly miserable.

"And all on account of Adolf Hitler!" he groans. "I had no idea jaundice was such a serious disease!"

"It's a lifesaver, though," Frank consoles him. "Where would you be now without jaundice?"

"Probably in a mass grave, I know. Still . . ." He rolls over, groaning. His wife smooths his forehead.

We set out for home; but at the next corner the world is boarded off, or rather shut off with beams—worn-out moving vans and nondescript scrap iron. Berlin has closed the barricades: first defense belt, second defense belt, third defense belt. Every bridge and every overpass is being built into a nest of resistance.

A woman hurries past us. "The Russians have taken Lichtenberg," she calls. Nobody thinks of the western powers any more; by now even the dullest realize that the Russians will conquer us alone. We pedal away as fast as we can go. Barriers wherever we turn. By a thousand detours we finally get home, perspiring, dirty, hands and knees raw from crawling across a carelessly guarded right of way.

Andrik receives us. "Russian tanks in Mariendorf, Köpenick, and Friedrichshain."

We fall into bed, and the Russian artillery grinds out our lullaby.

Tuesday, April 24, 1945.

"Get up! Get ready! We should have gone down long ago!" Joe yells at eight in the morning. I bound from bed. Crrrrash! The walls totter; sounds of breakage. Dirt splashes in my face.

"Andrik!" I roar. "Frank!" A whizz, a howl, another bang. This is the end! The noise has stopped my ears; the dirt has stuck my eyes shut. I fumble around like a blind woman. Am I still alive? Has the house fallen in?

"Quick, quick!" says Andrik's voice beside me. "Are you waiting for an invitation? Standing there with no shirt on in the thick of an artillery bombardment!"

"Invitation? Artillery bombardment?" Slowly I pull myself together. The room looks as if a hundredweight of mortar had been poured all over it. "So they've hit us at last."

"Nonsense," Andrik snaps. "A shell got the next building. If you'd only get busy and put on your shirt!"

Dress, shoes, stockings. I struggle with buttons and hooks.

"Come on," Andrik urges. "The others are downstairs long since!"

"It's mad—it's mad," I wail. "Do at least get the laundry basket out of the bathroom, and we can put in . . ." I shoot like an arrow through the apartment, grabbing whatever I can lay hands on—pillows, blankets, knives, cups. My alarm clock, the bag of potatoes, the sugar tin, the coffee mill. Don't forget anything important! One thing after another flies into the basket.

"Ready? Let's go!" We race down the stairs. The basement is teeming like an anthill. The narrow central passage is blocked with boxes, shopping nets, bundles, and miscellaneous objects. We work our way painfully to our own corner. Even that doesn't look exactly spacious. All the way up to the ceiling trunks are piled against the wall—trunks upon trunks, of every size and description. Here the last legacies of Jewish friends await the resurrection.

"Well, I hope it won't last long," Andrik sighs.

"I hope not" comes a hollow voice out of impenetrable darkness. Joe is building a search-proof hideout among boxes and shelves in the farthest corner of the basement. Frank is helping him. "Be it ever so humble," he says smugly, patting his rug-covered rathole with an architect's pride.

Life in the basement begins. We sit dumbly side by side, jammed in among all the rubbish and odds and ends. The war kicks up over our heads, making a monstrous noise of deadly cannonading.

At eleven o'clock the current goes off. It's cold and dark. The contrast between the inferno outside and our own forced inactivity grows more and more intolerable. Fabian winds up the phonograph, and puts on *The Beggars' Opera.* "You, sirs, who teach us to live blamelessly, shunning vice and sin" sounds out tinnily through the basement.

Ratatatatat. Those are the first machine guns. We hear the bullets slapping into the walls.

The front door flies open. Good God, a strange man's voice! Frank and Joe wriggle like eels into their carpet oubliette. Andrik rushes to the door. Through the basement passage races a soldier, with no cap, his blouse open. His hair sticks to his forehead; his face is as gray as dead ashes.

Andrik bars his way. "Stop! Where are you going?"

"Anywhere—anywhere but . . ." The stranger shudders. "Out there . . . You have no idea what's going on out there!"

We pat him on the shoulder. "Suppose you calm down, for a start. Do you want water?"

The soldier shakes his head. "Not water, clothes. Civilian clothes. If they find me like this—"

Andrik looks inquiringly at me.

"After all, we can't just hand the man over to be butchered," I whisper. "Go ahead. He won't give us away."

"What's your name?"

"Stolzberg. Panzergrenadier Fritz Stolzberg." The man looks at us as if his soul's salvation hung upon our lips.

"All right, Mr. Stolzberg, come with me. I think we take the same size." In five minutes the transformation is complete. We have one civilian more in the basement. Andrik surreptitiously sticks under an upturned box the bundle whose contents made Fritz Stolzberg the carpenter into a tank grenadier a year and a half ago.

Frank and Joe can surface again. "We've got to arrange this differently," says Frank, dusting off his sleeves. "We're no deep-sea divers, after all. And getting in there every time with one swift leap is something you can't always manage in five seconds."

"We ought to establish watches," Heike proposes. "Then we won't always have to sit in this damned hole. We'll change the guard every two hours. If we see danger coming, we just call out innocently, 'Erna, where are you?' When the danger is past, we'll holler 'Ilse!' through the building. Girls' names have a sort of unsuspicious sound. What do you think?"

The crowd agrees. Fabian takes the first watch.

"And I'm going for water. We'll all die of thirst here without water." Heike reaches firmly for the air-raid bucket.

"Are you crazy? With that barrage?"

"I hear a steel helmet will take care of that. Besides, they're just catching their breath again at the moment. *Carpe diem!* I'm off." We gaze admiringly at the courageous, child face.

"Anyway, keep close to the buildings. And when things start popping, you take cover," Frank calls after her.

"The rest of us might as well go to work too," says Joe. He pulls the potato dish toward him, and starts peeling deliberately. On the second-floor balcony is an iron stove. Suppose we were to sneak up there. . . . Suppose we were to get it going. All of us are gradually growing faint with hunger.

Frank and I volunteer for the expedition. Stooping, we dash up the stairs. All the hall windows are knocked out; the staircase is as airy as a railroad station. Anyone who sees us from outside will take us for werewolves. So no one must see us from outside. Civilians will remain in the basement during firing.

Thank goodness, the stove works. We burn up two chairs, and the potato soup is on the table.

Heike is back, at a gallop, with her pail full. "I had to hit the dirt twice," she reports. "Otherwise everything was fine. It seems to me as if the other side had fallen back."

Indeed it has become remarkably quiet in the last half hour—as if the front had moved away from us.

"Don't let there be any holdup now," Joe implores.

In the afternoon the fighting ebbs away. Only enemy fighter planes loop in endless succession about the water tower.

"What would you say to a walk?" Frank asks. Andrik and Dagmar have lain down to sleep. Joe, deep in the poems of

François Villon, is crouching beside the smoky oil lantern. Fabian, too, is asleep. Heike, our heroine, is on guard behind a pillar on the second floor.

I nod. "All right, let's go. But without any more disturbance than we can help." We turn into the Mountain Cemetery and stroll along a path lined with flowers and hedges. "Look, how lovely!"

A harsh whistling overhead. I feel a blow in the back, stagger forward, and plunge deep into the hedge.

Another whistling howl. Not twenty yards away the earth bursts open. Bits of tombstone fly through the air, broken wreaths, rotten planks. The dead! Merciful heaven! The dead! Something dangles eerily in the branches of a weeping willow before me. War has snatched the dead from their tombs. It's . . . no. Nobody can endure this. In my torment I dig my face deep into the ground.

Frank tugs at my skirt. "Has something happened? Are you hurt?"

"I don't know. I don't think so. But this is too ghastly."

"Stay where you are. After the third one comes over, we'll run."

Once again there is a howling right over our heads. Frank puts his arm around me. "Now, quick! By the time they've got their new range, we'll be out of the line of fire."

We head for the cemetery gate at a run. Enemy fighters are circling over the water tower, and the Mountain Cemetery is under fire from Russian artillery.

In the cellar they're getting supper ready. "Where have you two been all this time?" Andrik receives us.

I mumble something, and privately vow that this is my last walk until peace comes. We lie down to sleep early. Who knows what may be ahead of us in the next few days?

About eleven o'clock I'm summoned out. A man wants to see me, says our sleepy neighbor in the basement.

Wald is at the door, with bicycle and peaked cap.

"Man alive, where did you come from in the middle of the night?"

"You've got to give me the rubber stamp. My wife has no pass. They're driving us crazy with their police raids."

"Wait, I'll wake up Frank. Are you going to ride back?"

He nods. I duck into the basement. Frank's cot is empty. Not a sign of Joe, either. I look around in astonishment. Why, they were just there. . . . Of course! The carpet oubliette. This time the password missed fire. Much relieved, I fetch the two out of hiding.

"Off again, on again," Frank grumbles. But he's already rooting in his suitcase.

"Just stay alive," I say to Wald. "You can manage everything else all right."

He pedals slowly away into the night. Shall we see him again? Charles's Wain sparkles yellow above the cemetery. And the air is as still as if there were no wars, no Nazis, no horrors.

Wednesday, April 25, 1945.

At six o'clock in the morning hell breaks loose outside. At noon one flight of bombers after another roars over our building. The fried potatoes are burning on the iron stove on the second floor. "Look out, down cellar!" our sentry shouts every five minutes. Look out, down cellar! We drop everything and run for the basement until the next breathing spell— until we summon new courage to venture back to our field kitchen.

293

Joe pokes his nose out of doors. "Leaflets!" They flutter like pigeons from the silver belly of the planes.

"Erna, hello, Erna," comes a shout from upstairs at the same moment. Joe vanishes as if the wind had blown him away. A troop of German soldiers comes around the corner. Will they come in? I post myself in the door, occupying its whole width. They don't come in. Like me, they're squinting at the leaflets, which may not be picked up on pain of imprisonment. Evidently nobody trusts anybody else.

"Where's the front?" I call.

One of the men turns. "In Lankwitz, and over along the Teltow canal. It looks rotten, young lady! Damned rotten!" He turns to leave.

Heike slips behind him, stoops, and hastily stuffs something white into her pocket. She comes back radiant. "I got one after all!" She opens out the leaflet.

"Germans!" we read. "The Russians have occupied the greater part of East Prussia, Silesia, and Pomerania, and crossed the Oder. Russian tank columns are advancing on Berlin. Hitler Germany is doomed to destruction. The days of Hitler and his clique are numbered. Cut yourselves loose from the bankrupt Hitler and his clique. Fight for the immediate cessation of resistance. Persuade the officers and soldiers to capitulate. In that way you will improve your own situation and that of Germany. Soldiers! Give yourselves up. That is your only salvation."

"The water is gone," Heike reports in the afternoon. "One bucket is hardly worth it. Several of us'll have to go."

We put on our steel helmets. Hell is popping around the water tower. Apparently they're making good yesterday's holdup. In single file we walk next to the buildings. A few people are crowding around the well, hurriedly plying the handle, grabbing their pails, and rushing off. It's not pleasant to be roaming the streets when death lies in wait there—around every corner, outside every door, by every garden wall.

Not far from the well they have strung up four Home Guardsmen—deserters, with cardboard signs around their necks. We don't look as we go by. And afterward we don't feel like supper.

Thursday, April 26, 1945.

You don't sleep well when the couch you have to huddle on is only three feet long. I feel as if I'd gone through a wringer when I wake up in my corner in the morning. The others are no better off; seven lame ducks gather around the breakfast table. Fabian is hampered by his plaster cast to begin with, and goes hopping among chests and cases like a wounded heron.

"I don't see how you can take up so much room," says Andrik grumpily. We chew on bread and margarine, and drink cold tea. There won't be much cooking done today. There's the devil to pay outside again.

"Did any of you send Stolzberg upstairs?" Joe inquires. "I think he's running up and down much too much. There mustn't be any men seen in windows now." A dozen rifle bullets are already imbedded in the wall of the stairway. We can take our turn on watch only by crouching down as we go. Frank calls the Panzergrenadier to account, and Fritz Stolzberg is ordered restricted to the basement until evening.

Reserves go banging along the broad main street next to the Colony. Baggage trucks, field kitchens, ambulances.

"I didn't expect to be watching the war from our window," I say to Frank. We're standing together inside the metal front door, peering out through a crack. "Look, how awful!" Close before us they are carrying a dozen wounded, on stretchers, planks, and tent squares. Their faces are twisted with pain; their hands are yellow like the hands of dead men. Some are young, some old. There are two children, scarcely sixteen. They look completely baffled, as if someone had hurt their feelings terribly. The procession sways onward; two drops of blood appear dark red on the pavement.

Heike joins us, her steel helmet on her head, ready for some departure or other. "Do you think I dare?" She points to her two shopping bags. "I hear they're selling meat over there. If we're lucky, they may not even want stamps."

"You must have nerves of iron," I say, shaking my head, "but go ahead if you must."

The youngster skips away. Frank laughs. "Children and the righteous have their own guardian angel. She won't come to any harm."

Guardian angels are all very well; during the next two hours I start at every hit. By the time Heike gets back, my fingers are stiff from holding my thumb for luck.

She brings back four pounds of ham, and a rage that almost takes her breath away. "Those filthy beasts, those termagants," she exclaims. "Twenty women outside the shop, all cursing like teamsters. And whom, pray tell? Hitler? Nothing of the sort. They're cursing out the deserters, threatening to string them up, and five minutes later they're pulling hair over every ham bone."

"And that's what we've stuck out thirteen years for," says Andrik bitterly. "Is it worth while? People like that . . . Those women. . . ."

Joe raises his head. "We're the ones who have got to make it worth while. They don't find any solid bottom in themselves; so they cast their anchor upon others. We've got to be the others—we, who mean well by them."

"A tough job!"

"Worth-while jobs are always tough. But once Goebbels' propaganda fanfare stops, souls will be easier to save."

"You've got a lot of courage," sighs Andrik.

Joe smiles. "Just a little faith in a good example—in living as you want others to live, and—well, in the verities of psycho-analysis."

"What reminds you of Freud now, of all times?" I ask in surprise.

"Because Freud knew all about it—that the Germans are people with inhibitions. That they overcompensate for their sense of inferiority by arrogance; that they lack self-assurance, and hence a sense of responsibility to themselves. Or did you think it was just an accident, our countrymen's craving for uniforms and emblems, organizations and iron heels? I can tell you that rubber lasts just as long as iron. But you don't hear rubber soles. And 'you' have got to hear that 'they' are around. The society, the emblem, the stormtroop *Sturm*, the uniforms, all are nothing but the concrete framework that our feeble self-confidence wears as a corset. Alone I am nothing. But look—I'm not alone. Listen to me walk—see me march—a unit and a member of an imposing multitude. That's why they're all for Hitler—because he gives them uniforms— because he realizes where they feel naked and unsure of themselves."

Frank nods. "I expect you're right. Psychoanalytic treatment of sixty millions. Three cheers for the inferiority complex!"

"Not for the inferiority complex, but for the overcoming of the inferiority complex. If we can manage that—"

"First suppose we manage to get to sleep," I remark frostily. It's twelve o'clock. Our kerosene lantern is smoking out its last drops of oil. The battle front, too, seems to be asleep. Outdoors one hears nothing but the monotonous rustle of the trees.

Friday, April 27, 1945.

Shouts outside the door: "Open up!" Yells outside the door: *"Open up!"*

I start up, and shake Joe and Frank awake. "Duck!" Hastily I fling on my dressing gown. What time is it, anyway? Scarcely daylight. The front door is locked. I run to get the key.

"Open up!" comes a yell from outside. *"Open up!"*

My hands quake. "Now," I think. "Now."

The door flies open; I find myself staring into seven worn-out soldiers' faces.

"What is it?"

"Water!" says one of them hoarsely. "Water!" They wear SS emblems on their collars, the accursed runes of our mortal foes. They look as if they would collapse at any moment.

"We have no water," I say. The men look at me like whipped dogs. "Where's the front?"

They look at the ground. "Along the canal. They've broken through. Over on the Priesterweg, too."

"Well, then, be off with you."

They make a hopeless gesture. "Where to? We're bottled up. We've lost our squad leader. They'll shoot us if we come without a leader."

"My heart bleeds for you!"

The youngest of them tosses his head defiantly. "Don't rejoice too soon. You people are the first ones they'll mash to a pulp."

His neighbor nods. "They're bottled up too, the dirty dogs. And when the relief army gets here from the west—" He gives me a hostile stare. "Watch yourself, miss. Things haven't gone as far as you think."

"Or maybe they have!" I slam the door. But I don't feel comfortable about it. Shouldn't I have given them a glass of water after all?

At seven the battle opens up, growing more intense from minute to minute. They're bombarding the water tower. The first shell is a miss. The second is on. So is the third. The slate-roofed dome goes down in a cloud of dust and smoke.

Restlessness drives us out of the basement. It's dreadful to wait for death in a rathole. If you can see it, it must be easier. We peer anxiously through cracks.

A few soldiers race past, duck hurriedly, and run stooping toward the cemetery. A dead man, arms flung wide, lies at the corner. Rifle shots rattle; antiaircraft keeps barking. Enemy strafers describe their ominous curves under the blue morning sky. Somewhere in the distance a military whistle shrills.

"They're falling back!" I whisper. New swarms of soldiers come past to northward in a disorderly jumble. There are Home Guardsmen among them, medics, and antiaircraft personnel. Frank, Joe, and Andrik take the safety catches off their revolvers. If they burst into our building. . . . If anyone tries to make us a center of resistance. . . .

But nobody pays us any heed. The remnants of the German fighting units move hastily, in disorganized crowds, toward the middle of town.

Suddenly the shooting dies away. We hold our breath. Two or three more soldiers stumble across the plowed field of the cemetery garden. They stagger, fall, lie motionless.

Silence.

Ten minutes. Fifteen minutes. Twenty minutes. Not a soul far and wide. The streets are utterly deserted.

"Hey!" Heike grabs my arm. "Hey—over there!"

Something is moving beyond the gutted corner building. A rifle barrel pokes cautiously past the edge of the wall. For a matter of seconds a soldier's head appears behind it—disappears, appears again. A strange face; a strange uniform.

"Russians!" Andrik breathes.

The place is coming to life. Men run forward, peer mistrustfully at our building. Now one of them ventures ahead to the gate of the cemetery garden. He rushes across the garden in great bounds. Behind the greenhouse he ducks down, crouching over his automatic rifle like a hunter on station. The militia men lie ten feet beyond him. Will he fire? No. You don't fire at dead men.

The newcomer stands up. He gives his companions a sign. Two of them break away from the crowd and gallop across the roadway. What odd sort of vehicle are they dragging behind them? Have they got bottles on their cart? They stop outside the greenhouse, steady their gun carriage in a furrow, and look searchingly down the street.

Just don't do anything careless now. Just don't let them think we're resisting.

"Hide your revolvers," Frank hisses. Our men creep down to the basement on tiptoe. On tiptoe they come back, unarmed. Those whom we now await are friends.

"What about a white flag?" I ask in an undertone. Heike pulls the sheet off her bed. The flagpole? A broom handle.

With three quick motions she ties the sheet to it, and crawls upstairs on her stomach. We hear her moving around up there.

Anxiously we watch the Red soldiers beyond the greenhouse.

Fire! A bright streak of flame dazzles us. We stagger back.

"Heike!" I scream. An insufferable smell spreads through the building.

"The place is on fire!" they shout from the basement.

Heike races downstairs. "They're using incendiary ammunition. Get down out of here!"

"They are, then, after all! What about the flag?"

"It's hanging out. I just managed to put it there."

We sit in the basement, not stirring. We have no water to put out the fire. And before we'd risk our lives for a little old junk. . . .

After half an hour the fire goes out. Hesitantly we venture upstairs. The strange vehicle is still standing outside the greenhouse, and the three Red soldiers are still peering mistrustfully down the street.

Around the corner comes the first tank. A second follows it; a third. Trucks come next. The train turns slowly down the main street, and then disappears rapidly to northward.

Silence. Occasionally we hear the whistle of a rifle bullet.

Is this the conquest that we have dreamed of for five years, that we have gambled our lives for a hundred times over?

There! Heike grabs my arm again. "They're coming!"

A man is running toward us; we hear his boots pounding the pavement.

"Russians in the building!" a voice screeches.

Andrik and I jump up. At last! We rush down the long basement passage. On the front landing we stop, blinded. The beam of a flashlight is aimed at us. The world beyond is blackness.

"*Drusya!*" I say into the darkness: "Friends."

The beam of light drops slowly. I see a bearded face, two watchful eyes, slanted like a Tartar's, and the turned-up collar of a leather coat. The barrel of an automatic rifle gleams palely.

"*Drusya!*" the soldier smiles.

Andrik takes over the negotiations. "We've been waiting for you," he says in Russian. "We're glad you're here."

The Red soldier looks searchingly into our eyes. "Really?"

"Really!" He shines his light into the open basement doors, shrugs, and goes away again.

We go back numbly to our basement. There we find a radiantly victorious mood. Joe has uncorked the last bottle of red wine. We drink a toast to liberation in tin cups and teacups.

The afternoon passes. Evening falls. Neither Russians nor Germans show themselves. For sheer boredom Fabian puts *The Beggars' Opera* on the phonograph. Joe peels potatoes. The rattle of rolling tanks comes from a distance, approaches, fades away again.

Frank creeps upstairs, and is back in two minutes. "All quiet. They're bivouacking at the corner, with field kitchen and canteen. One of them is even playing the accordion."

The hours drag along. The clock says nine, half past nine.

"Hey!" Heike whispers suddenly. "Listen! Don't you hear something? There—there it is again!" A suspicious cracking sound beyond the wall. A brief bang, sharp, quick, whistling. More whistling. A rattle sets up from all sides.

We stare at one another aghast. Hell's fire! Those are werewolves! They're shooting from the buildings.

"Get out your revolvers!" Andrik orders. "Occupy the entrances. Quick!"

Everyone runs hither and thither. As they go, the men clap their helmets on their heads.

I peer through the crack of an open window. Isn't that a man creeping across the courtyard, bareheaded, in a dark jacket? He crouches behind the shrubbery. No doubt of it —he doesn't mean to be seen. Now he takes aim. A shot. I hear groans and stifled curses.

Frank rushes up the stairs. "They've barricaded themselves in the side wing. There must be a lot of them. Make sure none of them comes over here." He races downstairs again.

Andrik's head appears beyond the banister. "Come down. Right away. It's urgent!" We creep below on all fours. A shot cracks outside. Splinters of wood fly about us.

We hold a council of war in the basement. "Bar the doors, and post guards," Joe advises. "At the slightest noise, raise the alarm. Nobody undresses; everybody go to bed in his clothes."

"Pleasant night," Fabian grumbles, loading his revolver with elaborate care. "So sleep is what we don't get none of again. And I thought when the Russians got here. . . ."

"You aren't supposed to think. You're supposed to stand guard." Andrik gives him a fatherly push toward the door.

"Who's afraid of the big bad wolf?" we hear him whistling mournfully.

The werewolves rule the night. Who can have thought up that diabolical invention? Fabian wakes me at two. "Get up, it's your turn. All quiet so far."

I jump up from my Procrustean bed and stagger sleepily to the stairs. On the window sill in the second story lies Fabian's revolver, carefully left in reserve. Only, unfortunately, I don't know how to shoot. A cold wind blows through the building. I look over toward town. The north is on fire, and so is the west.

Heavenly Father! Wasn't that the basement door creaking? My knees shake like aspen leaves. Someone clears his throat on the staircase.

"It's me--don't be scared," I hear Frank's voice. "You ought . . . I thought. . . ." Sheepishly he takes a bottle from his coat pocket. "Armagnac. I thought. . . . Well, that we might have a drink."

"You dear good thing!" All at once my heart is calm and comforted. Together we peer into the gloom. The trees rustle; the sky is clear and starry. The cognac bottle passes between us.

"Imagine living through all this—imagine having the privilege of living through it," Frank whispers. "I wouldn't trade with anyone today."

"I wouldn't either. They say God loves those most whom he tries most sorely. He's tried us very sorely indeed. I guess he must mean well by us."

"By us—and by the Jews. He who stands idly by is never 'chosen.'"

"Only that being chosen gives you no rights, nothing but duties."

Frank nods. "The duty to do better. Even if we failed once. After all, we're only human. Our value is fixed not by our falling into a slough, but by whether we find our way out. We're going to find our way out. Even if a thousand werewolves—" he breaks off, and fumbles hurriedly for the revolver. A shot crashes through the darkness. "Well, we've scared him off," he says with satisfaction.

"Whom?"

"The bushwhacker. Over there back of the shrubbery."

I don't dare look. "Did you *kill* him?"

Frank looks at me indignantly. "Kill him? I wish I had. Or did you want him to kill us? Go on to sleep, you pacifist. It's three o'clock. We can knock off for now."

Rather shamefacedly I slink into the basement, roll up in my blanket, and reflect that I am probably no heroine after all.

Saturday, April 28, 1945.

The werewolves keep shooting. The Russians won't stand for it long. We have a guard on every floor. We want to help, and don't know how. We roam restlessly from basement to attic. No one feels like doing anything. The house doors are locked. Andrik tinkers with the radio, but there's no current. "Why didn't we get a crystal set?" he grumbles.

In the evening new tanks come rolling up. They stop at the street corner, and level their guns at us. The side wing stands deserted, with open, gaping windows. Mute, like a house accursed.

Ratatatat! Ratatatat!

The werewolves! Do they really dare? You hear the whistling, but you don't see the riflemen.

The tank guns slowly descend.

Ratat! Are they mad? Choosing this moment to fire?

Andrik pillows my head in his arm. "Think of something else," he whispers.

"Hickery, dickery, dock, the mouse ran up the clock," I babble stupidly.

A roar shakes the air; the floor heaves. We rush into a corner. They're shelling us. It thunders like the hammers of hell. Rifle butts bang against the front door.

"Now it's really going to start," Heike stammers.

Andrik gets up. Silently he looks at us; silently he goes to the door.

Frank tosses the revolvers behind a clothes cupboard. "Hickery, dickery, dock, the mouse ran up the clock!" Why can't I get that damned nonsense out of my head?

Men are all shouting at once—angrily, in a strange tongue. Andrik is talking too. I catch a word, *Padashditye*—"Wait." His voice is gentle and friendly. He talks at great length. The others are silent now. Now they seem to be asking him something. He answers in Russian. Heavy boots clump across the hall. "Andrik!" I can't stand it any longer, not if they shoot me dead on the spot. He mustn't be there alone.

His light overcoat shines beside the front door from among a tangle of dark uniforms. Russians are crowding around him, behind him, in front of him, beside him. They point their pistols at him. He looks at them and smiles. Then he goes on talking, talking, pleasantly, without a pause. His face is pale. His hair blows in the wind. He keeps his hands in his overcoat pockets—the only man who is unarmed.

Now he sees me, and summons me with his eyes.

"*Drusya,*" I stammer, and force my way among the soldiers. They stare at me suspiciously, then fall back and let me pass.

"They think we're werewolves," Andrik whispers in my ear. "I've got to convince them."

Someone jabs him in the ribs. "You, soldierr!"

They drag him outdoors.

"Andrik," I wail, running after him. A whirlpool of sparks greets me; the adjoining buildings are on fire. They stand like smoking torches in the night. Their glow stains the heavens dark red.

Soldiers are climbing over the garden fence. They come running up from all sides, more and more of them. They run hither and thither, yelling, gesticulating, moving like dancing shadows among the great bonfires. Now they charge the entrances to the buildings—ten, twenty, fifty. Others pour after them. Shouting and trampling. But we hear no shots.

I stand next to Andrik, looking in horror at the turmoil.

Isn't that Stolzberg they're bringing out? He's as pale as a corpse, staggering like a drunken man.

Two officers go over to him. "You Gerrman soldierr," they say angrily. "You come with."

Stolzberg's knees sag. "No, no," he stammers, looking to Andrik for help.

Andrik smiles at him. "They won't hurt us. We just mustn't be afraid."

Joe and Frank appear, escorted by six Red soldiers. They are quite calm, holding their hands high. They are told to step out on the lawn, searched, and dismissed.

Confused noises come from below, but they sound peaceable, and don't alarm us. The buildings to right and left are burning like torches.

And from the neighboring basements rattles the gunfire of the werewolves.

I reach for Andrik's hand. He squeezes my fingers reassuringly. We stand close together in the midst of the charging soldiers. Shots still ring out treacherously from the side wing.

There! That volley went home! Two Red soldiers fall headlong in the sand. Their steel helmets roll like tin pots across the pavement.

"We're lost," I stammer. Andrik, too, has turned pale. Great drops of perspiration stand out on his forehead. "Those thugs," he grits out. "Those irresponsible idiots."

Someone screams aloud; it sounds like a wild animal in its death agony.

"They're coming. . . . They're going to get us." I clutch Andrik's arm like a child. Out of the smoke and flame before us rises the enraged countenance of a huge Mongol. "You shooting," he roars, brandishing his automatic rifle.

In a moment we're surrounded. I feel a prod in the back. I totter forward. Something cold touches the back of my neck. "You shooting," come yells from all sides. I run. Andrik runs beside me. Suddenly Stolzberg is with us too: three Russians ahead of us, three Russians behind us. The muzzles of their automatic rifles stare like dead eyes. We are dragged off at a gallop. Our feet run of their own accord, run, stumble, run again. A fence looms before us. We're over it with a bound. I see shrubs, hedges, wooden crosses. The cemetery. A dead man lies directly across our path. German? Russian? What do we care? We just have to jump to keep from stepping on him.

They'll kill us in a moment, here behind the shrubbery. Dead to the dead. We're stopping. . . . This is it. . . .

I look at Andrik. His lips are tight; his eyes stare fixedly ahead. Stolzberg is shaking as if he had a fever.

Another prod in the back of the neck. Mechanically we put one foot in front of the other. Isn't that the water tower? The dome rises steep and shattered from the darkness.

At the iron gate we halt, then grope down a few steps.

So it'll be in a cellar—with no sky and no stars. . . . Dear God! Oughtn't we to run away? But where to? The muzzles of the automatic rifles stare at us like dead eyes.

Suddenly we hear voices. A door is swung open. I see a low vault. Candles flicker in the necks of tall bottles. I see stools, a table, two dark-green plush armchairs, collected indiscriminately to make the field headquarters of the Russian staff. The air is thick with cigarette smoke. Eight pairs of eyes look at us, severe, cold, hostile.

"You were shooting?" asks the commandant.

"No," Andrik replies in Russian. "We weren't shooting. Others were. We're innocent."

The officers do not move a muscle. Their faces are like iron masks. "You are partisans," the commandant says. "We shall shoot you."

Andrik bows his head. "We aren't partisans," he says tonelessly.

The colonel eyes him suspiciously. "Why do you speak Russian?"

"I was born in Moscow."

"Why are you living here?"

"My parents are German."

"Do you listen to our radio?"

"Every morning at eleven o'clock."

"When was the last time you listened?"

"Last Tuesday, when they broadcast the German news. Then the current was shut off."

"What did we say on Tuesday?"

"That fighting was going on in Lankwitz and Friedrichshain, and that the city was being entered from the south and east."

The colonel frowns. The faces of his officers stare like iron masks.

All the terrors of death have fallen away from him. Daring shines in his face—daring and unshakable confidence. "We hate the Nazis," he says loudly. "For twelve years we have been waiting for you. We were always on your side."

The other does not seem to hear him. He leans thoughtfully

over the map that is spread before him. "Show me where we are. Show me the Wilhelmstrasse and the Alexanderplatz."

Andrik's finger moves quickly and positively hither and thither on the map. "There . . . there . . . there. This is the main street that goes in town." He hesitates. "We aren't partisans," he repeats softly. "We want to help you!"

The officers say nothing. I look around cautiously. Stolzberg is as white as a sheet. Can't he realize that he looks like the very embodiment of a guilty conscience?

"You say you've listened to our radio," the colonel goes on. "Do you know what we do when we announce a victory over you?"

Andrik smiles. "You fire a salute."

"Do you know the Russian national anthem?"

"I do."

The officers look at him. Their faces are like iron masks. "Sing it to us. If you know it, you should be able to sing it."

His voice rings clear and calm through the room:

*"Soyus nerushimyy respublik svobodnych
Splotil na veki velikaya Rusy."*

He's singing for our lives. We know it. The candles sizzle. Otherwise, not a sound to be heard.

"Skvos grosy siyalo nam solnze svobody"

Slowly the expressions of the men sitting before us change. The masks turn to human faces.

"My v bitvach resheem sudybu pokoleniy"

A little lieutenant with a tiny blond beard holds his head in his hands. Perhaps he's thinking that he'd like to go home. Perhaps he's thinking it would be beautiful there.

"Pusty ot pobedy k pobede vedst."

The basement room is still. The candles smolder, and the smoke of countless cigarettes hangs in the air like a fog. The colonel pushes a half-filled glass of tea across the table. "Drink that, Tovarisch!"

Andrik downs the tea at a draught.

As if at a signal, the officers jump up. They surround us, slap us on the back, laugh, shake hands, and talk to us in their strange, incomprehensible tongue. Andrik hardly knows whom to answer first.

"Are you hungry?" "Sit down." "When was the last time you were in Moscow?" "You're a musician. Do you know Shostakovitch? Do you know Stanislavsky?"

They offer us food. Bacon, sausage, groats. "*Kushaitye, pazhaluista.*" Orderlies come running with fresh tea, sugar, and preserves. Everyone wants to give us something. "You have no meat? Here. Please take some. You're short of bread? There you are. Put it in your pocket. How can you carry it? Perfectly simple. Take our dish."

Loaded down like children on Christmas afternoon, we go back across the cemetery. The dead soldier lies there. I bend over him. It's a Russian, scarcely twenty. Poor friend, you had to die, and we can live.

"We ought to make a grave for him," Andrik says.

Then we're back at our home. The adjoining buildings are still burning. A sentry guards our door; soldiers with pails, bowls, and dishes run in and out. Something is steaming in their vessels.

"*Mozhno?*" I ask. "May we?" They let us pass in.

I hear Heike's yell. "You're back!" Laughing and crying, she falls upon my neck. For a long time we can't say anything at all, and when we finally do, it's just silly blubbering. They all appear, Frank, Dagmar, Joe, Heike, and Fabian. They beam, and act as if they were drunk. "Why, you did it! Why, you're alive!"

Yes, we did it—life and liberty are ours. For the first time we look around. We aren't alone in the basement. Wherever we look Russian soldiers are sitting—in passages and doors, on air-raid cots, on boxes and bundles. They lean against the walls, they squat on the floor. They're spooning Russian groats out of German dishes. One spoonful for you, one spoonful for me.

"It tastes wonderful!" Dagmar raves. The whole neighborhood has arrived. One spoonful for you, one spoonful for me. The crowd is big enough for a country fair. Kerosene lamps are lit in all the basements. Little stumps of candle, hastily stuck up somewhere. The war's over, the candle stumps say. Now we needn't be guarded any more.

The war is over. At that moment the peace begins for us. Frank Matthis, you're free. Joe Thäler, you're free. You're all free, you who have lived for years in hiding—Wald and Hartmann, Ralph, Rita, Konrad, you countless thousands who said *No* to Adolf Hitler's policy of misery. The great unrighteousness has ceased to be. We greet you, Helmuth von Moltke; we greet you, Sophie and Hans Scholl, Ursula Reuber, Heinrich Muehsam, Peter Tarnowsky, and Wolfgang Kühn. We will make a beginning. In your name we will make a beginning.

Afterword

Friday, August 24, 1945.

Andrik died at eleven o'clock yesterday evening. The stray bullet of an American patrol wounded him mortally. It was just after he had given his last concert for Allied troops. "Next time I'll play Bach for you," he said to his English friends. Then there was a shot. And then he said nothing more. Andrik Krassnow is dead. He was forty-six years old when he gave up his life. And he enjoyed living.